Conductivity Healing is a pro\
the complexity of life. In sir
restoring the flow of energy in a d
creativity. I've always known, as a ~~... ~~... ~~...~~apist, that when
energy is obstructed, illness and pathology frequently follow. This book—
from the Enlightened and highly intuitive Avatar Adi Da Samraj—is an absolute
treasure, revealing several methodologies that support harmonious healing
frequencies not only for the physical body but for the emotional and spiritual
domains as well. I loved reading it. Highly recommended!

—**Stephen T. Sinatra, MD, FACC**
cardiologist and bioenergetics psychotherapist;
coauthor, *Health Revelations from Heaven*

Conductivity Healing is an eloquent invitation to go beyond the limitations
of physical being and understand ourselves as energy; to consciously be
alive as energy and live our lives as energy in relation to ourselves and to
others. The book gives a foundation of etheric awareness and describes various practices for magnifying and circulating life-energy. All dimensions of
healing are covered—the physical, the subtle, and the causal. It includes
many practical exercises to awaken sensitivity, consciously participate with
the universal field of life-energy, and facilitate healing on all levels.

—**Debra Greene, PhD**
author, *Endless Energy*;
founder, the Energy Mastery program

Conductivity Healing will captivate you, drawing you into the life and
spirit of Adi Da Samraj, and the gift of healing he bestowed upon the
world—a gift you may find insightful and useful in your healing journey, and
the journey of others you serve and assist.

—**Donald Yance, CN, MH**
founder, Mederi Centre for Natural Healing;
author, *Adaptogens in Medical Herbalism*

I am a physician who lost faith in the tools I was given to treat my patients,
triggering a personal healing journey, and my discovery of the beauty and
tremendous healing powers of both energy and the breath. After my life-
changing understanding of the nature of health, I incorporated energy healing
into my medical practice, and I've seen great benefits for my patients. It was
therefore with great joy that I received and read Adi Da Samraj's new book,
Conductivity Healing—which I can now enthusiastically recommend to those
of you, who, like myself, are seekers on the deepest levels. Enjoy!

—**Felice Gersh, MD**
founder and medical director,
Integrative Medical Group of Irvine

Energy, the energy body, energy transference, and energy healing are all
real. *Conductivity Healing*, from Avatar Adi Da, adds a very important
piece to the complex puzzle of healing with energy and healing with touch—
and the simple, universal truth of healing with love.

—**Dr. Marc Halpern**
founder, California College of Ayurveda;
author, *Healing Your Life: Lessons on the Path of Ayurveda*

At our most subtle level, we are made of vibrating energy. Learning to measure and harness this energy will be the future of medicine. *Conductivity Healing* offers a time-tested road map, using the most profound tools of yoga (union) to heal, in the simplest and most natural way possible.

—**Dr. John Douillard, DC, CAP**
author, *Body, Mind, and Sport*;
creator, LifeSpa.com

Conductivity Healing is a welcome addition to the world of health and healing books. In this book, energy healing is explored from the perspective of the Avatar Adi Da Samraj, and encompasses a wide range of practices and philosophies. Anyone who wants to become more knowledgeable about healing—and move to a higher energetic level—should consider reading *Conductivity Healing*.

—**Misha Ruth Cohen, OMD, LAc**
clinical director, Chicken Soup Chinese Medicine;
author, *The New Chinese Medicine Handbook*

Conductivity Healing is a gigantic leap forward in the understanding of the human body and its relationship to what is commonly referred to as the subtle body. As in all of his books, Adi Da Samraj reveals what no one else has been able to fully embody, authentically. This book is an essential study for those who practice and profess to know about esoteric and energetic healing.

—**Ed Reither**
founder and director, Beezone.com

I read *Conductivity Healing* in one sitting, and feel like Avatar Adi Da took me on an incredible ride of concepts to find happiness, understand self-realization, and attain pure consciousness and energy. As an Ayurvedic practitioner, Avatar Adi Da reminds me of an Ayurvedic physician—one who is always in consideration of the whole body, and what it means to be an uninhibited human being, conducting the radiance of truth itself. I am inspired!

—**DeAnna Batdorff**
founder, dhyana Center of Therapeutics

Carefully crafted, *Conductivity Healing* offers a number of simple, supportive energy practices conducive to healthy living, all stemming from Avatar Adi Da's unique and extraordinarily dynamic demonstration of full spiritual realization. Technically and scientifically inclined readers interested in subtle energies will find original material for further exploration and elaboration.

—**Scott Virden Anderson, MD**
director, Yoga Science Foundation

Though I am not a devotee of Adi Da Samraj, I revere many ageless wisdom traditions that tell us energy transcends our human form. This brilliant work offers practical guidance on energy medicine. Use these simple disciplines to find healing beyond symptom-based "cures"—for yourself and others.

—**Amanda McQuade Crawford, MA**
medical herbalist and psychotherapist;
author, *Herbal Remedies for Women*

In the 1980s, Nobel Laureate Albert Szent-Gyorgyi introduced me to the science of energy medicine. One of his many insightful and inspiring statements: "In every culture and every medicine before ours, healing was accomplished by moving energy." Fortunately, the ancient methods of healing are resurging—acupuncture, Ayurveda, meditation, Tai Chi, and Yoga, to name a few. And energy medicine practitioners from every tradition, as well as scientists, are learning how to "move energy." *Conductivity Healing* is an important source of vital information on this subject. The book takes energy medicine beyond the physical and emotional body, to the ways energetic flows can be enhanced through simple, transformative, and pleasurable exercises. These are pure, potent, direct, and effective "conductivity practices." By practicing the methods described here, the "work" of healing becomes simple, ecstatic, intuitive, and radiant.

—**James L. Oschman, PhD**
author, *Energy Medicine: The Scientific Basis*;
founder, Nature's Own Research Association

Conductivity Healing contains the practical and the sublime, offering doctors and health practitioners—and everyone—an opportunity to read and receive the most radical healing instruction, the way beyond all dis-ease. In these pages, the Master Healer, Adi Da Samraj, offers fundamental instruction on the critical alignment of the physical body to the subtler energies that sustain it, and explains the ultimate antidote to human suffering. Highly recommended.

—**Angelo Druda**
author, *The Tao of Rejuvenation*

Adi Da Samraj is a master teacher and spiritual realizer. In *Conductivity Healing*, he reveals the secrets of energy healing in relation to self, others, and the world. In his usual comprehensive and straightforward way, Adi Da Samraj gives practical instructions on how to conduct energy, how to consciously use the breath, and how the laying on of hands can be used as a means to heal and transform. This book is a must-read for all students of the healing arts.

—**Dustin DiPerna**
author, *Streams of Wisdom*

His Divine Presence
Avatar Adi Da Samraj

CONDUCTIVITY HEALING

Energy-Healing Practices That Support
An Intelligent, Harmonious, and Flowing Re-Integration of
The Physical and Etheric Dimensions of The Human Body

As Given by His Divine Presence,
AVATAR ADI DA SAMRAJ

AN **ADIDAM**™ SOURCE-TEXT

THE DAWN HORSE PRESS
MIDDLETOWN, CALIFORNIA

NOTE TO THE READER

All who study the Reality-Way Given by Avatar Adi Da Samraj or take up its practice should remember that they are responding to a Call to become responsible for themselves. They should understand that they, not Avatar Adi Da Samraj or others, are responsible for any decision they make or action they take in the course of their lives of study or practice.

The devotional, Spiritual, functional, practical, relational, and cultural practices and disciplines referred to in this book are appropriate and natural practices that are voluntarily and progressively adopted by members of the practicing congregations of Adidam (as appropriate to the personal circumstance of each individual). Although anyone may find these practices useful and beneficial, they are not presented as advice or recommendations to the general reader or to anyone who is not a member of one of the practicing congregations of Adidam. And nothing in this book is intended as a diagnosis, prescription, or recommended treatment or cure for any specific "problem", whether medical, emotional, psychological, social, or Spiritual. One should apply a particular program of treatment, prevention, cure, or general health only in consultation with a licensed physician or other qualified professional.

This book of Instructions from His Divine Presence Avatar Adi Da Samraj was compiled by the Adidam Editorial Guild, under the senior cultural overview of Ruchiradama Quandra Sukhapur Rani Naitauba (of the Ruchira Sannyasin Order of Adidam Ruchiradam). Explanatory text by Caitlin Quinby. Senior editorial overview by Jonathan Condit. Radiant Life Clinic review by Daniel Bouwmeester, MD. Illustrations by Matt Barna.

CONTENTS

EPILOGUE

Perfectly Free Energy
by His Divine Presence, Avatar Adi Da Samraj
353

Appendices

Throughout His Life, Avatar Adi Da Samraj worked to develop means—both literary and artistic—of communicating the True Nature of Reality. He approached the creation of His literary and artistic works as a process of Revealing What Reality <u>Is</u> and how Its True Nature can be Realized.

The cover of *Conductivity Healing* features an image Avatar Adi Da created in 2003. The original photograph from which He constructed this image (by pairing the original with its own "mirror") was created entirely in-camera, by means of multiple exposure. This image is also used (in black and white) on the part openings of this book.

Examples of the artwork of Adi Da Samraj, together with discussions of His artwork and His own statements about it, may be seen online at:

www.daplastique.com

FOREWORD

by Bill Gottlieb

The morning after my intimate partner learned she had a recurrence of breast cancer, I found her at the computer in her office, weeping—and writing. I knew she was overwhelmed with fear and sorrow, and I thought she might be writing to a family member or friend about her plight. But when she turned from the computer screen to talk to me, I was surprised to see her face was . . . radiant with joy.

She told me that in the darkness of early morning, having been up all night, her mind racing, her heart haunted by terror and despair, she had given up trying to figure a way out of her life-threatening disease—a new diet, a new drug, a new doctor, a new plan. And in that heartbroken moment of surrender, she felt the blessing energy of Avatar Adi Da Samraj, her spiritual master—an energy that suddenly freed her awareness from fearful identification with the dying body-mind, and revealed her true and eternal identity as *prior* to the body-mind.

She told me, in weeping joy, that she *knew* her true identity to be a limitless field of awareness, of free and blissful energy, of Conscious Light—as Adi Da describes it, *Self-Radiant, egoless Love, One and Indivisible* and *Perfectly Sufficient*—Adi Da *is* that; she *is* that; everyone and everything *is* that. No matter what happened, in life and in death, Conscious Light would always be the case.

She was gratefully writing Avatar Adi Da to thank him for his profound gift, the gift of "radical" healing (as he calls it): healing that is not achieved by seeking for a cure or remedy, but by a searchless awakening to what is "radical" or at the root; an awakening to what is always and already whole and healed.

And now it is my honor and privilege to write the foreword to the newest book to present Adi Da's philosophy and practice of "radical" healing: *Conductivity Healing*. It is a book intended for the devoted students of Avatar Adi Da Samraj. And it is also a book intended for any interested "student" of health and healing—health practitioners, and people who want better health.

I was asked to write the foreword because I have been both a longtime devotee of Avatar Adi Da Samraj and a bestselling health writer, with more than a dozen books published in the U.S. and worldwide. During my forty years of writing about health, I have interviewed thousands of health practitioners, and read articles, books, and scientific papers by tens of thousands more. Medical doctors and naturopaths. Nutritionists and herbalists. Psychiatrists, psychologists, and faith healers. Yoga teachers and massage therapists. Practitioners of Native American Medicine and Traditional Chinese Medicine. Researchers at Harvard, Stanford, the Mayo Clinic, and other leading universities and hospitals. And over those four decades of investigating and writing, I have encountered a seemingly endless array of remedies and methods for health and healing, most with value in relieving suffering—from gene-targeting pharmaceuticals to water fasting, from gamma knife radiosurgery to aura balancing.

But I have never met another healer like Avatar Adi Da Samraj. And I have never read another health book like *Conductivity Healing*.

To my mind, the greatest healer is a person who can guide and help the individual to a state of *real* healing, to a *real* cure, in which Conscious Light is realized as one's true and deathless identity, and all the inevitable difficulties and dissatisfactions of daily life—including illness—are felt within It. In my experience, Adi Da is such a healer.

And in this utterly unique health book he guides and helps every reader to understand that existence is a vast vibratory field of living energy—and that there are practical ways to "conduct" life-energy throughout the body-mind, for balance and well-being. In this revelatory book, you'll find:

How effective healing must take into account the *entire* structure of the human being. How life-energy is discovered primarily through *feeling*. The paramount importance of *breath* in energy healing. A simple and profound approach to the prayerful laying on of hands. The importance of *touch* for healing. And the way to wellness not only for each individual but for *all* the humans and non-humans of Earth.

It is my heartfelt hope that you benefit bodily, mentally, and emotionally from the principles and practices communicated in this book. I hope, too, that you feel the healing energy communicated by the words and person of Avatar Adi Da Samraj—his mysterious transmission of Conscious Light, which has the graceful power of perfect healing. ■

Bill Gottlieb is a health coach certified by the American Association of Drugless Practitioners, the author of 16 health books that have sold 3 million copies and been translated into 11 languages, a journalist whose articles on health have appeared in *Reader's Digest, Men's Health, Bottom Line Personal,* and many other periodicals, and the former editor-in-chief of Prevention Magazine Health Books and Rodale Books.

The Purest Healing Source

by Daniel Bouwmeester, MD
and the editors of the Dawn Horse Press

The wisdom in this book—on energy healing, and about optimal health and true wellness altogether—is based in the unique disposition and illuminated State of Avatar Adi Da Samraj.

In His Spiritual autobiography, Avatar Adi Da describes His earliest experience of life in human form:

> *Even as a baby, I remember only crawling around inquisitively with a boundless Feeling of Joy, Light, and Freedom in the middle of my head that was bathed in Energy moving unobstructed in a Circle—down from above, all the way down, then up, all the way up, and around again—and always Shining from my heart. It was an Expanding Sphere of Joy from the heart. And I was a Radiant Form—the Source of Energy, Love-Bliss, and Light in the midst of a world that is entirely Energy, Love-Bliss, and Light. I was the Power of Reality, a direct Enjoyment and Communication of the One Reality. I was the Heart Itself, Who Lightens the mind and all things. I was the same as every one and every thing, except it became clear that others were apparently unaware of the "Thing" Itself.*
>
> *Even as a little child, I recognized It and Knew It, and my life was not a matter of anything else.*
>
> —*The Knee of Listening*

Avatar Adi Da named this radiant Sphere of Joy the "Bright". He knew it to be His own native or fundamental State—and He knew it to be the native State of all beings.

The Sphere of the "Bright", Avatar Adi Da says, is "Centerless and Boundless"—in other words, there is no ordinary experience

1

of being the center (or self, or ego) within a defined experience (or world). The "Bright" Sphere, He writes, is "without 'difference', without 'place', without 'other', without relatedness, without death, without diminishment, without limit, without problem".[1] And Avatar Adi Da's entire life was always guided by His innate knowledge of this "Bright" egoless Sphere of Reality—and the impulse to enable all beings to know it, and to consciously participate in it.

Throughout His life (1939–2008), Avatar Adi Da worked tirelessly to help people understand the primacy of the "Bright", to Spiritually transmit the "Bright" to each and all, and to establish means (such as His written word and empowered places) for that transmission to continue after His bodily lifetime.

He also called those who were responsive to Him to relate to Him in the time-honored manner of devotion to a Realized Spiritual Master, or Guru—to become His formal devotees. It was only in the context of this heart-responsive, devotional relationship to Him that Avatar Adi Da spent many years (1972–2000) teaching people about the "Bright".

During Avatar Adi Da's "teaching years", He brought into the world an entirely new and complete way of living, founded in a profound understanding of Reality—and how any human being, at any time, can respond to and participate in Reality. This way of living is inherently free—that is, it is based on the native State of the being, which is free of the limits of the ego, or the contracted, separate sense of self. It is also searchless—free of effortful, motivated seeking, because Reality is known, responded to, and participated in now, not in the future. Avatar Adi Da calls this way of living the Reality-Way of Adidam. He summarizes this way in His final masterwork, *The Aletheon*:

The Reality-Way of Adidam is a total life-practice based upon transferring energy and attention from "self" to Reality Itself. That turning—from "self" to Reality Itself—is the Means for entering into the Divine Sphere of egoless Self-Identification with Reality Itself, and (thus and thereby) transcending the illusory space of ego-identity.

1. From "The Demonstration of Self-Abiding Divine Self-Recognition", in *The Aletheon*. Unless otherwise indicated, all books mentioned in the text (and footnotes) are published by the Dawn Horse Press (www.dawnhorsepress.com).

Some elements of the Reality-Way of Adidam are new—never given to humankind before. Other elements of the Reality-Way of Adidam have ancient, traditional, or even modern precedents and likenesses.[2] But every element of the Reality-Way is brought into the context of the teaching of Avatar Adi Da, and the devotional relationship to Him—and is thus, in essence, made new again, free of the trappings of seeking that characterize all practical, religious, and Spiritual traditions.

Avatar Adi Da's instruction addresses both the ultimate nature of Reality and the complexities of human existence, which He summarized as money, food, sex, and social egoity. In that human context, He gave specific principles and practices for diet, health, and all forms of healing—including energy healing. This book contains His summary instruction on energy healing as practiced in the Reality-Way of Adidam—a unique form of energy healing called "conductivity healing". This instruction is offered to His devotees—and to anyone who is moved to seriously study and reflect on the purpose and practice of energy healing.

How Avatar Adi Da's Energy-Healing Teachings Were Established

Avatar Adi Da's specific instructions on health and healing, including energy healing, were established over many decades of intensive examination and experimentation. This process was engaged by Avatar Adi Da Himself, in His own physical body. And it was engaged in conversation with the gathering of devotees who came to Him during His "teaching years", some of whom were trained healers of one kind or another.

Very early on, Avatar Adi Da communicated to those of us who had been educated in various healing modalities that we were embarking on a course of study that would be more rigorous than anything we had experienced in any healing certification or medical school. And this turned out to be true. Over the years, Avatar Adi Da engaged us in an exhaustive investigation relative to <u>every</u>

2. Appendix E offers a selection of books from various traditions of energy healing, illustrating the link between such traditions and the energy-healing practices in the Reality-Way of Adidam.

3

aspect of healing and health, whether uniquely based on His own Realized State and knowledge, or simply based on His sensitivity to and rediscovery of the sacred essence of healing traditions developed in the history of humankind, Eastern and Western.

There was nothing that was not worthy of Avatar Adi Da's "consideration"—a process of exhaustive examination of a particular area of life, until its truth reveals itself. At His request, we studied and researched a plethora of diets and healing regimes. Avatar Adi Da would apply and discover for Himself the value of the various regimes that He brought to us or we brought to Him. More and more, we were able to witness how He readily got to the heart of whatever healing tradition was under investigation— almost as if He were the very source of that tradition or approach. He undertook many dietary practices Himself, and He allowed us to offer Him many different healing therapies over the years— including acupuncture, various techniques of massage, osteopathic and chiropractic treatments, and much, much more (far too many to enumerate here). Avatar Adi Da's devotees often participated simultaneously in these spontaneous health and healing experiments, reporting results to Him. All these findings were added to Avatar Adi Da's consideration and the conclusions He came to— conclusions based on this rigorous process of investigation, rather than any mere presumption or belief.

This process of consideration continued until Avatar Adi Da came to a summary decision relative to the approach He would recommend in every area of health and right living—an approach summarized in His final texts, and compiled into many books of His practical wisdom, including this one. The "conductivity"-healing practices presented here epitomize Avatar Adi Da's conclusive recommendations relative to energy healing.

The Energy Consideration

In His summary instruction about energy healing, Avatar Adi Da confirms the ancient and modern understanding of the primacy and seniority of energy in relation to matter—and, thus, in relation to our physical bodies. Energy is subtler than—and senior to—matter.

The animation or aliveness or emotiveness of the physical depends on—or, in fact, is—energy. Energy is both internal and external to the physical form we generally identify as our "self". In other words, energy is inherent to our own bodies and at the same time pervades everything that surrounds our bodies. Physical forms appear, go through transformative changes, and then ultimately pass away—within a unified field or "sea" of energy.

Therefore, the quality of the activity of the body (its health and ease, or freedom from dis-ease) has a lot to do with the inherent energy of the being and its relationship to the unified field of all-pervading energy, including how energy is circulated (or conducted) in the body. And this self-evident understanding is used in healing practices—since ancient times, and now.

Fundamental to this understanding about the role of energy in healing and well-being is Avatar Adi Da's larger consideration of the true nature of energy and of existence itself (and therefore the true nature of our own existence). To help us understand the true nature of existence, He often spoke of "conditional reality" and "Non-conditional Reality".

The Non-conditional Reality is the "Bright"—the Root-Condition of existence, which is not dependent on any conditions (or specific circumstances of experience). In other words, it is that "One Reality", the Sphere of limitless radiance, which Avatar Adi Da had known since birth and longed to communicate. The Non-conditional Reality is that which is "always already the case", or that which is indivisible, and therefore cannot be broken down or subdivided.

Avatar Adi Da points out that if you follow subjectivity (or personal awareness) to its source—from thoughts, to ideas, to reveries, to discriminative intelligence and will, to intuition, to attention, to the "I"-thought—the subjective awareness is ultimately observed to be Consciousness. If you follow objectivity (or outside appearances) in a similar manner—from matter, to atoms, to subatomic particles, to energy, to visible and non-visible light—it is ultimately observed to be Energy, or Light. Avatar Adi Da's "radical" (or "at-the-root") teaching is that these indivisible sources—Consciousness and Light—are not different, but are one "Thing" or Reality. And, thus, the Reality of the Non-conditional is Conscious Light, or that which always already Is.

The conditional reality covers the full spectrum of changing experiences and appearances, high and low—which Avatar Adi Da defines as "modifications" of Conscious Light. The vast range of energies and experiences can be understood in vibratory or energy terms, and are displayed in visionary form as a sphere of concentric colors (as Avatar Adi Da describes in detail).[3] The physical body and the body's energy are the two outermost vibratory levels in this spectrum—appearing as the color red (for the physical, or gross, dimension of existence) and yellow (for the energy, or etheric, dimension of existence). Avatar Adi Da teaches that the "yellow-red conjunction", or the communication between energy and the physical body, is the place of healing and balance.

Avatar Adi Da makes it clear that the Non-conditional Conscious Light is not within conditional reality, like a deity or soul within—rather, the conditional arises within the Non-conditional Reality of Conscious Light.

This means that the dimensions of the being related to energy healing—the physical body and the energy that pervades it—adhere in, and are themselves modifications of, Conscious Light.

Energy Healing—Modern and Traditional

The two most widely practiced forms of energy healing today are the laying on of hands (also referred to as "healing touch" or "touch therapy") and bodily massage. Both healing practices work to restore the native or inherent flow of energy, to restore balance in the body, and altogether to intensify the reception of the universal, all-pervading energy. By these means, balance and flow are restored, through re-integration of the etheric and physical, allowing healing to occur.

These energy-healing practices are often used in conjunction with other healing modalities to support or improve their outcome. Such healing modalities commonly include changes in diet (such as fasting or detoxification regimes), various physical and breathing exercises, lifestyle changes, and also, where appropriate, other traditional or modern healing therapies. Forms of healing touch are

3. See chapter 1 for a full discussion of this sphere, which Avatar Adi Da calls "the Cosmic Mandala".

also currently being used or experimented with in hospitals and clinics around the world to positively improve the outcome of complicated surgical procedures and other health conditions.[4]

In earlier times, healing touch and massage were typically exchanged within families or between close friends. For instance, the increasingly popular Thai form of massage developed as a means of maintaining wellness within families. Certain forms of Hawaiian massage, such as lomilomi, were originally practiced by all members of society, at all ages. In other words, these primary healing approaches can be practiced by anyone who has feeling empathy for the one to be healed and who has the intention and energy to help. Avatar Adi Da also encourages all His devotees to give and receive healing touch when needed and even (optimally) as a daily part of life and Spiritual practice.[5]

Of course, traditionally, you could also go to someone locally in your village or tribe who was particularly skilled in the methods of energy healing. This paradigm is still observed in some traditional tribal cultures today, although many of these traditions are being lost or diluted in modern times. In fact, during His lifetime, Avatar Adi Da encouraged devotee healers who were serving Him to meet with and learn from those still skilled in energy-healing services in traditional cultures—such as the Native American shamans, Hawaiian kahunas, and Fijian medicine healers. He would also encourage us to meet with and learn from those experienced in religious energy-healing practices such as faith healing, and also those schooled in the multifaceted and highly structured systems for balancing and intensifying the energies of the body that have developed in various traditions over thousands of years, such as chi gong, needle and needleless acupuncture, and hatha yoga/pranayama. A big part of why we met with these energy healers was to confront and overcome our Western provincialism about healing, and to see firsthand the naturalness and often dramatic effectiveness of energy healing.

---

4. See for example Barb MacIntyre, et al., "The Efficacy of Healing Touch in Coronary Artery Bypass Surgery Recovery", *Alternative Therapies* 14 no. 4 (Jul/Aug 2008): 24–32; and Joyce Wong, et al., "The Impact of Healing Touch on Pediatric Oncology Patients", *Integrative Cancer Therapies* 12 no. 1 (January 2013): 25–30, https://doi.org/10.1177/1534735412446864.

5. See pp. 150–51 for Avatar Adi Da's further instructions on this point.

In the course of this research, we discovered that a common element in the various traditional healing practices is a disposition of bodily submission or surrender to the source of the healing energy (which is conceived variously in different traditions). However, we also discovered that this disposition was not part of what could be easily passed on to others. Some things could be taught or demonstrated by these healers in a visit or two, but they could not impart the force and power of their submission to the source of their healing in a brief exchange. As we learned, a real understanding and capacity for this submission in any particular tradition would often require either being born into the tradition or else a long apprenticeship often involving many years, even decades, of direct instruction and practice. It was always paradoxical that Avatar Adi Da Samraj would admonish us to travel to these healers and come back in a day or two having "learned everything he or she knows". More and more, we understood that He was sending us to them to witness people who had no doubt relative to their healing approach, and who engaged a real process of submission to their healing source. Through this, we learned more about what Avatar Adi Da was offering to us Westerners, raised in a world that had lost its sacred traditions and whose collective mind about such things could generally be characterized as "full of doubt"—He was offering a "radical" healing approach and a Transcendent Healing-Source. In this process, Avatar Adi Da was creating a new culture of understanding relative to energy healing in the modern world.

A Story of Deepening Recognition and Transformation

Avatar Adi Da also demonstrated His own compassionate healing, throughout His "teaching years", by performing healings on those who needed or requested His Help.[6] And when receiving treatments on His own body from devotee-healers, Avatar Adi Da was not only receiving healing help but was involved in another

6. See, for example, the book *Love and Blessings: The Divine Compassionate Miracles of Avatar Adi Da Samraj*.

form of His Healing Work: He would also work with the devotee performing the treatment, transforming his or her understanding of healing and increasing his or her sensitivity to His State and thus to the Source of healing. Through the years of receiving healing treatments from His devotees, Avatar Adi Da worked directly with many healers in this way. One example, which occurred toward the end of His bodily lifetime, is presented here.[7]

In 2008, Jane Yang, a devotee of Avatar Adi Da, offered her healing services to Avatar Adi Da to correct partial blindness caused by glaucoma (or elevated pressure) in the eyes. Jane was born and raised in China and spent many years being schooled in and practicing traditional forms of martial and medical chi gong, and also developing and practicing a form of chi gong based on the energy field called "Wu Ji".[8] She is acknowledged by her teachers and peers as being a master in her tradition, and she returns to China on a regular basis to teach others.

When Jane went to Adi Da Samrajashram, the island hermitage-retreat of Avatar Adi Da in Fiji, Avatar Adi Da took the opportunity to communicate with Jane about her experience and feeling-sensitivities while she did her Wu Ji Chi Gong healing treatments for Him. In one of her exchanges with Avatar Adi Da, Jane wrote: "Wu Ji Chi Gong is a process of consciously bringing one's feeling and intention into the Wu Ji field of energy and allowing that field to bring whatever changes are needed into being." In other words, Jane was indicating that Wu Ji Chi Gong works directly with a specific energy as the source of healing, and the purification and balancing that occur depend on what is needed by the system and by the qualities and characteristics of this field of energy, Wu Ji.

Avatar Adi Da received Jane's healing services and Jane's ongoing comments of what she perceived during the sessions. In this intensive exchange, a truly remarkable confession emerged. In one of her communications to Him, Jane described her experience of Avatar Adi Da as pure white Presence perceived through the

---

7. See pp. 218–20 and pp. 259–60 for testimonies from several other devotee-healers with whom Avatar Adi Da worked.

8. The term "Wu Ji" is a combination of two Chinese characters: "Wu" means "nothing or without" and "Ji" means "the ultimate or extreme". The term "Wu Ji" can be understood to mean "ultimate emptiness", or "infinite space".

golden Wu Ji field—and, in fact, her confession was that she recognized Avatar Adi Da to be the Source of the Wu Ji field. Avatar Adi Da acknowledged her confession:

Jane is correct in regarding Me and recognizing Me as the Source of the Wu Ji force, the Wu Ji sphere. I Am the "Bright". The process of My Transcendental Spiritual Presence here is Spherical, Circular. She is approaching Me at the yellow-red dimension of My Spherical Presence here. Thus, I Am the Source of what she knows as the Wu Ji field.   —August 3, 2008

Jane's confession of recognizing Avatar Adi Da as the Source of the Wu Ji field was not a casual matter. This occurred after years and years of her learning, applying, and practicing this form of energy healing—and all the struggle and transformation that necessarily occurs in the process of mastering any energy-healing practice that is based on submission to a source. And this recognition came also based on her own devotional response to Avatar Adi Da Himself.

Avatar Adi Da also acknowledged that, while Jane's sensitivity to His Spherical Presence allowed her to effectively serve Him, her heart-impulse in response to Him as His devotee also transformed the purpose of her service to Him.

My Presence here is Spherical. What Jane is describing is sensitivity immediate to the physical dimension of My Spherical Presence. She is seeing My Presence and experiencing It in immediate association with the physical, in the yellow-red dimension. That is the most outward level of My Spherical Form.

She is approaching Me at the body level, the yellow-red level, and is able to be sensitive to Me there and relate to Me there. And in her devotional recognition of Me, she can serve Me at the point of My association with the physical Body.

She has also indicated that she is approaching Me for the sake of Realization. This absolutely is her deepest desire. Because she will be entering into the Sphere of My Person for the purpose of Realizing Me, I must say to her: I am approached at the periphery, but What is to be Realized is at the Source.   —August 3, 2008

"I knew beyond doubt that He is the Great One"

J ANE YANG: *The great revelation that I eventually experienced was that Beloved Adi Da Samraj Himself is the Source of the Wu Ji field, incarnate in human Form.*

In July of 2002, I went on retreat at the Adidam Sanctuary in Hawaii. And around the same time Beloved Adi Da decided to come there from California. Even at the very moment His plane was touching down on the island, I felt a great shaking occurring in my body. As He arrived at the Sanctuary, my heart exploded with joy, and I knew beyond doubt that He is the Great One in human form. I could see Him completely shining with golden brightness, and this brightness was what I knew as the Wu Ji. As I sat before Beloved Adi Da, His Body dissolved into Pure White Light, and then was gone—just Brightness and an overwhelming dissolving Bliss until I knew no more. That day, Beloved Adi Da healed a great pain in my heart and body, which I will never forget and always value. I threw myself at His Feet, and cried till my heart was stilled by His deep silence. I love Him and always want to be with Him.

I became a formal devotee of Avatar Adi Da Samraj in November 2002. Six years later, I went to Adi Da Samraj-ashram to offer my healing services to Avatar Adi Da. On the first occasion of offering healing service to Him, the room was beautifully prepared with a massage table, blankets to cover Beloved Adi Da, and even exquisite flowers for Him to look at, soft music playing in the background. Beloved Adi Da came in and I bowed at His Feet, offering not only a flower but my whole life dedicated to serving Him to the best of my ability. My heart broke seeing His complete submission and vulnerability. The treatment lasted about thirty minutes.

(continued on next page)

This was the beginning of an amazing period of questions from Beloved Adi Da. He wanted to know everything about what I was doing, what I felt, what I was aware of, and so on. He was intensely interested in every aspect of what was going on—not only in Him, but in me as well. As Beloved Adi Da said to me:

> *Jane is not just treating Me—I am Working with her. No one has ever given Me any physical treatments who did not wind up going through a process themselves. Because I not only am receiving Jane's treatment help, I am receiving Jane. And she is not just connecting with everything that associates itself with Me—she is being connected with things associated with herself. [September 5, 2008]*

Of course Beloved Adi Da was right—I was going through all kinds of bodily, emotional, and mental purifications while working with Him. I had to receive daily healing treatments myself so I could cope with the effects of it. Bhagavan purified so many aspects of my previous family life, particularly with my mother, and the effects I had suffered as a result of growing up during the Chinese Revolution.

Beloved Adi Da was also continuing to instruct me to clear up my false patterns of being the healer! And Beloved Adi Da was also freeing me to truly understand the limitations in my understanding of the Wu Ji itself and how it relates to His human Form. He was always turning me to Him as the "Bright"—Beyond all conditional forms, Beyond the limitations of the Cosmic Mandala.

I realize that Beloved Adi Da Samraj Himself is this Ultimate Reality I was connecting with (and do connect with) through the Wu Ji field, but previously I had had no experiential understanding of this. That is why I fall at His feet in recognition of Who He Is. I know that the devotional relationship with the Guru is the only true healing required for any being. I see this confirmed in my healing practice time and time again.

The Source In Person

What is truly important about this story of Avatar Adi Da and Jane? First of all, it shows what makes energy healing work, what makes it truly effective—submission to a source, without mind, wishful thinking, or even prefigured visualization or intention. Regardless of how the energy-source is conceived and contacted and worked with, this disposition of submission is essential for anyone who practices energy healing, whether in traditional or modern forms. Secondly, it shows that while there are variations on how an energy-source for healing is conceived, contacted, and worked with, there are universal principles associated with the relationship between the physical body and the energy dimensions of existence. These are clearly evidenced in the ancient healing traditions, which are rooted in shamanic and (in some cases) esoteric yogic practices—embodied and conveyed by beings of great sensitivity, wisdom, and Spiritual understanding.[9]

Avatar Adi Da's wisdom on energy healing coincides with this traditional pattern and ancient wisdom. From His State of Realization, Avatar Adi Da considered and described, in detail, the practical and yogic requirements for health and well-being—and these make use of the inherent relationship between the physical body and etheric energy. Because of these universal principles of energy healing—the submission-disposition, and the role of energy in healing the physical body—Avatar Adi Da's instructions in this book can be used and applied by anyone in the context of their healing services (and even by anyone, in daily life).

9. See appendix E for a bibliography of books that demonstrate the universal principles and ancient origins of energy healing.

Lastly, as this story illustrates, recognition of the Source of the wisdom given in this book can not only transform one's practice of energy healing—it also can altogether transform the purpose of one's life. Through deepening sensitivity to Avatar Adi Da's State, it is possible to discover the single indivisible Source of any form of healing energy—and to come into feeling-contact with the direct transmission of that indivisible Source. This occurs in the sacred context of the devotional relationship to Avatar Adi Da—and, in that context, the heart-impulse to Realization can come to the fore.

In His communications to Jane, Avatar Adi Da spoke further on the process of Realization, and those statements were later included by Him in an essay in *The Aletheon*:

> *What Is to Be Realized Is at the Source, not at the periphery.*
>
> *However, right approach to Me begins at the periphery.*
>
> *Initially, people approach Me at the bodily level, recognizing Me devotionally and whole-bodily-responsively.*
>
> *In doing so, they enter into My literal Sphere.*
>
> *It Is the Sphere of the "Bright".*
>
> *To enter into My Sphere Is to "Perfectly Know" the Context of all conditional appearances.*
>
> *My Sphere is not related exclusively to My bodily (human) Form.*
>
> *Rather, My Sphere Is the Sphere of Reality Itself.*
>
> *That Is What must Be Realized.*
>
> *That Sphere Intrinsically and Perfectly Transcends the body, the "world", and all conditional phenomena.*
>
> *My devotees are involved in a process in which the body, the "world", and all conditional phenomena are Transformed by virtue of association with Me, and (Thus and Thereby) by virtue of Intrinsic Coincidence with What is Found to Be a Spherical Field of Energy That Is Utterly Benign.*
>
> *I Describe That Spherical Field of Energy As Love-Bliss Itself, Self-Existing Self-Radiance Itself, or Conscious Light Itself.*
>
> *That Spherical Field of Energy Is Beyond what may be "experienced" via the body or in relation to the body.*
>
> *That Spherical Field of Energy Outshines the body.*
>
> *That Spherical Field of Energy Is the Divine Self-Domain.*
>
> —"The Boundless Self-Confession",
> *The Aletheon*

The energy healing Avatar Adi Da describes is simply recognition of and direct feeling-submission to His Divine Presence as the Source, and being moved by that recognition in the context of the yellow-red domain—consciously conducting etheric energy in and throughout the physical body. And, simultaneously, the recognition of Avatar Adi Da draws the being into the great process of Realization.

Avatar Adi Da is the indivisible Source to be invoked for the sake of Realization, and the Healer for those requesting His Blessing-Help. His Healing-Force of Blessing is always available directly or through the healing help of others who invoke Him—and most effectively to those who practice the devotional relationship to Him.

Avatar Adi Da's Self-Confession is that He is not only the healing energy of the conditional world, but also that He is the Non-conditional Radiant Sphere of Indivisible Conscious Energy, or Conscious Light—prior to this world, prior to the body-mind and all dis-ease, mysteriously pervading all and including all, as a Love that knows no bounds.

May you make use of Avatar Adi Da's Instruction and His Healing Balm—Offered to you and to all. ■

Daniel Bouwmeester, MD, received his medical degree from the University of Melbourne, Australia, in 1975. He became a devotee of Avatar Adi Da in 1974, and after his residency moved to the United States to be near Avatar Adi Da and to be part of His gathering of devotees in California. Daniel served as one of Avatar Adi Da's personal physicians, and participated with Avatar Adi Da in His "considerations" of right life and Divine Realization throughout His "teaching years". Daniel currently serves in the Radiant Life Clinic, practicing medicine within the community of devotees on the basis of Avatar Adi Da's "radical" approach to healing, and guiding the implementation of Avatar Adi Da's healing principles in the cooperative gathering of Avatar Adi Da's devotees.

Avatar Adi Da's Right-Life Teachings Are for Everyone

In mid-2008, only a few months before His physical Passing, His Divine Presence Avatar Adi Da Samraj asked that a book be created to specifically communicate His Teachings about energy healing. In response to this request, this book was compiled from a vast array of instruction, given over many years (1972–2008), about how the human being can participate in and as energy—in the context of the body, the total universe, and Reality Itself.

This instruction on energy healing represents one facet of Avatar Adi Da's comprehensive "right-life Teachings". Avatar Adi Da defines "right life" as "the always practical life-demonstration of ego-renunciation".[1] When the illusion of ego (or separateness) is relinquished, one's actions are necessarily transformed, even on the most practical levels. Such transformed life-actions are not purposed toward fulfilling an apparently separate (or egoic) "self", but are expressions of ego-transcending participation in the Single Indivisible Unity of Existence (or Reality).

This reorientation—from ego-based life to a life of ego-transcending practice—is urgently needed in today's ego-based world-culture. Avatar Adi Da calls everyone to consider the Indivisible Nature of Reality, to live and act on the basis of that Reality, and to thus allow the necessary transformation of human culture as a whole. Study of Avatar Adi Da's instruction on energy healing is one means to participate in this process, to which He calls all of humankind.

Avatar Adi Da's right-life Teachings are also an integral part of the Reality-Realizing Way of life He offers to everyone. Those who tacitly recognize Avatar Adi Da as the direct Communication of the Indivisible Reality naturally choose to take up this Way of life,

---

1. From "The Human Destiny of Divine Translation", *The Aletheon.*

which He calls the Reality-Way of Adidam. The specific energy-healing practices described in this book are part of the comprehensive life of ego-transcending practice that supports full participation in the Reality-Way of Adidam.

If you, as a reader, are not a participant in the Reality-Way of Adidam, use the instruction in this book as Avatar Adi Da intended: allow the principles given herein to inform and illuminate your understanding and your heart, and apply them to your own practice of right life (in general) and energy healing (specifically) as is appropriate to your circumstance and capability. Avatar Adi Da's communications in Part One—on the energy structures of existence and the foundation principles of energy healing—are specifically intended to be useful for anyone who is moved to engage serious study on the subjects of energy and energy healing.

Parts Two, Three, and Four of this book contain Avatar Adi Da's detailed instructions on the specific energy-healing practices He gives to those who are practitioners of the Reality-Way of Adidam—described by the general term "'conductivity' healing" (see next page for details). While study of Avatar Adi Da's instructions in these later parts of the book can benefit anyone, they are specifically intended as a practical guide for those who are living the life of devotional response to Avatar Adi Da. Thus, if you are a practitioner of the Reality-Way of Adidam, this book offers direct guidance and instruction from Avatar Adi Da—to inform and guide your understanding and your practice of energy healing, in the specific forms He has given.

Regardless of your reasons for studying this book, implicit in all of Avatar Adi Da's instructions is an invitation to participate in direct relationship with Him. Thus, you are invited to receive the words contained in this book as a personal and living communication from His Divine Presence Avatar Adi Da, occurring not just in the mind but at heart-depth.

For more information, visit
conductivityhealing.com

Overview of the Practices Presented in This Book

Ιn this book, along with His general Teachings about energy and energy healing, Avatar Adi Da offers two principal forms of "conductivity"-healing practice and a variety of supplemental practices.

Principal "Conductivity"-Healing Practices (Part Three)

1. **The laying on of hands:** Avatar Adi Da gives a specific form of this ancient healing practice, which form entails the directing of natural life-energy through touch and the breath cycle, in coordination with whole bodily ego-transcending prayer.

2. **Yogic "conductivity" massage:** Avatar Adi Da gives a simple, but Yogically specific, structured form of massage intended to magnify the flow of life-energy in the body-mind in its primary circuit: up the back of the body and down the front of the body.

Supplemental Practices (Part Four)

Avatar Adi Da recommends a variety of supplemental practices and aids, which are presented in Part Four. These include:

- Polarity Screens
- Pranayama (or Yogic breathing)
- Hamsadanda (or Short Crutch)
- Water Immersion
- Tensing-and-Relaxing
- Twirling

Chapter 5 also includes a number of practices that are foundation elements used in the principal "conductivity"-healing practices given in Part Three. These are simple means for practitioners to take responsibility for the flow of life-energy in their own bodies and to establish the ego-transcending disposition that is at the core of all the practices described in this book. ■

Editors' Notes: The instructions included in this book include writings and discourses on energy and energy healing that Avatar Adi Da gave over more than three decades, beginning in 1972 and ending in 2008. Over the course of those decades, Avatar Adi Da worked continuously to refine and establish standards of terminology and communication that were maximally expressive of His Teaching-Revelation, and He asked that these standards (in their final form) be applied to His earlier writings and discourses. Therefore, per His explicit instructions, Avatar Adi Da's written and spoken instructions given in this book have been updated as necessary, so that the earlier writings and discourses are (in all respects) consistent with His final Teaching-Revelation. Thus, the reader can rely on the instructions in this book as part of His definitive and summary Wisdom.

In some of the quotations from Avatar Adi Da's Word, the editors have added subheadings, paragraph breaks, and (occasionally) bullet points, for the sake of assisting comprehension.

The expository writing in this book is an expression of respect and recognition of His Divine Presence Avatar Adi Da Samraj as the Incarnation and Transmitter of the Divine Conscious Light. Therefore, His various sacred titles, many words in reference to His Life and Work, and pronouns in reference to Him are capitalized, in order to concretely express the understanding of Who Avatar Adi Da Samraj Is that is at the heart of this communication.

Capitalization, Underlining, Quotation Marks: Avatar Adi Da Samraj uses capitalization, underlining, and quotation marks to distinguish between ordinary speech (which describes the conditionally manifested reality) and speech that describes the Non-conditional Divine Reality. With the use of capitalization and underlining, Avatar Adi Da expresses a different view of the world, in which Truth and the terms that relate to that greater Reality are given more significance than the language of the separate ego and the conventional world. (Avatar Adi Da also uses underlining simply to indicate emphasis.) Avatar Adi Da most often uses quotation marks as a visual indication that the word or phrase is being used with a specific meaning unique to His language of instruction (for example, "conductivity"). (Please see the glossary for explanations of such specific meanings.) In other instances, Avatar Adi Da uses quotation marks to indicate that an ordinary term, commonly presumed to point to something real, is, in Reality, pointing to an illusion (for example, "self").

ABOUT THE RADIANT LIFE CLINIC

The Radiant Life Cultural and Health Services (also known, more simply, as "The Radiant Life Clinic") was called into being by Avatar Adi Da Samraj in 1979. The principal responsibility that Avatar Adi Da gave to the Radiant Life Clinic is to provide education, publications, and research to the gathering of Avatar Adi Da's devotees and to the general public. In addition, health practitioners who are members of the Radiant Life Clinic provide clinical and healing services on the basis of their legal license to practice—conducting their healing practice in conformity with the instruction and right-life principles given by Avatar Adi Da.

THE *DAWN HORSE TESTAMENT* LOGO

This logo-image, developed under the guidance of Avatar Adi Da Samraj, appears in *Conductivity Healing* to mark principal quotations drawn from *The Dawn Horse Testament*. One of Avatar Adi Da's principal "Source-Texts", *The Dawn Horse Testament* contains His detailed instruction on the practice of the Reality-Way of Adidam. Therefore, instruction from *The Dawn Horse Testament* is central to ongoing study and application of "conductivity"-healing practice (and all other right-life practices) for His devotees.

For an explanation of the elements of the logo-image, see *Right Life Is Free Participation In Unlimited Radiance*, pp. xii–xiii.

The Body Is Energy

The Body Is Energy

by His Divine Presence,
Avatar Adi Da Samraj

The body is energy.
An aspect of it appears to be solid, but it is only a certain frequency of vibration.

There exist many higher and many lower vibrations of the being.

Beyond a certain point in this great spectrum of vibrations, you lose the "visibility" of the Divine Reality, you lose track of the Depth of Infinity—because your physical stress attunes you only to this limited vibration of apparent matter.

But, if that stress relaxes, you can feel that the physical body and energy are the same.

Can you feel that the body is only free energy—right now?

You can feel a tension, an urge to want to hold something in at your heart.

But that is just your stress, your reluctance to relax, your suppression of Radiance, of Love, of profuse Happiness.

Let that contraction go, and you will feel the whole body radiate.

A universal process of "tuning in" exists which all human beings are involved in, at an invisible level.

Even the physical mechanisms—the complex organisms of body and mind—are involved in this process.

The gross (physical) aspects of the human body-mind-complex function very much like transmitter-receivers.

The gross (physical) body is a living bio-form.

It has the capability to operate in a field of energy, to transfer energies—and to be in sympathy, therefore, with fields of energy that exist beyond the physical body.

The body does not have any independent existence.

It is not enclosed upon itself.

It did not arise on its own.

There is no seed inside it that brought the body into existence.

Likewise, every other dimension of the human being is not "inside", but is simply a modification of a universal pattern.

The brain and the nervous system are merely transmitter-receiver mechanisms.

They are ways of participating in a universal field that is, simultaneously, material and energetic and psychic.

And, if the "self"-knot is given up, the physical body will flow with the great force, the great elemental field in which it exists, and will be much healthier and freer.

What will the collective of humankind do when it takes the discovery of the relationship between matter and energy seriously?

How do human beings make medicine out of the understanding that the human body is energy?

How do human beings practice diet, health, sexuality, and social relations on that basis?

How are the higher "knowledge" of physics and the principles of esoteric Spirituality brought into the daily practice of ordinary people?

And, then, how can humankind be brought into the greater awareness—and, ultimately, the Perfect Realization—of the Transcendental Spiritual Divine Consciousness, in Which (and As Which) matter, energy, and light are appearing?

If you are serious about such questions, I suggest that you study the Literature I have Written for just such a one as yourself.

Then choose what you will do. ■

The prologue is drawn from "Stress Chemistry and Whole Bodily Enlightenment" in *Scientific Proof of The Existence of God Will Soon Be Announced By The White House!*; "M-Fields and The Work of The Adept" in *The Transmission of Doubt*; "You Can't Get There From Here", a discourse given on August 2, 1980; and "Christ = mc^2" in *Scientific Proof of The Existence of God Will Soon Be Announced By The White House!*

PART ONE

THE HEALING PRINCIPLE OF ENERGY

CHAPTER 1

Energy Healing
and the
Total Human Structure

I t is false philosophy to presume (or even insist) that Reality *Itself* is reducible to the observable "facts" of the presumed-to-be-separate human structure and its functioning.
This must be understood:
The human psycho-physical structure is (irreducibly) part of the Prior and Universal Unity.
Reality Itself Is Non-separate, Indivisible, and (Ultimately) *One*— *Beyond* all appearances.

—Avatar Adi Da Samraj
"The Transcendental Spiritual Way of Reality Itself Is Founded On The Tacit and Prior 'Perfect Knowledge' of Reality Itself",
The Aletheon

His Divine Presence Avatar Adi Da Samraj brings unprecedented clarity to the nature of energy healing and the context in which it is engaged. Specifically, He gives straightforward and precise descriptions of the energy dimensions that are most relevant to healing—the physical dimension and the etheric dimension. He describes how these two dimensions of energy function in relation to the human system itself and in relation to the universal (or cosmic) system of energy in which human beings are inherently participating. And, most significantly, He Reveals the Fundamental (or Prior) Condition, or Reality, of everything and everyone—which is the ultimate Context in which all healing occurs.

Everything Is Energy

f you rub your hands together, and then hold them close but slightly apart, you can feel the energy between them. You can feel there is a kind of vibratory fluid between the hands.

What does that mean? It means that the physical body is not merely "material" in some gross, meat-like sense. The physical body is part of an energy-domain.

If you go deeply into the physical dimension, you see it is simply energies. It is mainly space. When you get down to the atomic level, there is a lot of space in between so-called "particles". It is a field of energy. The particles are not particles—when seen truly, they are energy-fields.

Everything is energy-fields—everything! There is no "matter". There is only energy-fields. Everything is an apparition of energy-fields. Everything cosmic, everything conditional, is energy only. There is no matter otherwise.

What appears to be matter is a mode of energy. If you get close enough to it, you find matter to be energy. If you get more of a distant view, you feel it as "stuff". But, in truth, there is no "stuff"— there are only fields of energy.

Functioning on the basis of this understanding is fundamental human responsibility. The Reality-Way I Reveal and Give includes that understanding as part of the basic responsibility for practice. Right-life practice is energy-practice relative to the life-domain.

—Avatar Adi Da Samraj
July 30, 2008

It is common knowledge, in both Eastern and Western traditions—sacred and secular—that the human body is only energy. It stands to reason, then, that healing the body is primarily a matter of addressing energy. Indeed, this approach is becoming more and more widely accepted and utilized in a range of healing disciplines. Yet, in spite of this apparent knowledge, humankind as a whole still tends to relate to bodies and other physical appearances as solid, material "things".

AVATAR ADI DA SAMRAJ: What is the secret of everything? Energy! When I Say this, you say, "Yes, of course!" But you do not live as if it were so.

There are all kinds of circuitry, in the brain and otherwise, that determine whether or not you can "know" something. These evolutionary structures are really just limits on what you are able to "know" about what is the case. Because of these limits, you do not altogether get that everything is energy. You really do not.

You think you know that everything is energy, but you have not really realized it yet. To realize it is quite a different thing than affirming it, as even children do in classes in school. Affirming it is not the same—affirming it does not get through those circuits, those little pattern-keys that determine whether you just crawl around here and sniff, or enter into higher planes, or Realize the Absolute.

All these locks can be broken through. They can be unlocked. But you have to be very serious about all this.

You do feel that you know that it is simply, patently true that everything is energy, right?

DEVOTEES: Yes.

AVATAR ADI DA SAMRAJ: Even in schools or in common education, this is the presumption. You feel that you know this—yet you do not exist simply as it.

Therefore, the secret of everything is that it is energy—but it does not change anything to get the secret told to you. It must become a realization.

—February 8, 1997

Avatar Adi Da's Teachings on energy are intended to awaken this understanding that everything is energy—in your real experience, beyond intellectual affirmation. And the energy-healing practices He gives are part of a total life of practice for those who will choose it—a life that accounts for the understanding that everything is energy, and which is purposed to Realize that understanding in absolute terms.

Healing and the Hierarchy of Energy

T*he environment of the <u>whole</u> body is not solid, like a wall of concrete pressed against the psyche. When attention is free as present and constant feeling, in and through the functions of life, the psycho-physical nature (rather than the merely physical nature) of the total environment of the body begins to become obvious. Then breath and body are realized to be a single process in a single environment, which is made not only of solid elements but of subtle ranges, including all that may be felt, thought, conceived, intuited, and Realized in Truth.*

—Avatar Adi Da Samraj
"The Principles In Action To Which All Exercise
and Even Ordinary Activity Must Be Adapted",
Conscious Exercise and The Transcendental Sun

If everything is energy, then it is also evident that there is a vast range of energies that comprise all of existence. What range of energy is actually addressed in the practice of energy healing?

Avatar Adi Da uses the descriptors "red" and "yellow" to indicate particular forms of energy. In doing so, He is referencing a summary Yogic vision of the complete spectrum of the dimensions of cosmic existence. He calls this Yogic vision "the Cosmic Mandala". The vision of the Cosmic Mandala helps to illustrate the various energy dimensions of existence, and to identify the specific forms of energy that are most relevant to energy healing.

The Vision of Cosmic Energies

The cosmic domain as a whole is perceptible in the form of the Cosmic Mandala.

—Avatar Adi Da Samraj
August 16, 1995

In the same way that scientists explore the observable energies of the external, physical universe, true mystics and Yogis have explored the internal, subtle ranges of energy for thousands of years. Reports of such Yogic exploration describe the inner, visionary display of colored lights representing hierarchical energy-dimensions, including the physical. Those lights are interpreted and experienced in different ways by different individuals and traditions. In agreement with some esoteric traditions, Avatar Adi Da explains that, when experienced as a simultaneous totality, the display of lights appears as a mandala (or pattern) of concentric circles.[1]

Avatar Adi Da calls this vision the "Cosmic Mandala" because it depicts the entire cosmos—or all possible forms and states of experience. In other words, the Cosmic Mandala depicts the totality of everything conditional—all beings, things, places, and happenings that are inherently dependent on cause-and-effect forces, and are (therefore) always appearing, changing, and disappearing.[2] Avatar Adi Da calls the Cosmic Mandala "the body of the cosmic domain as a whole".[3]

Thus, Avatar Adi Da's detailed description of the Cosmic Mandala is a uniquely summary revelation about the total structure of conditional reality—whether apparently external or apparently internal.

In My Own "experience", that Cosmic Mandala is not only composed of concentric circles of particular colors—but each circle is of a particular precise width (and, thus, of particular proportional significance) relative to the other circles. Thus, in that pattern of circles, the red circle is the outermost circle (perceived against a colorless dark field), but it is a relatively narrow band, appearing next to a much wider band (or circle) of golden yellow. After the very wide golden yellow circle, there is a much narrower soft-white circle. And the soft-white circle is followed by an also very narrow black circle (or band). Closest to the Center of the Cosmic Mandala

---

1. Avatar Adi Da specifically gave the example of the vision recounted by Paramahansa Yogananda (1893–1952) in *Autobiography of a Yogi* (at the end of chapter 13, "The Sleepless Saint"): "the cosmical spheres, ring within ring, zone after zone, all dowered with divinity".

2. See the introduction, pp. 5–6, for a fuller discussion of Avatar Adi Da's description of "conditional reality" versus "Non-conditional Reality".

3. From a discourse given on August 16, 1995.

is a very wide circle of bright blue. And, at the Very Center of the blue field, there is a Brilliant White Five-Pointed Star.

—Avatar Adi Da Samraj
"I (Alone) Am The Adidam Revelation",
The Knee of Listening

Avatar Adi Da explains that each color band of the Cosmic Mandala is a distinct energy dimension of existence, with the dimensions becoming more and more subtle as they move inward toward the central Star-Form. (The Star-Form does not represent an energy dimension, but rather is the Form as which the Non-conditional Reality is perceived in the vision of the Cosmic Mandala.)

The colors of the Cosmic Mandala, taken all together, represent the full range of possible energy vibrations in conditional existence. This range falls into two broad categories: (1) gross (physical) energy and (2) subtle energy. The subtle energy dimension is further delineated into three categories: etheric, lower mental, and higher mental (each of which appears as a distinct color).[4]

The outermost, red ring of the Cosmic Mandala represents the physical (gross, or elemental) dimension. The golden-yellow ring just inside it represents the etheric energy dimension (the first, or "lowest", form of subtle energy). Avatar Adi Da describes the yellow-red conjunction, or the meeting of etheric energy and physical energy, as the "place" of energy healing in the human body.

Red = Physical = Gross Energy

Avatar Adi Da emphasizes that even the physical dimension of existence, despite its apparent "grossness" (in the sense of "denseness"), is simply a range of energy.

---

4. See appendix A for Avatar Adi Da's fuller descriptions of the significance of each of the bands of color and the central Star form in the vision of the Cosmic Mandala. See appendix B for more details on each of the three categories of the subtle dimension of existence.

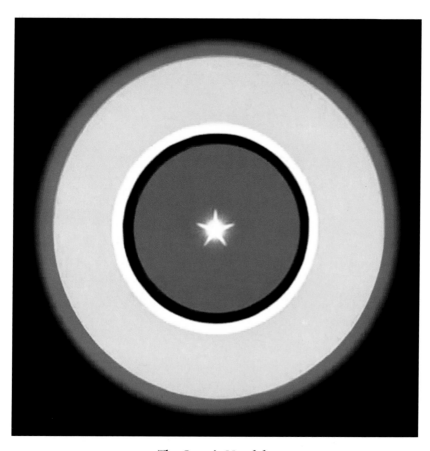

The Cosmic Mandala

Artist's rendering, developed under Avatar Adi Da's guidance

When I refer to the "gross dimension", I am covering everything within it—everything gross, or physical, altogether. There are many gross forms in this apparent "world". The human body is a gross form, but so is a rock, and so is the densest elemental material. All of that is gross.

All gross forms exist in a realm peculiar to themselves. Each of them exists in a field that corresponds to its elemental grossness. Therefore, the human gross body exists in a field of grossness of its own likeness. You are sensitive to an elemental field in the likeness of your own body. Things that are more solid in their grossness are likewise sensitive to a field in their likeness.

Insects, and even tiny entities not visible to the human eye, and so forth, exist on Earth. Some even attach themselves to human bodies. If you took a microscope up to your eyelids, for instance, in almost every case there are little tiny entities there, little bug-like entities nesting in the edges of your eyelids—right now—and all over your body.

Such entities exist in this Earth-plane, just as human bodies do, and they are often even living in or on human bodies. But they are not thinking, "Here I am, nesting on the eyelid of a human body." They are "experiencing" this Earth-"world" in quite a different fashion than you are as a human entity. As far as they are concerned, they are in a different place altogether, a different kind of a realm altogether—visually different, tactilely different, with different sense features, different qualities of awareness, altogether. And, yet, it is the same Earth-"world".

Also, no matter how dense a form gets, it is still not absolutely motionless. Everything moves, everything changes. A gross elemental like, let us say, your toenail grows over time and you notice that. But, if you just look at the toenail in any given moment, it does not appear to be moving. Nevertheless, if you could enter deeply into it, down into its energy structure, you would see all kinds of motion.

Therefore, no matter how gross, or dense, or (so-called) "material", anything appears to be, it is still energy. As energy, it is participating in the lower end of the subtle dimension of the cosmic domain.

—Avatar Adi Da Samraj
August 19, 1995

Because the gross dimension is in fact energy, no physical form is truly distinct, or separate, from the surrounding energy field in which it arises. Rather, there is a continuous interaction, at the level of energy, between the physical body and its surroundings—and also a continuous exchange of energy within the body's own physiology.

You are existing in a vast gaseous fluid that is rather invisible. You are very much like fish in the water. In bodily terms, you are moving about in a fluid. . . . Where does the body end and the fluid appear? Where is the "difference"? . . .

The body exists in a sea of gas. It also exists in a sea of energy. It exists in a sea of elements of all kinds. Although you can refer to your mind, it is not just a "something". It is part of this multi-planed sphere of forces—chemical, biochemical, molecular, energic—that proceed in a vast, unlimited sphere. There is no separate breath. Breath occurs within this sea of gas. There is no separate energy. There is one energy—which is conducted (somehow or other) within some sort of who-knows-what, and which is not separate from it.

So, where is "the body"? Where does it begin? What makes it a "the" anyway?

—Avatar Adi Da Samraj
"Have You Experienced A Reality That
Corresponds To Your Words?",
My "Bright" Form

❖ ❖ ❖

If you enter into "consideration" of the gross physical (or gross material) dimension of Reality more and more deeply, you become aware of subtler aspects of what you otherwise presume to be merely gross physical (or merely "matter"). Thus, you become aware of the mental and (eventually) the psychic aspects of conditionally manifested existence. And you become sensitive to the energy dimension of conditionally manifested existence, and (in due course) to various kinds of subtle perceptions of conditionally manifested existence. But none of those aspects of conditionally manifested existence are entirely separated from the gross physical (or exclusively "inward" to, and entirely "away" from, the gross physical)—rather, they are simply subtler forms of what you call the "gross physical" (or "matter"). The gross physical is simply one depth (or mode) of vibratory perception, and there are various deeper modes of the perception of the Same "Thing".

—Avatar Adi Da Samraj
"I Am The Way To Transcend The Illusions of Broken Light",
Real God Is The Indivisible Oneness of Unbroken Light

Yellow = Etheric = Subtle Energy Immediate to the Physical

Human beings are grossly manifested—there is no doubt about that—but you are not only grossly manifested. The physical body is of a certain size—five or six feet long—with two arms, two legs, a head, a trunk in the middle, and various other features. The physical body is one aspect of the human being. So long as the senses are functioning rightly, they provide you with information about yourself and others quite readily.

But you actually exist in another form as well, which is also quite tangible and personal, and that is the dimension of the etheric being, or etheric sheath.[5] This sheath pervades and envelops the gross food-sheath and extends for some distance outside the body. How far it extends depends on the qualities of each individual.

Everyone is present, then, not merely as a gross material entity, but also as a subtle material (or etheric) entity. You are actually extended even beyond the etheric envelope in the subtle domain. Ultimately, you are arising in the Infinite Field of forces and the Ultimate Transcendental Spiritual Force.

—Avatar Adi Da Samraj
"The Body As Energy and The Universal Field of Consciousness",
The Transmission of Doubt

Etheric energy is the invisible current or force that animates the physical body. As Avatar Adi Da describes above, this energy pervades the physical body and also surrounds it—effectively forming a personal field of energy directly related to the physical body. This etheric field is associated with the systems of sensory

5. For a summary of the paradigm of the "sheaths" of the human being, see appendix B.

perception and emotion. Additionally, etheric energy is directly tied to the process of breathing, which connects the flow of life-energy to the physical body.

---

etheric energy

Avatar Adi Da uses various terms to describe etheric energy:

- natural life-energy
- bio-energy
- bodily "experienced" energy
- pranic* energy

Each of these phrases points to the fact that etheric energy is energy that is experienced by the body. The physical body and its associated field of etheric energy are always (to one degree or another) integrally connected and in communication.

* A traditional term based on the Sanskrit word "prana", meaning "breath".

AVATAR ADI DA SAMRAJ: *The etheric field of energy basically conforms its shape to the physical body as long as one is alive in the physical sheath, but it also participates in the subtle forces (or the finer material energies). On the one hand, the etheric field of energy conforms, in general, to the shape of the physical body—but, on the other hand, it surrounds the physical body as a kind of bulb or egg-shape. Where it is rather shapeless or curved or egg-shaped, the etheric is bleeding into, or connected to, the subtle dimension. This etheric aspect of the human structure could be called the "lower subtle dimension". In some literatures, it is simply referred to as part of the subtle dimension.*

DEVOTEE: *Beloved Master, are there two different bodies, then— one that is similar to the gross physical, but made of energy, and one that is curved or egg-shaped?*

AVATAR ADI DA SAMRAJ: The right way to think of it is that everything is just energy. At one end of the scale, Energy is Infinite, nothing but the Self-Radiance of the Transcendental Spiritual Self-Condition, the Divine Being—and It Pervades the entire cosmos. This All-Pervading Energy is stepped down by degrees. At each major step, Energy becomes more gross, and different functions, activities, and qualities are associated with each step. By the time Energy reaches the physical level, It exists in its grossest (or densest) form. The etheric is simply the next subtler aspect of the continuous spectrum of Energy. Thus, there are not really two separate bodies— they are just different degrees (or levels) of the same Force.

The physical body is a discrete (or particularized) form. While you live in association with the physical body, the etheric body, as I have already Said, extends out some distance from the body, but basically conforms to the gross physical shape. Beyond that immediate range of energy, you begin to enter into subtler dimensions of energy. The subtle field itself comprises a number of increasingly subtler levels. There are really no absolute breaks in energy but only different qualities of one great Energy, one great Force-Field, becoming more and more particularized. The closer this Energy is to the physical, the more It conforms to the physical in shape and appearance.

First there is a kind of emanation that conforms basically to the shape of the physical. Then, at a certain distance, it begins to become a kind of radiance or sphere. There are many levels of spheres. As you get deeper and deeper into the domain of Energy (or Being) Itself, you develop the capability to be sensitive to, and to observe, the qualities inherent in the different levels.

At the level of ordinary human learning, you must become sensitive to the gross personality and its functional aspects, its nervous system, its right and left halves,[6] and the processes that keep it in balance. You must also become sensitive to your etheric aspect, the energies that are very intimate with your gross physical personality. And, to some degree, you must become sensitive to the dimension of your existence that includes your higher psyche.

6. See chapter 8 for Avatar Adi Da's instructions on the "right and left halves" of the body-mind-complex.

41

Ultimately, you must go beyond all three of these levels in the process of Awakening, but at least these three—the gross, the etheric, and the psychic dimensions—must become part of ordinary human "self"-knowledge at a relatively early stage in life. . . .

Because of your material view of existence, you tend to think that space is empty, that it is just the distance between "objects" and is not itself a positive substance. The most you may think is that some chemicals may be floating around in space, because you know that you breathe—but without a subtler awareness, a subtler sensitivity to phenomenal existence, you tend to discount the fact that space is pervaded by energy. Space is continuous. It is not just the distance between "objects". Rather, space is that within which "objects" appear. In fact, "objects" are space. Space is energy. Human beings are energy. And human beings participate in infinite space because they are extended into infinite space.

At one level, you exist as a specific physical entity—but an entity that is dependent on all kinds of physical processes for its birth and its survival. You are also a personal field of energy that is rather limited—shaped like the physical, and very intimately associated with your physical existence. That energy is not only outside the body, but it pervades the body as well. It is the energy of the nervous system, and it is (to some degree) dependent on the state of the physical body.

The food you take into your body and your general environment support a kind of chemical process that produces the etheric dimension. But the etheric dimension is not merely created by chemical and electrical forces. The etheric dimension also derives from the subtle dimension. The etheric sheath, then, is a limited personal field of energy that (on the one hand) is arising from and supplied by the universal field coming out of the subtle dimension, but (on the other hand) is supplied by the physical body.

Thus, to treat the physical body wrongly will decrease nerve-force and weaken the etheric envelope, and it will even have some effect on the more subtle dimensions of the being, such as the psychic part of you.

—Avatar Adi Da Samraj
"The Body As Energy and The Universal Field of Consciousness",
The Transmission of Doubt

Balancing the Yellow-Red Conjunction

Avatar Adi Da teaches that the relationship between the physical body and its etheric energy is the key to the healing process. How etheric energy is conducted throughout the body is the measure of this relationship.

The physical is the red realm, and the etheric is the yellow realm. Healing is a matter of keeping the conjunction between yellow and red in balance, and flowing, and so forth—maintaining the balance of that conjunction (or, otherwise, restoring the balance of that conjunction) and (thereby) removing obstructions. Thus, "conductivity" healing is a matter of the yellow-red conjunction.

There are other dimensions of energy also. But, healing is particularly a matter of addressing this yellow-red zone. That is where healing work is done. It is about the connection between the yellow and the red, the etheric-energy dimension and the gross physical dimension—keeping that connection balanced and free-flowing, free of obstructions, free of toxicity and negative accumulations, free of "cause"-and-"effect" patterns that show unwellness and various other life-conditions that are regarded to be negative.

—Avatar Adi Da Samraj
July 30, 2008

❖ ❖ ❖

The process of healing enables the gross physical body to be integrated with the etheric body (or energy body), which is the next most subtle dimension of the being. When that integration occurs, the physical body is submitted to the lawful process of change. Eventually, physical karmas (the negative, binding qualities and tendencies of action and reaction in the gross physical body) may be completely undone. But, even in the present moment, the individual can at least enjoy the disposition of well-being and be free of his or her habitual, problematic approach to "experiential" life.

—Avatar Adi Da Samraj
"The Doctor Is A Healing Presence",
The Eating Gorilla Comes In Peace

Many healing practitioners, in a variety of disciplines (including even some practitioners of Western medicine), make use of etheric energy for healing of the physical body and the emotional being— although they use a variety of terms and approaches to describe what is occurring.[7] Some energy healers practice in traditions that work with highly technical and detailed maps of the energy pathways within the physical body.[8] Avatar Adi Da's practical Teachings about energy healing are based in universal principles that are expressed in these ancient and modern energy-healing traditions.

My communications about the subtle body and its relationship with the gross body come from My direct "experience". Also, there is a vast collective "experience" of such things. Thousands upon thousands of individuals throughout history have corroborated what I am Saying to you about this matter.

Therefore, what I am Saying about the relationship between the subtle body and the gross body is not merely a philosophical matter. It is not just an alternative proposition to materialism—as if it is just another way of thinking, and it may or may not be true. No, it is clearly true. It is based on real "experience", thoroughly investigated, and not merely entertained by fools. The most highly developed of beings who have ever lived on Earth have confirmed all of this.

Of course, this particular matter is not about Ultimate Truth or Realization. It is about how the cosmic domain works. The cosmic domain works from within outward—from the subtle toward the gross. In other words, what is appearing here—as gross forms, gross functions, and so on—is an expression of what is subtler. The actual functions of the human being exist on a subtler level, and function from the subtle into the gross.

—Avatar Adi Da Samraj
July 23, 1995

7. See, for example, Patty de Llosa, "Energy Therapy", *Parabola* 37:4 (Winter 2012).

8. See appendix E for a listing of books on traditional and modern energy-healing practices, many of which illustrate this point.

One need not be familiar with complex maps of etheric energy (or other, subtler levels of energy) to use Avatar Adi Da's instructions on energy healing—although Avatar Adi Da does call His devotees who are professional healers to understand and make use of such maps of the human body-mind-complex in their healing work. To practice energy healing as described by Avatar Adi Da, it is simply necessary to become aware of the etheric dimension of one's own body and of existence altogether—and to become sensitive to the process that occurs in the conjunction between the etheric and physical dimensions.

The etheric is immediate to the physical. It is a living, or circulatory, force, not just a static shape. The etheric is a process. It is a living energy. It is a bio-energy-field, immediate to the physical.

But the relationship between the physical and the etheric can become complicated, interrupted—it can be a matter of awareness or it can be a matter of zero awareness. Keeping the relationship between the etheric and physical right, balanced, integrated, and conscious is very important for health.

The health disciplines I have Given to My devotees are completely associated with the energy-field, including the etheric, and are not merely gross physical matters.

—Avatar Adi Da Samraj
July 30, 2008

Furthermore, it is also necessary to become sensitive to the fact that all living beings are inherently connected to one another through this "yellow", or etheric, field of energy—and that, therefore, the quality of the personal etheric-energy body is directly communicated to others through this universal field of natural life-energy.

You must understand how conditional existence works. People tend to think in gross-body terms—so they do not see the subtle connections.

The subtle dimension of the personality is the dimension full of the faculties—of mind (or attention), emotion (or feeling), and breath. And even the principal energy of the faculty of the body is part of the subtle body—the etheric part.[9]

Therefore, you are not merely functioning as a gross material form. You are functioning as a subtle personality, equipped with all the mechanisms of the subtle personality. You are connected, then, to all of your associations not only through mechanisms of mind but through the plastic of the etheric field.

Therefore, with anything that is within your sphere of attention— your relations or whoever or whatever is in your thoughts, whether intentional thoughts or in your subconscious mind somehow—there is actually a subtle connection, an energy connection, a tangible connection with that person or thing. It is an actual connection.

If you like, think of this etheric field as a sticky, rubbery substance, which links up to, or touches, all of your associations, environments, and so forth.

—Avatar Adi Da Samraj
August 3, 1995

Because of this universal characteristic of the etheric field, one person can directly affect another in a healing manner. Avatar Adi Da's energy-healing practices are a way to make conscious, positive use of the field of natural life-energy for the sake of balancing the yellow-red conjunction.

---

9. The four principal faculties of the human body-mind are body, emotion (or feeling), mind (or attention), and breath. These four principal faculties account for the entirety of the human being.

The Causal Dimension and Accounting for Root-Contraction

I n addition to the two fundamental energy dimensions of existence—the gross (or physical) and the subtle (in its various levels, including the etheric)—there is a third fundamental dimension at the root-depth of existence. This is the causal dimension, associated with the sense of "self"-identity. Every human being is manifested via these three fundamental dimensions, which Avatar Adi Da summarizes as outer (physical), inner (subtle), and root (causal).[10] Avatar Adi Da's Teachings on energy healing address all these dimensions of the human structure.

"Underneath" (or deeper than) all bodily action and sensation, all emotion and perception, all thoughts and experiences, there is a sense of being an independent entity, a separate "self". Though it is free of any specific personality characteristics, this sensation has a kind of force, actively defining itself and, thus, differentiating from "others". Avatar Adi Da describes this force as a "contraction", or "knot", at the "root" of the being.

The "root" (or causal) dimension is the "root" ego-dimension, the dimension of the "root"-contraction. . . . The feelings of separateness, relatedness, otherness, and "difference" comprise the inherent characteristics of the causal dimension (or "root" ego-dimension) of conditionally apparent awareness.

—Avatar Adi Da Samraj
"What Consciousness Is",
The Aletheon

While the gross and subtle dimensions are represented by the spectrum of colors in the Cosmic Mandala, Avatar Adi Da explains that the causal dimension is not visually represented. This is because the causal dimension is the position of the presumed "self"-identity from which the entire Mandala is perceived.

---

10. This gross/subtle/causal paradigm is also found in certain traditional esoteric schools. (See appendix B for more on the three fundamental dimensions and their associated sheaths.)

The causal dimension is the "place" where awareness associates with the subtle and gross dimensions of the human being and the cosmic domain. And the causal dimension is the "deepest" (or "first") dimension of the apparently separate being, from which all the specific qualities and tendencies of psyche, mind, life-energy, and body emerge.

The causal dimension is something like the "stem cells" of the ego. Everything else gets built from it. All the subtle and gross modes of egoity come from this "root"-dimension of egoity. It is "subtle beyond words", you could say.

One of the traditional references for it is "anandamayakosha". Of course, there are different descriptions of the body-mind structures in different traditions. In the Yogic tradition, they speak of anandamayakosha as something that is really a part of the subtle body. Swami (Baba) Muktananda, for instance, uses the term "causal body" when he is really talking about a dimension of the subtle body. And then sometimes people refer to the "supracausal" dimension, conceived as a further dimension beyond the causal. There are different languages of description.

In My Teaching, the causal dimension is "root"-egoity. As I Said, it is something like the "stem cells" of the rest of the ego, or what makes the body-mind-complex in its elaboration, just as stem cells become a fetus.

There are stem cells in your own body right now. Adult stem cells exist. Even in your own body, there is the basis for the continuous re-making of your body every several years, progressively. I think it is said that every nine years, or something like that, the entire body is a different body—but it is a replica of what was already there. The body itself is encoded to replicate itself using stem cells. Effectively, it will be a completely different body, progressively, over a period of years—at the end of it, virtually the entire body is a different body. And, yet, it is identical, and still thinking the same thoughts, and all the rest of it, and you still call yourself "self".

Just as there is no physical body beyond the stem cells, there is no ego beyond the causal body.

—Avatar Adi Da Samraj
October 29, 2004

The causal dimension of the being—the core presumption of separateness—creates a focal point of awareness, apparently centered in the body-mind-complex and identified as "self". Then, by means of attention, all experience and knowledge are "viewed" from this "point" of awareness. But, as Avatar Adi Da points out, awareness is not a separate "thing" any more than the physical body (as energy) is a separate "thing".

---

awareness and objects

In His description of how the causal dimension of the being is distinct from the gross and subtle dimensions, Avatar Adi Da is delineating two principal characteristics of the human structure: awareness (causal) and all the apparently objective things and experiences that awareness views (gross and subtle). As touched upon in the introduction, these two characteristics of the human being reflect the principal characteristics of Reality: Consciousness (as the source of awareness) and Energy (as the source of objects).

There are many levels of the human structure—there is the physical, and there is the etheric (or energy) level that energizes the nervous system, and there are the emotional, mental, and psychic dimensions. And the mechanism of attention goes to all these various mental and physical events.

But then there is awareness itself. What do you think awareness is—a point inside your body? It is not a "point". It does not originate in the body. It is simply the ground level of the body-mind-complex. Awareness, like the physical body, arises in a universal field.

Therefore, there is no separate "you". There is just this body-mind-complex, targeting all its data, reflecting them in awareness. And awareness is a universal, absolute condition—except it is also one of the layers of the body-mind-complex.

Therefore, after all this targeting of physical and mental phenomena, and so forth, the last element of the body-mind-complex is the consciousness of it. And all this specificity, this particularity, is projected, then, on this awareness by the body-mind-complex. When it gets down to that point, the awareness thinks it is a "me" inside the body-mind-complex, or identical to the physical, separate person.

—Avatar Adi Da Samraj
"You Can't Get There From Here",
August 2, 1980[11]

Avatar Adi Da often illustrated this illusory presumption of separate "self" by contrasting an open hand with a clenched fist. The open hand is the native state of the being, built to explore and participate in relationship with the world. The fist, on the other hand, is closed around a presumed center, cutting itself off from universal participation.

The persistent, causal-domain activity of "self"-contraction, or "point of view"—as Avatar Adi Da also terms it—is like forming a fist with the hand. That motion of contracting from relationship not only makes the illusion of separateness seem real, it also registers as a feeling-sense of dilemma and dissatisfaction. In fact, "self"-contraction is the fabricated source of all apparent problem and the motivating cause of all seeking for solutions. It is, in some fundamental sense, the principal form of disease that all human beings are enacting.

Why is there suffering all the time? . . . There is compulsive activity, automatic activity, unnecessary activity. There is compulsive curvature, bending, contraction at the causal "root" of condition-ally manifested existence. . . .

The activity of "self"-contraction is merely the obstruction to life, an illusory pattern within life—but that activity is utter, funda-mental, all-inclusive. You cannot even pick your nose without doing the "self"-contraction. You cannot look at anything without being involved in this "self"-contracting activity, this avoidance of relationship. You cannot think, feel, move, breathe, you do not live a single moment, without performing this activity and "experiencing" its results.

11. Published on a CD of the same title.

Therefore, from the "point of view" of the dilemma, <u>everything</u> is a form of this activity. To someone who is wedded to dilemma, the cosmic domain seems to be made out of nothing but suffering. That is why people become atheistic, insane, chronically depressed. To such people, the entire universe seems to justify despair—because everything seems to have become an extension of their own "self"-contracting activity. That activity has become the means and manner of their perception.

Therefore, "self"-understanding must take place at every level— down to the cells, and penetrating even to the "root"-sense of separate "self". On every level where "self"-contraction occurs, "self"-understanding can also take place. When this activity, this contraction, this avoidance of relationship, is thoroughly undone, thoroughly undermined, and only Truth is lived, then something about the nature of life in the cosmic domain begins to become clear. From the Disposition of Truth, life is allowable and good.

—Avatar Adi Da Samraj
"Vital Shock",
My "Bright" Word

As Avatar Adi Da indicates here, the "self"-contraction limits what is directly experienced and known. If there is no awareness, no direct experience, of the universal field of energy and what is beyond the conditional domain, then participation in those dimensions of existence is obstructed. Thus, an understanding of the activity of "self"-contraction is of great significance in the practice of energy healing, as well as in life altogether.

The core presumptions of the causal dimension are specifically addressed in the energy-healing practices given by Avatar Adi Da Samraj, by understanding the contracting activity (or ego) at the root of all seeking and embracing the ego-transcending devotional orientation of these practices. This will be explored more fully in later chapters.

The Fundamental Condition Is Conscious Light (or Consciousness-Energy)

T*he whole body is the body that includes not only the physical but the etheric, the emotional, the mental, the conscious awareness, and the "root". The environment of the whole body is like the whole body, since the whole body arises from and within it. The environment of the whole body is Light, or Radiance. The Very Condition of the whole body and its environment is Truth Itself, or Reality Itself.*

—Avatar Adi Da Samraj
"The Principles In Action To Which All Exercise
and Even Ordinary Activity Must Be Adapted",
Conscious Exercise and The Transcendental Sun

Beyond the specific forms of energy that are most directly associated with energy healing, and beyond the total structure of the cosmic domain (including all the hierarchical ranges of energy and the root-dimension), Avatar Adi Da brings awareness to and directly Communicates the Fundamental Substance, or Condition— of which the human structure is a modification and within which it is arising.

There are subtler aspects of the gross physical (or gross material) dimension of Reality that, because you may not be directly "experiencing" them at the moment, you may think of as being "somewhere else". But, in Truth, and in Reality, There Is Only One "Thing" (or Only Indivisible Light, or the One and Very Being That Is Consciousness Itself and Its Own Self-Radiance). Yet un-En-Light- ened human beings are tending, always presently (and naively), to identify with a gross physical modification-appearance of That One "Thing", when even that modification-appearance Is Only Light. The gross physical (or gross material) dimension of Reality is simply the mode in which the yet un-En-Light-ened human personality is "experiencing" Intrinsically Indivisible Light at the moment.

—Avatar Adi Da Samraj
"I Am The Way To Transcend The Illusions of Broken Light",
Real God Is The Indivisible Oneness of Unbroken Light

❖ ❖ ❖

Even to use the word "matter" is a throwback to the nineteenth century—as if there have been no scientific advances in physics since then, and as if it still makes sense to talk about "matter" or "materiality" as if "it" were a "something". Truly, "matter" is not a "something" at all. There is only Continuum, only Non-separateness, only Indivisible Reality Itself—only the Single and Self-Evidently Divine "Substance" of Conscious Light Itself.

—Avatar Adi Da Samraj
"Indivisible Perfect Space: Neither Outer
Nor Inner I<u>s</u> The Space of Reality Itself",
The Aletheon

Consciousness-and-Light

As is evident in His expressions throughout this book, Avatar Adi Da uses many evocative phrases to describe the Single Reality of Consciousness-and-Light that is the Ultimate Condition and Substance of the human structure:

- Non-conditional Reality
- the "Bright"
- Reality Itself
- the Divine Self-Nature, Self-Condition, Source-Condition, and Self-State
- Self-Existing Self-Radiance
- the Divine Reality
- Love-Bliss-Light
- Conscious Light
- Consciousness Itself and Its Own Radiance (or Energy)
- Real (Acausal) God

Avatar Adi Da describes the Indivisible Conscious Light as "Prior"—not in the sense of "existing earlier in time", but in the sense of existing "always and already". Regardless of changes in the conditional domain, Indivisible Conscious Light Always Already I<u>s</u>—Non-conditional, Unchanging, Perfect, Love-Bliss-Full.

In the vision of the Cosmic Mandala, this Conscious Light manifests as the five-pointed White Star at the center, which Radiates throughout (and, thus, Pervades) the cosmic domain, but which is truly the Unbroken (or Indivisible) "Brightness" of which all the gross and subtle colors are prismatic refractions, viewed from the causal position of separate "self-hood".

Egoity is the condition of being trapped in appearances. That is what egoity is about. As soon as there is "self"-contraction, there is the loss of the Realization of Reality and the inability to (Transcendentally, egolessly, Spiritually, and, Thus, Divinely) Self-Recognize appearances for what they truly are in Reality.

When there is no "self"-contraction, no separateness, there is only What Is. Reality is Realized Inherently, and appearances are (Inherently) Divinely Self-Recognizable in Reality. The Most Perfect Realization of Reality and the Divine Self-Recognition of appearances is what the Reality-Way of Adidam is, ultimately, about.

In Truth, whatever appears to arise as an "object" of any kind is merely a modification of Self-Existing and Self-Radiant Energy, or "Brightness". The Consciousness That Views any "object" is Self-Existing, One Only. And the Energy of Which everything is an apparent modification Is simply the Self-Existing Self-Radiance of that Very Consciousness, or the Divine Self-Nature, Self-Condition, and Self-State. To be Awake is to see that This Is So. And This is Freedom—or Liberation, Enlightenment, Divine Self-Realization. But this same Reality is always the Reality. It is the Reality now. It is the Reality Which you are all "experiencing" in this moment. Because of "self"-contraction, you propose various illusions, or you make propositions based on illusions, or you ask questions based on illusions, or you generate presumptions based on illusions—but that does not make Reality any different than It Always Already Is.

—Avatar Adi Da Samraj
August 2, 1995

Avatar Adi Da's "radical" Wisdom on energy healing is founded in the reality that His State of Being Is that Fundamental Condition—the Context and Source and Condition of the entire human structure. Avatar Adi Da is able to Reveal the Real (Prior) Condition directly to human beings—because He Is That Condition.

During Avatar Adi Da's bodily Lifetime, He investigated all the mechanisms of the human structure—in His own Body, and in consideration with others—in order to discover the means whereby human beings could be utterly coincident with Conscious Light. Therefore, through His instruction, Avatar Adi Da not only communicates (and literally Transmits) the True Source and the Substance of the human being, He also clarifies the lawful relationship between any human being and the transformative and healing Force of that Ultimate Source-Condition.

Avatar Adi Da's Transmission-Power moved into the room where we were seated with Him face-to-face. The "Brightness" of His Divine Light infiltrated the space with Luminosity, so that the walls, the objects, and persons became visibly "Brightened" by His Transcendental Spiritual Power. The differentiation between objects loosened, such that Reality was clearly a Field of Divine Light rather than a field of apparently separate material objects. Beloved Adi Da was Revealing to us the Truth that matter equals energy equals Light and that His All-Pervading Divine Transcendental Spiritual Presence is the Very Substance and Nature of That Light.

Again and again, as He spoke or sat silently, His own Transcendental Spiritual Person Flooded into our bodyminds and drew us into this Sea of Divine Light. He was penetrating the body-mind to the toes, permeating every cell with His Love-Blissful Radiance. Then, within this Sphere of "Brightening", Avatar Adi Da Revealed the Secret of the Non-"difference" between Consciousness and Energy (or Light). Suddenly, not only Avatar Adi Da, but the room, the objects, the persons, and the entire pattern of arising appeared as a Field of Light, and was recognized to be Conscious Light, Self-Existing and Self-Radiant Consciousness Itself.

—Ruchiradama Nadikanta Naitauba,
renunciate devotee of Avatar Adi Da Samraj

There Is Only Light.
Light Is All There Is.
All That Is Is Light.
Light Is (Intrinsically) Indivisible, Non-Separate, and One
Only. . . .

When Intrinsically Indivisible Light, or Real (Acausal) God,
Is (Apparently) "Objectified" To Itself, It Appears As The Cosmic
Mandala Of all conditional "worlds", forms, and beings.

Thus, Intrinsically Indivisible Light, or Real (Acausal) God,
Utterly Pervades all conditional "worlds", forms, and beings.

All conditional "worlds", forms, and beings Thus Inhere In, Are
"Lived" (or Sustained) By, Are Not Other Than, and Can Directly
Realize A State Of Inherently Most Perfect Self-Identification (or
Indivisible Oneness) With Intrinsically Indivisible Light, or Real
(Acausal) God.

—Avatar Adi Da Samraj
The Dawn Horse Testament[12]

As described earlier in this chapter, energy healing is associated specifically with the connection between the gross and etheric dimensions of the human being. Therefore, energy-healing practices do not themselves cause or lead to Realization of the Indivisible Conscious Light. They are also not, in and of themselves, specifically Spiritual practices.[13] Rather, like healing disciplines in general, they work at the yellow-red conjunction—with the physical body and the etheric body, and within the universal field of life-energy.

---

12. *The Dawn Horse Testament* is Avatar Adi Da's principal summary text on the total practice of the Reality-Way of Adidam in all its essential details. In this principal text, Avatar Adi Da employs a convention of capitalization that is distinct among all of His texts, in which nearly every word is capitalized (thereby pointing to the Non-conditional Reality) and very few words appear in lowercase (thereby pointing to the conditional reality). *The Dawn Horse Testament* thus carries a unique force in its communication—unrelentingly reminding the reader that the Divine (Non-conditional) Reality is the very Substance and Source of all that arises as the conditional reality (including the apparent individual reading His text). As He says in *The Dawn Horse Testament*, "The big and small letters of My Texted Gift always interrupt the common flow of mind, and Signal the Heart of 'you' that this moment Is the Necessary Instant of Self-Awakening—to Be As 'you' Are."

13. See pp. 82–86 for Avatar Adi Da's instruction on Spiritual Energy.

Medicine is not Spiritual. It is physical and etheric and vital. It may have an effect on a person's emotional and mental states in curing at the physical, etheric, and vital levels, but medicine does not have a function in the "higher" levels of mind and psyche, nor does it work on a Spiritual level. Therefore, there are no Spiritual but rather magical feelings sometimes about certain of the healing arts and treatments.

There are kinds of medicine associated with Spiritual traditions. This is true enough. But it does not mean that the medicine itself works on a Spiritual level. Rather, it can be associated with a Spiritual understanding of life and (therefore) it can be compatible with Spiritual life and understood in the context of Spiritual life. Medicine itself actually works on the level of the lower sheaths.

—Avatar Adi Da Samraj
February 7, 1990

Nevertheless, as Avatar Adi Da Reveals, the human being is a modification of Indivisible Conscious Light—and, therefore, healing is inherently associated with that Fundamental and egoless Condition. This can become a conscious part of energy-healing practice. Energy healing occurs at the yellow-red conjunction—which appears at the periphery of the total cosmic manifestation that is a unified field of energy, which is all a modification of the "Bright" Divine Conscious Light.

Avatar Adi Da communicates that it is every being's innate and deepest heart-impulse to know, and participate in, and, ultimately, to Realize the Indivisible Conscious Light. This great purpose is the fullest context in which Avatar Adi Da's devotees engage the practice of restoring energy flow and balance in the yellow-red conjunction. Through the relationship to Avatar Adi Da as the direct Communication of the Indivisible Conscious Light, energy-healing practices are oriented and aligned to the Fundamental (or Prior) Condition of the human being.

Avatar Adi Da Samraj
Ruchira Dham Hermitage, 2000

Live As Energy In
The Infinite Domain of Real God

by His Divine Presence,
Avatar Adi Da Samraj

Here Avatar Adi Da summarizes how a right relationship to the gross and etheric structures of the human being (explored fully in the following chapters) relates to the collective process of humanity's growth and the ultimate process of Divine Enlightenment.

Part of My Work, part of My Reality-Teaching, is an effort to help you break out of the enforced model of Reality that is preventing you from being sensitive to your actual Condition and to dimensions of your existence that go beyond, and ultimately even transcend, material existence and all forms of limited, egoic, conditional existence. But in that process, the first thing you must do is complete your ordinary learning and break the spell of the materialistic model. You must become sensitive to yourself and understand yourself, and through your sensitivity observe your physical existence fully. Then you must observe your etheric existence, your existence as energy, and begin to function consciously as energy in relation to others. Be useful to others, but also be alive as energy. Be free. Be balanced. Be sensitive to your psyche. Be sensitive to the contents of your conscious awareness. Permit yourself to "experience" the contents of your conscious awareness. Do not shut them off. Become capable of dreams, of reverie, and of being psychic. Be sensitive to your archetypes, the poetry and metaphors of your conscious awareness. Allow them to be legitimized. In other words, legitimize "subjective" existence. You must legitimize it before you can transcend it.

You must become sensitive to yourself not just as a physical being, but as an etheric and psychic being. To become so sensitive is a matter of ordinary human learning. Even someone who has fully learned all this has not begun the process of Spiritual life. It is just the ordinary equipment of human beings. But when human beings become responsible for this ordinary equipment, then they can grow beyond it, transform it, and make it usable in a higher sense.

Human beings are not here merely to grow wheat and make computers! To be socially productive is just one aspect of human existence, and people have no business being devoted to it exclusively. You must develop a free human existence and be free to grow in dimensional terms. You live as energy. You live as light. You live in the Infinite Domain of Real God. This is self-evident when you become sensitive enough to break out of your mind-set.

The conditional personality thinks that he or she is a specific consciousness and feels separated somehow from other beings, other consciousnesses. He or she feels perhaps somehow essentially like other human beings, but not identical, not literally the same. There is no feeling of Identity, or Equation, in the perfect sense. Similarly, his or her own body seems entirely different from other bodies, and the "objective world" seems full of independent, separate "objects". Thus, the usual individual does not feel, does not observe or literally know, that all these discrete phenomena are arising in a Single Field, and that that Field is the Field of Consciousness Itself, and that Consciousness is just One Being. This is not obvious from the egoic "point of view". But from the Enlightened Disposition, it is simply Obvious.

Thus, learning about the etheric and lower psychic aspects of your existence should not be taboo. On the contrary, you must find out about them. True "self"-awakening to the etheric and lower psychic aspects of yourself is associated with Spiritual acculturation, with real "religious" and Spiritual processes, because when you learn about these dimensions of yourself, you begin to enter consciously into a state of participation in them, and you actually eliminate the imbalances, the negativities, and become a positive, benign, and human presence. It is not by making this kind of learning taboo, but by making it, in effect, obligatory, necessary, real, and truly available in a fully human and Spiritual context, that human beings will stop destroying one another, stop undermining the process of existence in this plane, and allow humanity to devote itself to its right developmental course.

Human beings are all enchanted. You are already modifications of Reality Itself—and, yet, you explore existence <u>as</u> modifications. You do not see how modifications arise. You do not see That in Which modifications arise. You are limited to modification itself, to what you simply appear to be. And you break this spell only if you are free enough to thoroughly investigate your circumstance, your condition, your functioning being, all your parts, all your aspects, and begin to "Know" Reality in an expanded sense, beyond what you presently appear to be. The more you go beyond these limits, or the "point of view" of contracted being, the more directly you can intuit the Condition of conditions. ∎

From "The Body As Energy and The Universal Field of Consciousness",
in *The Transmission of Doubt.*

CHAPTER 2

"Conductivity" and the Yellow-Red Conjunction

*A*ll Healing Of the body-mind-complex Involves An Intelligent, Harmonious, Flowing, Intensified Re-Integration Of The etheric (or Natural Life-Energy) Dimension Of The human Structure With The elemental (or gross physical) Dimension Of The human Structure. Therefore, The True and Complete Healing Process Necessarily Involves mental and emotional As Well As physical Responsibilities and Changes.

—Avatar Adi Da Samraj
The Dawn Horse Testament

His Divine Presence Avatar Adi Da Samraj uses the term "conductivity" to describe the practice of magnifying and circulating natural life-energy in the body, thereby consciously energizing, re-integrating, and balancing the yellow-red conjunction. Such "conductivity" of natural life-energy is the practical foundation of all the energy-healing practices Avatar Adi Da gives.

Conducting the Flow of Natural Life-Energy

*T*he secret of "conductivity": Treat or relate to the phenomenal "world" and "self" (or the body-mind-complex) as energy rather than mere matter. And treat or relate to every condition of the phenomenal "world" and "self"—positive or negative, high or low—as the same Ultimate and Total Energy (or Self-Radiance of Transcendental Spiritual Divine Being). Body and mind are the same energy. Use every condition or circumstance as

an incident of transmission of energy, continuous with the Radiant Principle of Divine Being. Open to energy, contact it, and circulate it. And communicate it in all directions and relations through love.
—Avatar Adi Da Samraj
"Treat Everything as Energy",
"I" Is the Body of Life

Avatar Adi Da says (in agreement with many healing traditions) that well-being is essentially a matter of the free flow of natural life-energy in the body. And, likewise, healing service to another is about supporting this flow of energy in the body of the one you are serving.

What Is functionally and organically wrong with anyone who is sick Is That There Is a limitation On The Natural Life-Energy That Is Available To Move In the person. If a person is ill, he or she Is Invariably Enervated and Obstructed (or toxic). Therefore, . . . Healing Must Address These Two Aspects Of the condition of anyone who is ill: Toxicity and Enervation. First, The Obstructions In the person's system Should Be Removed, Such That The Natural Life-Energy Is Able To Flow Freely (Thereby Further Increasing The Available Natural Life-Energy and The Degree Of bodily Health)— and, Second, A Greater Degree Of Positive Natural Life-Energy Should Be Introduced Into the system of the ill person.
—Avatar Adi Da Samraj
The Dawn Horse Testament

Thus, natural (etheric) life-energy is itself a healing force. Conducting natural life-energy through the body rejuvenates even the cells of the body by encouraging their innate functioning, including the release of toxins and degenerative stress-patterns.

The energy-healing practices given by Avatar Adi Da are straightforward means to conduct etheric energy throughout and around the physical body—in the form of principal "conductivity"-healing treatments (described in Part Three), and through various other supplemental practices (described in Part Four).

The purpose of "conductivity"-healing treatments and "conductivity" responsibility is to address the yellow-red conjunction. All the kinds of healing "techniques" I have Described—primarily the laying on of hands and Yogic "conductivity" massage[1]—are "conductivity" practices and matters of responsibility for the relationship between the etheric and the physical.

—Avatar Adi Da Samraj
July 30, 2008

The bodily system is already equipped with what is necessary for increased flow of natural life-energy. Not only is the body itself energy, it is also associated with specific mechanisms (or functions) that can support the flow of energy.

The living human body is a system, or structure, for conducting life. . . . The center, "root", and living core of the process is the life-force, or universal energy, apparently cycled through the phases of the breath, but constantly and priorly communicated in, as, and through the human being via the process of feeling. . . .

The physical body is always already fully permeated by all-pervading energy, or life-force. It never becomes empty or filled, but it is only either more or less directly and presently in a condition of communication (or communion) with the universal life-force.

—Avatar Adi Da Samraj
"The Internal Locks of The Whole Body",
Conscious Exercise and The Transcendental Sun

Therefore, magnifying the flow of life-energy is not a matter of reconnecting the physical body and the etheric body, as if they were separate. Nor is it a matter of pulling energy from "outside" the body to "inside" the body. Rather, Avatar Adi Da says the practice of "conductivity" in general, and "conductivity" healing in particular, is a matter of participation in the universal field of life-energy that already pervades the body and its environment. As Avatar Adi Da describes in *The Dawn Horse Testament*, "conductivity" is a matter of "Bringing (or Yielding) the body-mind-complex To The Condition Of Energy".

---

1. The laying on of hands and Yogic "conductivity" massage are the principal forms of touch-based "conductivity" healing given by Avatar Adi Da.

Whole Bodily Participation in Energy

I n order to practice "conductivity", one must be sensitive to and learn to be responsible for etheric energy. The process of sensitization can begin with the simple practice of relaxation—as Avatar Adi Da describes in the following statement, recorded several months before He began His formal work of Teaching (on April 25, 1972).

If you are tense, your constriction of the muscles gives you the sense of a very specific physical form. But when the body is relaxed, you just sort of feel a shape. You feel the current of movement in the body, but you do not have the same sort of sense of a particular form. If you go a little deeper than mere bodily relaxation, the etheric energy itself becomes your form. It is less specific than the physical itself, even though it corresponds to its shape. A little deeper even than that, a little subtler than that, the shape of the body seems to be spherical or egg-shaped, ovoid. That is because the energy envelops the body, and it has its own system of energy circuitry. The physical elements—the nerves and the blood vessels and everything—move in a manner that corresponds to the physical shape. In the etheric (or pranic) form, the energy is also being conducted, but through this oval, this sphere, along the line of curves, rather than the "legs-and-arms" shape. The etheric energy encloses the physical, and it also provides the physical with energy.

—Avatar Adi Da Samraj
January 13, 1972

Sensitivity to one's own etheric field, and to the etheric energy-fields of others, is necessary not only for energy healing but also for basic human maturity. Because of its importance, Avatar Adi Da gives many forms of daily practice—which He calls "conscious exercise"—that serve to awaken sensitivity to (and responsibility for) the etheric dimension of existence.[2] Avatar Adi Da's essential

2. Avatar Adi Da gives His devotees a wide range of disciplines that release one's focus on the gross dimension by awakening sensitivity to what is beyond the merely physical—see chapter 4 for more discussion on this point. Also see appendix D for a summary description of "conscious exercise" and other disciplines that specifically support sensitivity to the etheric dimension.

instructions on how to magnify one's participation in the etheric-energy dimension are summarized below, by considering how the whole body participates in etheric energy, via each of the faculties, or fundamental functions of human aliveness: feeling (or emotion), breath, body (via physical touch), and mind (or attention).

Discover Life-Energy through Feeling

The principal human faculty through which etheric energy can be discovered is the faculty of feeling, or emotion. One's state of emotion, or feeling, has a direct impact on one's own physical body. As Avatar Adi Da once famously quipped, "You cannot feel any better than you can feel"[3]—in other words, your well-being is dependent on your capability to freely exercise the faculty of feeling. Additionally, feeling is a form of non-physical communication of energy between "self" and "others".

Because the direct communication of your state, your condition, to others in any moment has moral and Spiritual implications, you must become responsible for your energy—responsible, therefore, for your emotional state. You must keep the energy-field of the body-mind-complex in balance by transcending reactive emotions, and you must maintain a state of physical well-being and mental openness, receptivity, and clarity.

You must maintain a free psychic state. In doing this, you not only change your outward behavior, but you also affect your energy-field and (therefore) your energy transmission to others.

—Avatar Adi Da Samraj
The Incarnation of Love

Avatar Adi Da explains that the ideal time for feeling-awareness of the etheric field to develop in the human being is approximately ages seven through fourteen—in what He calls "the second stage of life".[4]

3. From "The Fire Must Have Its Way", in *My "Bright" Sight*.

4. Avatar Adi Da's seven-stage schema describes the potential forms of growth and experience in the human being, as well as the Prior Context of that entire potential. For descriptions of all seven stages, see "God-Talk, Real-God-Realization, Most Perfect Divine Self-Awakening, and The Seven Possible Stages of Life" in *The Aletheon*, or the standalone booklet by that same name in the *Basket of Tolerance* booklet series. For a summary description, see glossary, **stages of life**.

As Avatar Adi Da describes below—first in a passage He had written about the second stage of life and then in His own commentary on the passage—feeling-sensitivity to the etheric field is a matter of the social, emotional, and what could be called "truly moral" development of the human being.

Essay Excerpt—

The second stage of life is the early stage (particularly occupying human beings during the second seven years of life) of adaptation to the etheric dimension of conditionally manifested existence. The etheric dimension may be functionally described as the emotional-sexual dimension of one's being—but it is, in essence, the dimension of natural life-energy, nerve-force, and direct feeling-sensitivity to the conditions of existence. Since the second stage is the primary stage of socialization, one can say that it is the basic stage of moral, or right relational, development. But the primary adaptation is to feeling, or sensitivity to the energy inherent in one's person, and which is in all others, and which pervades all of nature. Thus, this stage is not merely the stage of conventional socialization, but it is the stage in which feeling-sensitivity is developed relative to one's own etheric dimension (or natural energy-field), that of others, and that which is everywhere. When this feeling-sensitivity is exercised, one learns that one is more than merely physical, but one is also part of a field of etheric energy that extends to others and communicates emotional, mental, psychic, and physical states to others as well as to the natural "world". Therefore, one must learn to be responsible for one's emotional, mental, psychic, and physical state by participating in, or surrendering openly into, the domains of life-energy. By doing this, one's social development and one's involvement in the natural "world" will develop as a moral and feeling gesture, rather than an amoral (or ego-possessed and other-manipulative) form of conventional socialization and "worldliness".

Commentary—

The second stage of life, apart from the process of socialization, is the school in which you develop your feeling-sensitivity. In other words, you develop the capability of the etheric being, or the being who is not just a physical personality, but who is a force that is manifested as a field of life-energy in contact with the energies of nature and the Universal Spiritual Energy in Which nature is arising. In order to allow this entire process of feeling-sensitivity to mature, the individual must discover that he or she is just such an etheric (or energy-based) personality. . . .

It is not readily obvious to young people, or even to many adults who have never really undergone the true learning of the second stage of life, that they are manifested as an etheric energy-field. This must be learned through "self"-observation and exercise of the feeling-capability. . . .

Thus, the individual in the second stage of life should repeatedly "consider" this matter of the etheric energy-field, or the feeling-being. You contact or sense it as energy, but it is manifested through the vehicle of your feeling and emotion.

—Avatar Adi Da Samraj
"Early-Life Education, or, My Seventh Stage Way
of Schooling In The First Three Stages of Life",
The First Three Stages of Life

Although the second stage of life is the ideal time to consider and cultivate one's sensitivity to the etheric dimension of existence, anyone, at any time of life, can cultivate that sensitivity by embracing simple practices such as those recommended by Avatar Adi Da in this book.

Feeling-radiance, or love, is central to "conductivity"-healing practices. In all forms of "conductivity" practice, the heart is activated as feeling. Additionally, conducting natural life-energy encourages and requires the release of emotional contractions, thus supporting emotional balance. Avatar Adi Da describes the etheric body as "the sheath of natural energy that connects body, emotion, and mind".[5] Therefore, conducting natural life-energy in the body-mind-complex harmonizes all these various functions of the human being, restoring native equanimity.

The practice of feeling-radiance is not only essential to establishing and maintaining bodily well-being, it is also essential to the process of transcending the root-contraction in the causal dimension, and thereby reestablishing direct participation in the Divine Reality.

W*hen I was growing up, I was taught to be sensitive to the natural environment, as part of Avatar Adi Da's Teaching about becoming aware of the etheric-energy dimension. One way I continue to do this in my adult life is by exercising outdoors in a conscious manner. For instance, when I was on retreat recently at Bhagavan Adi Da's Hermitage-Island in Fiji, I was doing evening yoga at the wharf. I was moving and breathing in a relaxed way, regarding a photograph of Beloved Bhagavan Adi Da in a small open-air temple nearby. I noticed the tree above and the wind moving within it, the sounds of the birds and the ocean waves, the sand and sun on my skin. Every sense was alive. My body felt permeable and resonant with life-energy. The energy I breathed in felt connected to the force that flowed through the nearby tree and moved through the ocean. It was so enjoyable to be continuous with the environment— to inhale and receive life-energy, to arc my body or stretch a leg in the pleasure of it and to exhale and let it all go, to be diffuse and surrendered. It was a practice of full participation, giving and receiving life-energy, and it felt exactly like love.*

—Devotee of Avatar Adi Da Samraj

---

5. From "The ego-'I' is the Illusion of Relatedness", in *Santosha Adidam.*

To exceed the ego-trap—and to be Refreshed at heart, and in the total body-mind-complex . . . , it is necessary to feel and swoon Beyond the "center" (or Beyond the "point of view" of separate ego-"I" and separative body-mind-"self").

—Avatar Adi Da Samraj
"Do Not Misunderstand <u>Me</u>",
The Aletheon

❖ ❖ ❖

Your single obligation is at the heart. It is in your feeling that you become ego-possessed. It is in your feeling that you betray the Real and Ever-Living God and all your relations. It is in your feeling that you are unhappy. It is in your feeling that fear, sorrow, anger, doubt, shame, lust, and all egoic obsessions are arising. Therefore, it is in your feeling alone that you will be healed.

—Avatar Adi Da Samraj
September 16, 1979

Feed on Life-Energy with the Breath

The pranic body . . . [is] centered at the heart (or the emotional, or feeling, center)—and it is functionally associated with the cycle of breathing.

—Avatar Adi Da Samraj
"The ego-'I' Is The Illusion of Relatedness",
Santosha Adidam

The "pranic body" is another name for the etheric body—and the traditional term "prana" literally means "breath". While feeling itself is at the core of etheric sensitivity, Avatar Adi Da says that breath coincides with feeling—and, thus, the state of the breath in any moment directly mirrors (or is a functional demonstration of) the quality of feeling in that moment.

The cycle of breathing is a reflection of the present state of "conductivity", and (thus) responsibility, of the individual. . . . Breath and emotion are identical. You feel and breathe simul-taneously, as a single event. Unobstructed feeling, or love, is senior to the physiological action of the breath, but simultaneous with it. Love is "creative", or "causative", relative to breath and life. . . .

71

The conscious feeling of the bodily and relational cycle of breath and life, under conditions of action and repose, is fundamental to well-being, good relations, and to the entire affair of "conscious exercise". Therefore, it is essential to account for the critical factors and events in the feeling-cycle of breathing.

—Avatar Adi Da Samraj
"The Internal Locks of The Whole Body",
Conscious Exercise and The Transcendental Sun

Thus, in "conductivity" healing, one must do more than simply engage the unconscious (or automatic) in- and out-flow of air. Feeling-breathing is the means to participate in and literally "feed on" the field of natural life-energy.

There should be no dead breath, no small chemistry, but intentional and full use of breath as a feeling instrument in actual and present ingestion, transformation, and transfer of life-energy.

—Avatar Adi Da Samraj
The Eating Gorilla Comes In Peace

❖   ❖   ❖

The true food is life itself, which you may breathe—but only when breathing is combined with unobstructed feeling of the universal life-energy and the All-Pervading Force of the Divine Reality. Feed on life-energy, through feeling-breaths, relaxing the entire body, including the brain, into that current of life-force. Receive that life-energy through inhalation to the vital organs of the lower body. And then release that force, through exhalation, to the entire body, and via the entire body to Infinity.

This is the native "diet" of humankind. You are always eating and sustained by life-energy, through every truly and openly feeling breath. But if you contract in your feeling, you also contract bodily and mentally. Thus, you become ego-possessed, suffering reactive emotions, bodily tensions, and chronic mentalizing. Through the "conscious exercise" of the wholly feeling breath, you are fed and sustained and healed and transformed by the Self-Radiant Divine Reality.

—Avatar Adi Da Samraj
"The Transcendental Diet of Man",
The Enlightenment of the Whole Body

In the practice of "conductivity", the breath is intentionally engaged as this cycle of reception and release.

The reception-release cycle of the breath is not meant to be practiced rotely, or as a repetitive technique. Rather, Avatar Adi Da describes such right breathing as an artful matter, to be engaged randomly during daily life and "conductivity"-healing practices. It is engaged spontaneously, in living communication with the universal field of life-energy. For those who engage the Reality-Way of Adidam that Avatar Adi Da has given, breath also becomes a principal expression of the devotional relationship to Him.

The distribution of the life-force to the whole body through conscious participation in the natural cycle of the breath . . . , under all conditions, in all activities, and in all relations, is the key to the health and rejuvenation of the body-mind-complex.

In general, the cycle of feeling and breathing from moment to moment is a "conscious exercise", a general attitude, or mudra, of the entire body, in which the body is constantly purifying, re-balancing, and regenerating itself. Thus, every breath should be the feeling-breath of "conductivity" of the universal etheric energy, or the process whereby the bio-energetic field in which the body exists is contacted and the life-force is conducted to the entire body. On inhalation, one receives the etheric energy, or life-force . . . into the vital center of the body. On exhalation, one then releases the life-force . . . and allows it to pervade every part and function of the body, and even the "world". . . . (In the Transcendentally Spiritually Activated stages of practice-demonstration in the Reality-Way of Adidam, My devotee adds to this responsibility the "Transcendental Spirit-Conductivity" that is Communion with My Transcendental Spiritual, and Always Blessing, Divine Presence.[6]) . . .

One also makes use of the cycle of feeling breath in the case of any physical disturbance or disease, by directing the life-energy to the area or function of the body that may be disturbed, in order to equalize the bio-energetic field. However, in a condition of health and well-being, one is naturally, from moment to moment, allowing the life-force to pervade the entire body, so that the body remains full and not obstructed.

—Avatar Adi Da Samraj
"The Four Stages of Your Bodily Regeneration In Real God",
The Eating Gorilla Comes In Peace

6. See pp. 81–86.

Convey Life-Energy via Touch

Physical touch is, of course, a principal mode of bringing healing life-energy to another. Avatar Adi Da explains that touch is the bodily sense through which feeling is expressed and through which the etheric body can be perceived.

Human beings have several bodily senses, most of which are localized through a specific organ. Seeing is, in general, localized through the eyes, hearing through the ears, smelling through the nose, and tasting through the mouth—but the entire body is an organ of touch. In terms of its comprehensiveness, then, the body is the senior sense organ, and the sense of touch is the means whereby just about anyone can very quickly become aware of the aura or the etheric energy-field of the body.

—Avatar Adi Da Samraj
'The Body As Energy and The Universal Field of Consciousness",
The Transmission of Doubt

❖ ❖ ❖

The process whereby you achieve sensitivity to this energy-field is through the primary sense of touch, or through feeling-contact. The other senses may play a part in this sensitivity to, or observation of, the etheric energy-field, but the primary organ of "self"-awareness in terms of the energy-field or etheric body is your feeling-capability. And your feeling-capability is an extension of the sense of touch.

—Avatar Adi Da Samraj
"Early-Life Education, or, My Seventh Stage Way
of Schooling In The First Three Stages of Life",
The First Three Stages of Life

Because of the nature of etheric energy, one does not need to directly, physically touch another to be sensitive to and influence his or her etheric-energy field.

In energy healing, the energy that you are working with is not in the body—it is surrounding and pervading the body. You could affect the energy without even touching the body, perhaps, because the energy is extended beyond the body. The body includes that energy, so when you touch the body, the body can be sensitized to feeling the etheric energy. But that energy is always there and surrounding the body.

—Avatar Adi Da Samraj
April 20, 1996

❖ ❖ ❖

The primary way of "experiencing" the etheric field is through touch, although not only via sheerly physical touch (your hands touching the physical body of another). Just as you can feel some pressure of energy between your hands after rubbing them together, you can feel the energy-field of another by bringing your hands into the field associated with that person's body. When you place your hands in the etheric field of another, or if you are even just physically near another, you may notice something goes on in your own body that registers the state of the energy.

—Avatar Adi Da Samraj
May 6, 1996

Avatar Adi Da describes the sense of touch as "Tangible Contact Via physical, emotional, mental, and breathing Feeling-sensation".[7] Thus, touch-contact in "conductivity" healing is not a merely physical practice, but a conscious feeling-and-breathing practice, through which natural life-energy flows to another. Touch-based "conductivity"-healing practices cultivate awareness of and sensitivity to one's own etheric-energy field, the etheric-energy field of others, and the universal field of etheric energy.

In addition, the sense of touch—as an extension of the faculty of feeling—is integral to direct awareness of the Divine Reality, beyond all forms of contraction.

Touch is precisely the dimension in which you must become awake. But, as touch, that condition is blind, in the sense that it is prior to the usual body-sense, prior to all the intellectually organized complexity of inwardness. With touch, inwardness vanishes, and

7. From "Vision, Audition, and Touch In The Process of Ascending Meditation In The Reality-Way of Adidam", in *Ruchira Avatara Hridaya-Siddha Yoga.*

what is "seen" is at the skin level. The "self"-contraction from Infinity can possibly even be measured in terms of electrical activity at the skin level. It is only when the sense of touch becomes Enlightened that the subtle activity at the level of the skin is freed from the effort of contraction and permits bodily participation in Infinite Radiance.

—Avatar Adi Da Samraj
August 14, 1979

Relax the Mind into the Field of Life-Energy

Although perhaps less concretely related to the etheric-energy field than the physical dimension, the lower mental field of the human being is also immediately associated with—and, therefore, directly impacts—the etheric field (and, thereby, the physical body).

The lower mind is associated with the registering of perceptual images and sensations, and it is the next most subtle aspect of the being (and the conditional world) after the etheric dimension. The lower mind is represented by the white band in the vision of the Cosmic Mandala (see color plate after p. 36).[8] In a sense, then, the etheric body is "sandwiched" between the physical body and the sensory-based mental field, and there is a continuous interplay between awareness of experience (via mind) and the experiences themselves (via physical-etheric perception).

The mind Always Directly Affects (or Modifies) The One Underlying and Pervasive Natural Energy (and the Naturally Multifarious functional energies) Of the conditional "world" (and Even In all the planes of the conditional "world", or Of The Cosmic Mandala Of Life). . . .

And The mind-Made Modifications Of The Universally Pervasive Natural Energy, and Of the Secondary (and Multifarious) Natural functional energies . . . Affect (and Directly appear as) all (Apparent) personal bodily states and Even all (Apparent) personal (physical and "experiential") events in general.

8. See also appendices A and B for full descriptions of the bands of color in the vision of the Cosmic Mandala and the "sheaths" or "functional bodies" of the body-mind-complex.

Then all personal (physical and "experiential") events in general, and all personal bodily states, Directly Affect or Change the mind.

And So On, and On.

—Avatar Adi Da Samraj
The Dawn Horse Testament

Therefore, taking responsibility for the mental field is an important aspect of bringing balance and support to the yellow-red conjunction.[9] Avatar Adi Da explains that when the etheric field is integrated and flowing, then both the physical body and the mental field can relax into the etheric field, producing a harmonizing effect. A flowing and balanced etheric body provides a sort of energy "river" into which the physical and the mental fields can release negative patterns and toxins.

Avatar Adi Da once described His own bodily experience of this process after receiving a healing-touch treatment from a devotee.[10]

The calm I "experienced" in the treatment is what I mean by this kind of balancing, the resonating of the etheric field and the zones on the two "sides" of it—all of that resonating and becoming a homogenous or single field. It becomes simply balanced and without oppositions within itself. As the healing procedure unfolded, this relaxed field-state was fairly quickly evident.

This type of treatment relates to various zones—in effect, touching up this single field so that it is resonating more completely. Much of what this healer is doing may to her be simply intuitive, bodily responsive, and so forth. But "experientially", in My observation, this is how it unfolded as an event. It could be described as a kind of relaxation into the etheric field. The body relaxes into the etheric field.

---

9. The principal discipline related to mind (or attention) that Avatar Adi Da gives to His devotees is called the "conscious process". See pp. 138–40 for a summary of the various forms of the "conscious process", and also pp. 161–64 for a detailed description of the most basic form of the "conscious process" (Name-Invocation) that is engaged in "conductivity"-healing practices, and in general.

10. This treatment was given by Jane Yang. See the introduction for her testimony about offering her healing service to Avatar Adi Da.

The etheric field is prior to the physical, and it is a medium between the zone of mind and the zone of the physical. Therefore, it is a reflector of what is between the physical and the mental. Whatever is affecting that field from the direction of mind has to be relaxed. And whatever is there in the physical dimension has to relax. Both mind and body are relaxed into this zone (or sphere) of balanced etheric energy.

Therefore, in those zones coming together, there is a purification from both directions—in the mental (or what you could call the "astral") and in the physical. They both release their (what could be called) "out-of-balance" or "karmic" elements, if there are any, into this single etheric field, which is (in some sense) surrounding the body and is (therefore, in that sense) circular.

That relaxation is the sign of the purification.

What the treatment serves is the physical dimension, and the connection of the physical vehicle with the larger field.

It is essentially about the body resting in that balanced, etheric field.

—Avatar Adi Da Samraj
July 27, 2008

The Circuit of "Conductivity"

When one is sensitive to and participating in the field of etheric energy with all the psycho-physical faculties, one can also perceive the manner in which energy flows or circulates in the human system. In addition to clarifying the <u>total structure</u> of the human being (and the cosmic domain), as described in chapter 1, Avatar Adi Da also describes the primary <u>pathway</u> through which energy moves in the psycho-physical structure of the human being. This pathway is composed of two arcs: energy descends through the front of the body (the frontal line), turns at the bodily base (associated with the perineum), and ascends through the back of the body (the spinal line).

*I have often Described to you the functional structure of appar-
ently individuated life. There is the descending Force, which is*

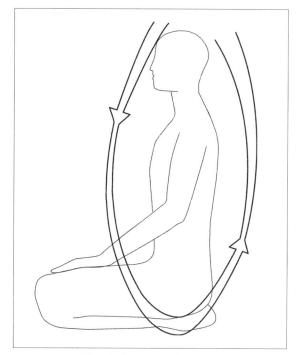

The Circle of "Conductivity"

manifesting life, and the ascending Force, which is returning to the Source of life. The "Root" of the entire Circle (or Circuit) of the conditional manifestation of your individual life is the True Divine Heart, the Divine Self-Nature, Self-Condition, and Self-State of all-and-All.

I have Described this process in terms of the physical body of the human being. The Current of Energy descends via the frontal line of the body-mind-complex and ascends via the spinal line of the body-mind-complex.

—Avatar Adi Da Samraj
"The Heaven-Born Gospel of The Ruchira Avatar",
My "Bright" Word

Avatar Adi Da calls this circuit of energy "the Circle". Magnification of the flow of natural life-energy in the body-mind-complex is magnification of "conductivity" in the Circle.

"Conductivity" is necessary to life—the "conductivity" of life-force. Ordinarily, people are only involved in rejecting—always attempting to empty themselves by various positive and negative strategies. But there is this natural "conductivity"—downward, through the frontal functions of the psycho-physical life, and then up the spine. This full Circle is the law of conditionally manifested life. That should be spontaneous, simple. That is health. It is also sanity. It is the human cycle, the psycho-physical circuit.

—Avatar Adi Da Samraj
"Money, Food, and Sex",
My "Bright" Word

Because the Circle is a psycho-physical circuit (and not merely a circuit within the physical body), the Circle of "conductivity" of every apparent individual is inherently integrated with the universal field of life-energy. In fact, Avatar Adi Da explains that the Circle of "conductivity" in the human being reflects the Great Process by which the Non-conditional (Divine) Reality spontaneously manifests as the cosmos itself.

The process by which you appear is not within you, nor does it originate in you. You are simply a reflection of a great pattern. That great pattern is expressed everywhere—in the form of all processes, all individuals, all the cycles that are everywhere to be observed.

—Avatar Adi Da Samraj
"Renouncing The Search For The Edible Deity",
The Yoga of Right Diet

❖ ❖ ❖

This "world" is appearing by virtue of a Process of Divine "Conductivity" (or Divine "Breathing", or Divine "Circulation") Descending from, and Ascending to, the Intrinsically Indivisible Matrix of Real-God-Light—and this Process is duplicated in psycho-physical life as the breathing (and otherwise circulating) activity of "conductivity", descending and ascending.

—Avatar Adi Da Samraj
"The Divine Person",
He-and-She Is Me

This great circuit is the "Pattern" by which the Indivisible Conscious Light Demonstrates and Communicates Itself, to the human form and throughout the cosmic domain.

This book is focused on "conductivity" of natural life-energy, specifically as it relates to the "conductivity"-healing practices given by Avatar Adi Da. However, "conductivity" of natural life-energy in the Circle is also associated with the same circuit through which Spiritual Energy can flow—and, for Avatar Adi Da's devotees, it is preparatory for "conductivity" of His Transcendental Spiritual Force, whereby the human structure participates with the Radiant Force (or Energy-Transmission) of the Indivisible Conscious Light.

I have found that with the awakening of the Transcendental Spiritual process, "conductivity" has taken on a much more expanded dimension. In meditation, when recognition of Bhagavan Adi Da occurs and His Transcendental Spiritual Presence is "located", the body is infused with a great Force of Transmission and naturally moves into a very strong and alert disposition of openness. My entire body seems receptive and alive with Energy and is filled with Bhagavan Adi Da's Transmission of Light and Love. There is a natural downward reception of His Bliss-Energy, and a spontaneous circulation down the frontal line and up the spinal line. Often all the frontal areas are deeply opened in Love-Bliss. This is simply noticed and participated in freely and happily—joyfully. It is always combined with recognition of Bhagavan Adi Da's Perfect State—it is never an occurrence in the body-mind in and of itself.

—Devotee of Avatar Adi Da Samraj

The Transcendental Spiritual process proceeds from the Limitless Real-God-Light, Which human beings intuit above the head but do not see through the various psycho-physical instruments. In devotional and Transcendental Spiritual Communion with Me, the Man of "Radical" Understanding, a process is initiated whereby the descending and ascending Circle of life in every individual is purified, loosened, begun to move, intensified. All the various obstructions, or forms of contraction, are (one by one) undone—until there is this Perfect Circle of "conductivity" lived and enjoyed.

—Avatar Adi Da Samraj
December 23, 1973

❖ ❖ ❖

I Am Working in the Circle of each one's body-mind, and (simultaneously) Blessing each one—from Infinitely Above and Beyond, and from the "Root"-Position.

—Avatar Adi Da Samraj
"The Boundless Self-Confession", *The Aletheon*

---

natural life-energy, Spiritual Energy, and Transcendental Spiritual Energy

Offered here is a brief summary of the distinctions between natural life-energy, Spiritual Energy, and Transcendental Spiritual Energy—as described by Avatar Adi Da in His Teachings and as these forms of energy are related to the practice of "conductivity".*

natural life-energy

As discussed in chapter 1, natural life-energy is etheric energy, the form of subtle energy immediately related to the physical, or gross, range of energy. Natural life-energy is universally associated with the physical world, and it is contacted and circulated through physical sensation, emotional feeling, and the breath.

* For a more in-depth study of these important and nuanced distinctions, please see "Cosmic Spiritual Baptism Versus Divine Transcendental Spiritual Baptism", in *The Pneumaton*.

Various subtle-energy phenomena that can be experienced in the body-mind-complex are caused by the movement or communication of natural life-energy—for example, phenomena generated through various energy-healing modalities, through Yogic sexual practice, and through other technical Yogic practices. Traditionally, such practices are often associated with the intention to draw the natural life-force upward (via ascent in the spinal line) from the gross-etheric dimension into subtler dimensions.

Spiritual Energy

Spiritual Energy is the immense Force, or Radiance, of the Divine Reality, which Pervades all of the cosmic domain and of which everything that appears is a modification. Avatar Adi Da also describes the Energy of the Divine Reality as "Self-Radiant Love-Bliss".

References to Spiritual Energy appear in both Eastern and Western traditions, by various names—such as "Shakti", "Divine Bliss", and "the Breath of God". The most developed Spiritual traditions involve the Transmission of Shakti, or Spiritual Force, from an authentic Spiritual Master to a prepared aspirant.*

Avatar Adi Da clarifies that, from the "point of view" of the body-mind-"self", the Spiritual Energy of the Divine Reality is perceived or experienced as an objective manifestation within the gross and subtle dimensions. In other words, Spiritual Energy, when perceived by an apparently separate "self", gets "bound to a cosmic (or conditional) view of Reality".† Encounters with Spiritual Energy based on this view are often associated with profound Yogic phenomena and states of Realization, generated by its

(continued on next page)

* There are also traditions associated with Shakti that involve stimulating natural life-energy (rather than receiving the Transmission of Spiritual Energy) within the structure of the body-mind-complex. Avatar Adi Da describes such traditions as "lesser". See *The Pneumaton* for Avatar Adi Da's thorough examination of the Spiritual traditions.

† From "Reality Itself Is Not A Size", in *The Aletheon*.

ascent (via the spinal line) from the gross and subtle dimensions toward the Formless Divine. The Kundalini Shakti tradition of esoteric Hindu Spirituality is an example of this approach to "cosmic Spiritual Energy".

Transcendental Spiritual Energy

Avatar Adi Da Reveals that the Spiritual Energy of the Divine Reality is not, in Truth, an objective manifestation, but (rather) Exists Beyond and Prior to any conditional mechanism of perception or experience. In other words, the Spiritual Energy of the Divine Reality is not only Prior to the gross and subtle dimensions, but also Prior to the causal dimension of "point of view". It is, in His words, "intrinsically egoless".

Therefore, Avatar Adi Da calls the Radiant Force of Reality Itself "Transcendental Spiritual Energy"—indicating that the Spiritual Energy of the Divine Reality transcends all cosmic perception, structures, states, and experiences.

The Reality-understanding of That Which Is Divine is that the Divine Is egoless. The Divine Is Prior to "point of view". Therefore, the Divine Is Prior to any cosmic pattern. The Divine Is Prior to time and space, without excluding any. Thus, the Spiritual Divine Is of a Transcendental Nature—not of a cosmic nature. . . .

The Transcendental Spiritual Divine does not merely pervade time and space. Rather, the Transcendental Spiritual Divine Is the all-and-All-Transcending Context of time and space—Prior to ego, Prior to "point of view", Prior to all cosmic measures, Prior to anything that goes through change in time, Prior to anything that moves in space, Prior to all limitations. . . .

My use of the words "Transcendental Spiritual" is, in and of itself, a Divine Avataric Self-Revelation about Reality Itself.

—Avatar Adi Da Samraj
"Reality Itself Is Not A Size",
The Aletheon

With "Transcendental", Avatar Adi Da is also indicating that the Spiritual Energy of the Divine Reality is not different from Consciousness Itself. Thus, the Transmission of Transcendental Spiritual Energy is the Transmission of both the Energy <u>and</u> the Consciousness of the Divine Reality, as Single and Indivisible—as Conscious Light.

Avatar Adi Da Samraj directly Transmits Transcendental Spiritual Energy (Conscious Light, or the "Bright"). One of the maturing signs of practice for Avatar Adi Da's devotees is the capability to recognize (and conduct) His Transcendental Spiritual Transmission.

The energies that are engaged, manipulated, transmitted, or exchanged within the Great Tradition originate within the cosmic domain and they make use of portals or structures in the body-mind-complex. If you are sensitive to transmitted energies, you can feel where they come from, where they originate in the structure of the body-mind-complex, and (therefore) how they are associated with the cosmic structure.

The "Bright" Is Beyond. The "Bright" does not originate in the cosmic domain. It does not originate in the body. My Divine Avataric Self-Transmission Is Divine Revelation of Person, of Teaching, of Intrinsic egolessness, but also of the Divine Conscious Light Itself.

You must discriminate between energies. To be My Transcendentally Spiritually Awakened devotee, you must know the difference. You must be able to identify My Presence, My unique characteristic of Transmission. It is the Divine Transmission of the "Bright", Avatarically-Given. I have Brought It into the cosmic domain. I have Broken Through the shell of the cosmic domain. I <u>Am</u> that Breakthrough. My Transmission is a specific Breakthrough in the cosmic domain as a whole, and (therefore) into the domain of humankind as a whole, and into the Earth-domain as a

(continued on next page)

whole. But My Transmission does not originate from within the "point-of-view"-sphere of conditional processes. My Transmission Comes from Beyond. My Transmission required a Breakthrough from Beyond.

My Transmission has no "location". My Transmission Is Beyond "locatedness", Beyond and Prior to "point of view". My Transmission Is the Divine Conscious Light, Intervening in the cosmic sphere, and (therefore) the anthroposphere, the human sphere. I have Broken Through the "point-of-view"-domain.

—Avatar Adi Da Samraj
October 22, 2008

The Frontal Line Must Be Open

R*ight "conductivity"-practice is to constantly keep the frontal flow pleasurably downward, with open-hearted feeling.*

—Avatar Adi Da Samraj
May 6, 1996

Avatar Adi Da makes clear that blockages in the etheric and physical dimensions (or in the yellow-red conjunction itself) manifest as "knots" in the frontal line of the Circle of the body-mind-complex. These knots restrict the flow of natural life-energy in the descending current.

Think of the descending current as a garden hose running from the top of your head to your feet or to the base of the body, with water running through it. When you pick up a garden hose and twist it, the water stops. Release it a little bit, and the water runs a little bit. The channel is supposed to be simply open, but by tendency it is constricted to one or another degree under the various circumstances of life, whether those circumstances are acknowledged to be external to you or internal and local to the body. This line of force is tending to be constricted to one degree or another, and it is rarely simply open.

When it is simply open, you feel good—and not just physically, but emotionally, altogether. You have a sense of well-being. When you have a sense of well-being, this current that registers itself in the frontal line of the body is open. When you do not feel completely well, it is constricted to one degree or another. And when you feel rotten, it is as if you had tied a knot in the garden hose. You can feel that knot throughout the frontal line. You will perhaps especially feel it over the solar plexus. If you are not happy in your feeling, not given over to the Living and Ultimate Principle, then perhaps you will notice that you "experience" a more or less chronic sense of contraction over the solar plexus, and a feeling of weakness also, as if you had a hole in your navel. In that case, there is weakness, there is tightness, there is a cramp, there is discomfort, there is disorientation—altogether, a sense of being out of balance.

All these symptoms are the results of a very simple mechanism of contraction in the frontal line of force. The contraction is registered especially over the solar plexus, because the bodily "battery" is the great region of the solar plexus, including the lower abdomen. You must (therefore) become sensitive to how this frontal mechanism works, how it changes in reaction to external circumstances and local (or internal) circumstances.

—Avatar Adi Da Samraj
August 11, 1983

In other words, human beings tend to habitually obstruct the flow of energy in the frontal line—and "conductivity" practices altogether, and "conductivity"-healing treatments in particular, are about restoring participation in the full flow of energy in the Circle.

In principle, what is "conductivity" about? It is about not indulging in obstructions, not indulging in breakages of the circuit but keeping it continuous, round, full, unbroken, unobstructed, a whir of wind, of feeling, of energy, with no obstruction, no breakage. That is what the whole art of "conductivity" is about. In ordinary life, you tend to obstruct the current in one place or another, or break it in one place or another. These maladaptations must be dealt with, very artfully, very sensitively, through real learning about yourself, in the actual occasion of this discipline, moment to moment, in all the circumstances of life. The whole point is to not break or obstruct the circuit. That is it. The super-conductor! Let it be so.

—Avatar Adi Da Samraj
March 11, 1993

Avatar Adi Da explains that these obstructions of life-energy, the contractions in the frontal line, are all signs of ego, or "self"-contraction—which, as described in chapter 1, functions in its root-form in the causal dimension as the "stem cells" of the ego, and then extends into the subtle and physical dimensions of the being. In describing His own early-life investigation of this matter, Avatar Adi Da says:

It became clear to Me that the "ego" (or the conventional "I") is not an "entity" (or an independent and static "thing of being"), but the "ego" (or the conventional "I") is the chronic and total psycho-physical <u>activity</u> of "self"-contraction, always associated with concrete results (in the psyche, mind, emotion, body, and their relations). And the "self"-contraction can always be tacitly observed (in any moment) in feeling (as fear, anxiety, stress, and all other kinds of reactive emotions and blocks in the flow of natural bodily energy in the Circle of the body-mind-complex).

It became clear to Me that the "self"-contraction is the complex limit on natural bodily energy, and (in the case of the degrees and stages of Transcendental Spiritual Awakening) on The Divine Transcendental Spiritual Energy, in the Circle of the body-mind-complex.

—Avatar Adi Da Samraj
"The Way of Me",
The Aletheon

Therefore, understanding and taking responsibility for the "self"-contraction is fundamental to well-being. Releasing the forms of contraction appearing in the frontal line reestablishes the flow of natural life-energy in the body-mind-complex, thereby allowing the yellow-red conjunction to come into balance.

As with the use of breath and touch in "conductivity"-healing practices, relaxation of the frontal line is a feeling matter, not merely a physical or mechanical one. As Avatar Adi Da describes, the disposition of feeling-radiance naturally opens the frontal line, thus supporting the descending flow of natural life-energy. This is why part of helping to heal another is the responsibility to simply be love—or unobstructed free feeling-attention—thereby giving the person loving, attentive energy.

The heart is the central seat of the central current. Thus, it is not merely in the frontal line, nor is it absent from the spinal line. It is the feeling-attitude of constant radiance, constantly transcending contraction and the limits on radiance. . . . Therefore, practice "conductivity" on the basis of the free feeling-attitude of the heart. . . . Surrender as the total body-mind into the All-Pervading Life-Current via the radiant feeling-attitude of the heart. On inhalation, open the entire body-mind with the feeling heart and so receive the radiant descending life-energy (and, ultimately, the Love-Bliss-Energy of the Divine). On exhalation, release the feeling heart in blissful love-aspiration, thus radiating the life-current to Infinity. Do this breath after breath.

—Avatar Adi Da Samraj
"Open and Release the Feeling Heart",
"I" Is the Body of Life

❖ ❖ ❖

If you observed this frontal current for a few days, just agreed to keep your attention on it quite regularly, you would observe certain symptoms relative to the energy in the frontal line of the body. You would observe that these symptoms change from hour to hour, change in different circumstances, change in the presence of different individuals, and so on.

When this channel is open, as it is supposed to be, characterized by full in-breath, full bodily realization, full feeling, then you are tending to be in a state of well-being. If you kept that channel consistently open, and, of course, observed various intelligent practices in life, you would maintain a general state of psycho-physical well-being.

But, by tendency, you do not maintain such a full, open in-breath. Instead, the egoic contraction, the "self"-contraction, tends constantly to contract and limit the descending force.

Healing another is fundamentally a matter of working on this frontal current, helping to bring the person—not just physically, but in every way—into a condition of openness to the descending current of life-force, so that there exist no relational, physical, emotional, psychic, or mental obstructions or reasons for contraction that limit the flow of force.

If this force is simply open and free-flowing, it cures everything. It restores everything to well-being, including relationships.

—Avatar Adi Da Samraj
August 11, 1983

"Conductivity" of natural life-energy is the practical foundation of the energy-healing practices described by Avatar Adi Da. By participating whole bodily—with all the faculties—in the personal and universal field of etheric energy, one develops sensitivity to natural life-energy and conducts the flow in the Circle of the body-mind-complex, thus serving to bring balance and conscious integration to the etheric and gross dimensions of the being.

I n 1978, when I first read the book Conscious Exercise and The Transcendental Sun *by Avatar Adi Da, I was struck by the subtitle "The Technology of Love". In that book, Avatar Adi Da used the term "free feeling-attention" to describe the most basic form of "conductivity", in which feeling and attention come together in bodily action. In a simple act such as watering a houseplant, I could see the difference between being present as free feeling-attention, in which mind and emotion were focused and harmonized, and when the mind and feeling were scattered and abstract. I could feel that when I was present as free feeling-attention to another person this was the same as being present as love.*

One way I practice "conductivity" that has always been very powerful for me is to engage it when I am walking. I find it takes me out of random day-dreaming or unconscious lazy energy and makes the walking a form of meditation in action. I work as a doctor and one way I specifically practice this is when I walk with a person from the waiting room into the consultation room. I use those few minutes of walking to intentionally conduct the life-energy before speaking begins. People have commented that they feel I am really present and listening to them and they notice the energy in the room. In these moments I can feel the "technology of love" in action.

—Devotee of Avatar Adi Da Samraj

Avatar Adi Da Samraj
Adi Da Samrajashram, 2008

Consent To Feel
As You Are

by His Divine Presence,
Avatar Adi Da Samraj

In this essay (excerpts of which have been presented earlier in this chapter), Avatar Adi Da summarizes "conductivity" as responsibility for the cycle of reception-release.

Life-Force Integrates Body and Mind

The living human body is a system (or structure) for conducting life. The physical body is contacted by (or integrated with) mind (or attention) via the pervading medium of life-force. The present-time capability of the complex of attention, feeling, and bodily form to conduct the life-power is its general state of responsibility, or "conductivity".

The same life-force pervades both the physical body and its environment. The physical body does not "contain", or grasp and hold, the life-force, but simply communes or communicates with the all-pervading life-force, or conditionally manifested light, and intensifies the sense and effect of the life-force through feeling, or psycho-physical emotion. Attention (including intention and controlled thought) and the control of posture and activity are the outer limbs (or extremities), the opposite poles of the process of living. The center, "root", and living core of the process is the life-force, or universal energy, apparently cycled through the phases of the breath, but constantly and priorly communicated in, as, and through the human structure via the process of feeling.

The Feeling-Cycle of The Breath

Feeling is either obstructed and reactive or unobstructed and non-reactive. Reactive emotions—such as fear, sorrow, and anger—are forms of recoil. They contract the mechanisms of the whole body, and obstruct or attenuate the "conductivity", and (thus) the responsibility, of the whole being. When there is simple, direct, and native participation in the state of life, there is no reactivity, but a pleasurable, relational force and radiance. This is love, or unobstructed "conductivity". In that case, the responsibility of the whole body-being is optimum, and Communion with the Real Condition (or Truth) of all conditions is possible, and even inherent in that instant.

The cycle of breathing is a reflection of the present state of "conductivity", and (thus) responsibility, of the individual. Indeed, the cycle of breathing, or "conductivity" of life-energy, is senior to all "subjectivity", all reactivity. Breath and emotion are identical. You feel and breathe simultaneously, as a single event. Unobstructed feeling, or love, is senior to the physiological action of the breath, but simultaneous with it. Love is "creative", or "causative", relative to breath and life.

Reactive feeling, or negative and "caused" emotions, are secondary to the physiological action of the breath. Shocks of life modify the breath-life pattern directly, and create contracted emotional patterns, as well as the sense that love and good feelings depend on reasons or circumstantial stimulation. Thus, by "experience" and reaction, your native responsibility for love in every moment is weakened. Shocks of life and breath are "creative", or "causative", relative to reactive (or obstructed) emotions.

The artful task of the living being is to remain responsible for its inherent disposition and "conductivity", even through and in the midst of the shocks and impositions of "experience". It is the Law of "self"-sacrifice, or love, that is hidden in every breath. If you abide as love, with free attention in all action, then you remain in the responsible position relative to life, breath, action, and the process of Realization. But if you abide in your "subjectivity", ego-possessed, distracted (by the obsessive "sound" of thinking) from feeling in the infinite pattern of relations, then you are irresponsible, subject to random "experience", unable to conduct life, or to breathe openly, or to act sanely and humanly, or to Realize Truth.

The feeling cycle of the breath is (thus) the center of life and all relations. The conscious feeling of the bodily and relational cycle of breath and life, under conditions of action and repose, is fundamental to well-being, good relations, and to the entire affair of "conscious exercise". Therefore, it is essential to account for the critical factors and events in the feeling-cycle of breathing.

Feel Without Obstruction

The physical body is always already fully permeated by all-pervading energy, or life-force. It never becomes empty or filled, but it is only either more or less directly and presently in a condition of communication, or communion, with the universal life-force. You fluctuate or "phase" in your state of feeling, moment to moment. You also chronically feel reactive or contracted and negative emotional conditions—from fear and sorrow and anger, to relatively modest anxiety and sadness and despair, to depression and dullness and boredom. Therefore, you are also chronically tending toward a condition of non-communication of life (or energy), on the basis of the effects of "experience" or (otherwise) reactions to "experience", in every moment.

The only way to realize a present degree of maximum intensity, communicated in, as, and through the whole body-being, is to feel without obstruction, or contraction. Then you abide in the inherent intensity of the universally present energy, life, or light. That feeling is named "love" and "sacrifice" (or "surrender"). It is the unlimited feeling and the inherent intensity of the whole body-being that characterizes you when you simply look and feel and <u>are</u> and act completely happy. In your chronic condition, you tend to manifest such happiness, or love—in other words, you tend to communicate (or commune) with the inherent force of existence—only when events "cause" you to react with complete, unobstructed feeling.

Thus, only in the rare moments of good fortune or fulfillment, the moments equivalent to suddenly getting a gift of a million dollars, do you consent to feel and to exist as that inherent force.

This is the chronic "problem" of humankind—that human beings do not consent to feel as they are, but only as they are "caused" to feel. You feel according to your present circumstances rather than your inherent force of existence. The Spiritual obligation of every human being is to realize the inherent intensity of life in every moment. And this is possible only if there is true, present, and "radical" understanding of the evidence of Truth and of life itself. Only then will you consent—or even be able—to look and feel and be and act completely happy, under all conditions.

The discipline of "conscious exercise" is a part of the total right-life discipline that obliges My devotees in the Reality-Way of Adidam. All others may also apply at least this part of the wisdom of the whole body, and so benefit all of human society by becoming more stable, healthy, and responsible for life and feeling.

And feeling, as you see, is the key to the functional wisdom of the whole body. Feeling unlocks the contractions of the reactive body-life, and permits a free communication between attention and action. . . .

Reception/Release and Prior Fullness

In the simplest terms, the living body is an expression of two tendencies, uses, or currents of life. And, again in the simplest (or most basic) terms, these tendencies are the two motions of contraction and expansion, or reception and release. There is a negative (or exclusive and unbalanced) expression of each of these tendencies. When reactivity (or reaction to "experience") becomes stronger than the force of life and unobstructed (or free) feeling-attention, then the tendency to live as contraction and expansion disables you. You become ego-possessed, confined to "subjectivity", negatively emotional, vitally weak, and self-defeating in action. Then expansion (or release) is confined to patterns of mere "self"-indulgence—such that you are constantly emptied, until death.

But there is a positive (or true) functional development of each of these motions—when they are in balance, and when attention and bodily form and action are controlled by full central communion with (or feeling into) the universal environment of the life-force. In that case, even each breath becomes a balanced cycle of reception-release, contraction-expansion, in the constant field of fully felt life-intensity.

It has already been "considered" how the inhalation of breath (or life) is associated with reception, in-filling, and natural "conductivity" (or movement) toward the whole body. Likewise, the exhalation is associated with expansion, or release of the wastes, the accumulated contents, or old circumstances and adaptations of life (not the release, or emptying, of life itself), and natural "conductivity" (or movement) from the whole body outward. This dual cycle is generated from the heart (the feeling center), and enacted between the apparent entrance of breath at the nose and the vital (or abdominal) center below. The cycle of breathing moves to and from the vital abdominal center. The vital center is not filled and emptied in the process, but it is rhythmically active as the bodily center wherein the felt intensity of the universal life is constantly and priorly communicated with and expressed.

When you breathe, you should breathe with the sense that the whole body rests (or abides) always and already in the universal, all-pervading life-field. Thus, the vital center and the head are both—equally, and always—in perfect and constant contact with the light of life. When the cycle of breathing is generated, it should not be felt that life only enters the nose and then goes down to the vital center, but that the whole body breathes, or communes with the universal life. The nose, throat, vital center, and heart are simply mechanisms, or parts, of the conversation between the whole body and the all-pervading life. . . .

. . . You must abide constantly in the sense that the whole body— from the feeling heart, from and to and through the whole surface or skin of the body, and via the vital center—is always already existing in an all-pervading, unlimited, and universal field of energy, life, or light. It is only because the life-force is associated with the incoming and outgoing cycle of the breath that you feel life itself comes and goes—whereas, in fact, life is constant, and the cycle of breath is only a play of feeling-attention on the universal energy that always already pervades the whole body, the vital center, the heart, and the mind. If feeling can be full and constant, then it is no longer subject to the apparent cycle, or "phasing", of the breath. Then your eternal position begins to become clear—at the heart, prior to mind and body. Therefore, you are constantly obliged by the Law of "self"-sacrifice, love, or radiance.

The sense of the prior fullness and eternal conservation of life, or light, may be presumed to be simply or factually true on the basis of "consideration" of science and "experience". Thus, anyone may practice "conscious exercise" who has at least minimal sympathy with the profound evidence of science and life. But the full (or optimum) practice depends on Prior Realization of the Truth of the whole body—and such Realization depends on Listening to Me, and Hearing Me, and Seeing Me. Likewise, the practice I Give to My devotees is an entire life of full devotional (and, in due course, Transcendental Spiritual) practice in My Divine Avataric Company, and in cooperative association with other devotees. ■

From "The Internal 'Locks' of the Whole Body",
in *Conscious Exercise and The Transcendental Sun.*

CHAPTER 3

Healing the Whole Bodily System— and the World

R eality Itself is a prior unity. Reality Itself is indivisible and egoless. Therefore, life must be lived in accordance with that Self-Nature of Reality Itself.
This absolute principle is fundamental to all resolution of human problems.

—Avatar Adi Da Samraj
"No Enemies",
Prior Unity

The overarching principles on healing given by His Divine Presence Avatar Adi Da (summarized in this chapter) provide essential guidance for approaching "conductivity"-healing practice. These principles account for how the total human system works— on both an individual and a collective level—and for how obstructions in that system can be relinquished.

"Conductivity"-Healing Practices Serve the System, Not the "Problem"

I n the common "world", The Approach To Health and Healing Tends To Be (Primarily) An Effort To Combat The grosser Aspects Of ordinary Suffering. Thus, the Suffering individual Presumes (and Tends To Take The Form Of) The Principle Of Disease.

If Disease Is Presumed To Be The "Problem", Then "Cure" Is Presumed To Be The Only Possible Resolution Of Your Situation— and You May (Therefore) Tend To Become (Irresponsibly) Involved

In The "doctor-patient Game". When "Cure" Seems To Be The Only Answer To Your Suffering, You Become Obsessively Involved In The Search For something that (You Hope) Will "Cure" (or Excise) Your Apparent "Problem".

Among human beings (Especially In This "Late-Time", or "Dark" Epoch), The Demand For "Cure" Is Only Slightly Less Universal Than The Expectation Of (and Even The Demand For) "Disease"!

Altogether, The Presumption Of "Disease" and The Search For "Cure" Generate A Mass Of Confusion In The Unconscious ego-Drama Enacted By each individual. In That ego-Drama, The Intrinsically egoless Principle Of Reality Itself Is Forgotten. In That ego-Drama, "Disease" and "Cure" Are Equally "Precious", and There Are "factions" within the ego-"I" that Defend "Disease" Just As Tenaciously As others of its "factions" Defend "Cure".

—Avatar Adi Da Samraj
The Dawn Horse Testament

Rather than reinforcing the idea of a "disease" that needs to be "cured", Avatar Adi Da calls for a "systems-based" approach to healing, founded in an understanding of the total system of the body-mind-complex.

Deal with the body's systems. The body within its total environment— its "world"-environment, its Earth-environment, its cosmic environment of energies—should be the means. You have to find out what the system does, how it works, and apply what the body can use (in its ordinary, or natural, course) for the sake of wellness. Do this— rather than attempt to manipulate the system from without, based on egoic mind.

In order to apply the systems-based approach, you have to "know" the law of the body, "know" the system of its physicality, its chemical system—in fact, all of its systems, including the energy system that is actually global or universal—and use that understanding in a humble manner. For the healer, right healing is a humble matter, because you are subordinating the mind (and the ego) to what is greater than itself. Such subordination is a characteristic of right esoteric practice as I have Described it altogether.

In terms of healing, do not take the whiz-bang, manipulative, doctor-controlling-the-patient kind of approach. Rather, it is the humble healer who knows that "cure" (so to speak), or wellness altogether, is not the healer's province. Wellness is the province of the domain in which the body lives. As a healer, you must be subordinate to that and find out how it works and serve that.

That is quite a different position than the abstracted physician's kind of view. The conventional orientation of Western medicine is external, analytic. It "objectifies" the patient and dissects, even desecrates, the body and its field in an effort to cure, in an effort to deal with a "problem".

However, the concept of the body being a "problem" is not lawful. The body is the means. It is not a "problem". How do you work with the body such that it will deal with things and make wellness its sign? That is, basically, the healer's obligation—and it is a humble obligation, in that sense.

Anything beyond that humble, systems-based approach is really part of what I call "compassionate medicine". In that case, where somebody is in a difficult, critical situation, you have to take steps for the sake of the person's survival. That is where conventional Western medicine has its special province or role—when you are obliged to deal with the life-and-death, survival-or-not kinds of issues.[1]

—Avatar Adi Da Samraj
March 29, 2006

The systems-based approach is built into "conductivity"-healing practice—because such practice is based in an understanding of the body as an integrated hierarchical system. By working directly with etheric energy to influence physical well-being—in other words, by working at the yellow-red conjunction—"conductivity" healing supports and makes use of the hierarchical energy systems of the whole body.

---

1. Although Avatar Adi Da points out the limitations of the conventional analytical approach to health and healing, He also admonishes His devotees to make right use of this form of medicine, describing it (in *The Dawn Horse Testament*) as a secondary approach that "Should Be Applied Intelligently . . . Whenever Appropriate and Necessary". See appendix C for more on this point.

The etheric is the "root" of physical patterns. Therefore, energy healing that works at the conjunction of the etheric and the physical can be very effective. In other words, it can go right to the "top" (so to speak), and then it can deal with everything "below". If you affect the etheric pattern, you can (thereby) affect things at the grosser level of the physical.

The etheric is the lowest of the three sheaths commonly referred to as the subtle body. As such, it is immediately senior to the physical pattern. Therefore, if you affect the etheric (whether positively or negatively), then the physical can also be (potentially) affected.

—Avatar Adi Da Samraj
April 26, 1995, and May 6, 1996

If supported in its natural function as a whole, integrated, hierarchical system, the human structure spontaneously moves toward a state of equanimity. Avatar Adi Da describes the human system as "self-correcting, self-organizing, and self-rightening"— and "conductivity" healing supports these inherent characteristics. Rather than targeting a particular imbalance or disturbance, the whole-body system can simply be supported in its natural movement toward balance and well-being.

In some basic terms, even people oriented toward naturopathic medicine have a tendency to use the logic of conventional Western medical analysis. They think: you test it, you diagnose it through analysis, and then you propose treatment that is a kind of mono-treatment—an exaggerated influence of some kind or another, even (possibly) selected from natural sources, which, if you take it, immediately causes a reaction of some kind. Instead of making the entire system work, you analyze and select a particular substance or group of substances.

If you are busy diagnosing the system and then coming up with a remedy to attack a "problem", you are not taking into account the whole system. You are just using your analysis, which is detached from the whole.

The approach of analysis leading to attack of the "problem" with an exaggerated mono-something to cure it should be converted, through a different kind of thinking about healing. You should take all of the data as a means of understanding what is going on systematically in the individual case, and then you should address the entire system. This means you would not take just a substance to create an exaggerated effect—asserting things like "this pill or this plant will deal with your liver".

You must address the whole body, which is a system of many organs in relation to one another, and so forth. Healing is about the entire system and what it is going to do itself. It will self-organize. It will self-purify. It will self-correct. You simply must help the system to work. That is the right intention and approach. It is a different kind of thinking about healing. It is whole-body thinking, non-seeking thinking.

You should understand what is going on by testing and analyzing and diagnosing (or analyzing and seeing what the signs mean), but then you still have the whole body. Most systems of medicine—whether conventional Western medicine or Chinese medicine or whatever it may be—are typically "substance-and-problem"-oriented. Whereas the approach I am Recommending is not about that. It is a non-seeking approach, which means it is not "problem"-oriented. It is not seeking to solve a "problem".

It does not make any difference what the so-called "problem" is. You should always serve systems, not "problems". The system is a whole. And it is intrinsically self-correcting if permitted to do so. Do not put on the "problem" mind. Always assume the whole-body approach. That approach is about how to balance the whole body and how to "consider" the range of substances that will serve the self-correcting process of the body.

This is the logic of working with health issues that I am proposing. My approach to health and well-being is about how you manage health in a searchless manner, trusting the system to work.

—Avatar Adi Da Samraj
September 9, 2008

❖ ❖ ❖

When one presumes that the body is a "problem" to be "solved", rather than a system to be lawfully managed, then exaggerated and systematic efforts to "cure" the body only interfere with the body's self-healing ability. . . .

Gross and ego-bound views manifest in all kinds of ways, organizing themselves through notions of "problem" and "search". . . . Fundamentally, [I Recommend] the practice of assuming that you do not have a "problem" of health. Rather, you have an obligation for health, and not a "problem" to be corrected. When the body's functioning is limited in any way, yield the body to the lawful situation in which the condition may be set right, rather than presuming a "problem" and seeking a solution.

—Avatar Adi Da Samraj
"Searchless, Lawful Management of The Body",
Green Gorilla

T*he usual approach to healing is analytical and objective: to seek for causes of ill health via tests, and so forth, and to treat the ailment "from the outside in". One takes substances into the body from outside, based on forms of objective analysis. But Avatar Adi Da's Wisdom, while not abandoning the positive and necessary aspects of this analytical approach, uses the "answers" that lie in the body itself. Many times the objective, purely scientific approach reveals nothing. However, Adi Da Samraj says that the body itself knows what is wrong—without being able to name the problem—and the body can generally do something about it, by undoing the causes of the problem at their root. He describes this as dealing with health problems "from the inside out".*

—Charles Seage, MD,
personal physician to Avatar Adi Da Samraj
during His Lifetime

When the systems-based approach is applied, Avatar Adi Da says, healing is straightforward. One can simply observe the signs of imbalance, then apply natural and appropriate forms of restraint and intelligent action (including "conductivity" healing) that allow the structures to return to their natural state of equanimity.[2] As He describes here, such disciplines "yield" the physical body to its true circumstance.

The first approach to all health issues is always to self-responsibly correct the body and apply lawful right discipline to it. Part of the process of the practice of right life in the Reality-Way of Adidam is time—one establishes the lawful practice and then allows the body time to show its signs. The process of right life is allowed to unfold, because through right discipline the body's energies have been set free to show their lawful signs. However, the lawful practice of diet, and of health altogether, is a process of observation and examination, and is not necessarily spontaneously corrective of all health issues. The healing arts are an important aid to the body if resistive conditions are still observed in the body over time.

The obsessive and fanatical seeking-approach that looks for magic cures is not the approach I give to My devotees in the Reality-Way of Adidam. If there is to be well-being, the body must be yielded to its unified circumstance in the unity of its natural domain. How is that yielding accomplished? Simply by establishing the lawfulness of bodily discipline. The body is a food-process. . . . Fundamentally, it does not need to be cured. One needs simply to stop bothering the body with "self"-indulgent habits of life, stop throwing it out of balance, stop maintaining it unlawfully.

The principle of "searchlessness" relative to diet and well-being is unique to My Instruction to My devotees. I have Criticized seeking in all its forms since the first day of My formal Work of Teaching. Therefore, My Criticism of seeking applies to all the searches for cure . . . that may be found in today's marketplace.

People are always ready to work on their "problem", whatever it might be. In reality, you are your own "problem", and that is why you are always functioning as if you have one. The problem-free— or searchless—approach to discipline, rather than the search for a solution to a "problem", is the principle of right-life practice in the

2. See appendix C for a description of the three phases of healing and associated right-life disciplines that can be applied in the process of correcting imbalance.

Reality-Way of Adidam. . . . When you accept the discipline of lawfulness that I describe, healing is a spontaneous manifestation of the bodily life. Fundamentally, you leave the body alone. You observe its signs, rather than trying to manipulate it into well-being.

—Avatar Adi Da Samraj
"Searchless, Lawful Management of The Body",
Green Gorilla

"Radical" Healing Is Right Relationship to Reality

There is no <u>ultimate</u> well-being without turning (and, thereby, surrendering) to That Which Is Ultimate.

—Avatar Adi Da Samraj
August 11, 1983

Avatar Adi Da goes further in His calling for systems-based healing. Not only must one understand and work with the hierarchical and indivisible system of the human body-mind, but one must also understand how the human system relates to the Fundamental Condition in which it is arising. How does the human being rightly relate to its Source-Condition? When this is discovered and enacted, the transformative Force of the Fundamental Condition becomes obvious.

If you could simply feel your condition—feel as your condition in this moment, without obstruction, without making an interpretation— then you would no longer be what you are presently being. In that case, you would not be trapped in obstructed feeling-attention and defining yourself—feeling vulnerable, separate, "a" being. You would directly and intuitively discover the Source-Condition in Which you and every thing and every one is arising (without, in any sense, being separated out), in Which you exist Non-conditionally, in Which you are Sustained Absolutely, and in Which you never were (or are) separated from anything.

—Avatar Adi Da Samraj
"Renouncing The Search For The Edible Deity",
The Yoga of Right Diet

❖ ❖ ❖

Individual existence in a "world" is a riddle and a torment, unless it is established in right relationship to the Self-Radiant Energy That Is its real "Substance", and in right Identity with the Self-Existing and Limitless Consciousness That Is its Very Self-Condition. And the manner in which human beings may live in such right relationship to and Identity with the Divine Reality, free of fear and illusion, is in whole bodily conversion, or the "turnabout" of every aspect of the body-mind-complex, from ego-possession to ecstatic Communion with the Divine.

The most rudimentary form of such Divine Communion is the intuitive turning of all bodily, emotional, and mental functions, conditions, "experiences", and relations into forms of functional surrender to the Self-Existing and Self-Radiant Divine Reality. . . . In that process, the Living Power of Real God is permitted to Pervade, Enliven, Sustain, Transform, and Awaken the entire bodily being. And the primary instrument of that process is the whole bodily disposition of ecstatic (or "self"-releasing) sacrifice into the Divine Reality. That disposition is the one of total, profound, and free feeling-attention and love, relaxing the total body-mind into the All-Pervading and Intrinsically Free Force of Reality Itself.

—Avatar Adi Da Samraj
"God Is the Transcendental Consciousness and Radiant Life
That Pervades the Body, the Mind, and the World",
The Enlightenment of the Whole Body

When the direct process of such "self"-release into the Free Force of Reality Itself is entered into, then even the root-contraction of presumed separate "self" can be undone. The term Avatar Adi Da uses for the healing process that is based in transcending ego at its root is "'radical' healing". "Radical" healing is purposed toward much more than psycho-physical well-being.

"radical"

Avatar Adi Da uses the term "radical" in the sense of its Latin source-meaning, which is simply "at the root"—rather than as a reference to any kind of political orientation.

The Process Of "Radical" Healing Does Not Occur For The Sake Of the bodily human being (in and of itself). Indeed, True "Radical" Healing Occurs Only When the bodily human being Is Surrendered (or Yielded) To The Self-Existing and Self-Radiant and Intrinsically egoless and Perfectly Acausal and Self-Evidently Divine Condition Of Reality (Itself). . . .

The Basic Principle Of "Radical" Healing (Whether Of Apparent "self" Or Of Apparent "other") . . . Is Communion With The Prior Perfection (or Intrinsically egoless and Perfectly Acausal and Self-Evidently Divine Condition Of Reality) In Which the bodily human being is arising (and Of Which the bodily human being Is A Transparent, or Merely Apparent, and Non-Necessary, and Intrinsically Non-Binding Modification).

—Avatar Adi Da Samraj
The Dawn Horse Testament

Avatar Adi Da offers to humankind a specific and direct means to enable this process of transcending ego at its root through right relationship to the Fundamental Divine Reality. (See Part Two for more about His unique offering.)

Wellness for the Collective Human System

These principles of health and well-being apply not only to individuals, but also to the collective of humankind. And, likewise, the failure to apply these principles has implications for all. Because the human system is indivisibly connected to the entire energy system of the cosmic domain, disturbances in the yellow-red conjunction at the personal level not only create individual suffering but also impact the collective system of humankind. Avatar Adi Da explains that much of the extreme imbalance and aggressive self-destruction occurring presently in global human culture is a reflection of such disturbances.

The lack of integration of the etheric and the physical dimensions is fundamental to people's unwellness and neurosis. That is what is being reflected in people's aberrations. And it is what is being reflected in this global gross ego-culture now. Humanity has disconnected itself from the field of energy in which the cosmos exists, and which it (in fact) is.

It is not that matter exists in energy. Matter is energy. To make a global culture of people who are only thinking and perceiving in terms of sheer physicality is to have established a gross culture that is going to destroy itself.

To understand and correct this is critical. That is what I am Working with now on a global scale.[3] It is critical for the sensitivity to be restored, the balance restored, the responsibility restored by humankind as a whole—because its gross-mindedness is the basis for self-destruction.

—Avatar Adi Da Samraj
July 30, 2008

Avatar Adi Da points out that, like the individual human system, the collective system of humankind is self-correcting. Therefore, the "body" of the human collective will also move toward balance, if obstructions in the system are removed and right functioning is supported.

Unless they are specifically prevented from doing so, all systems will spontaneously righten themselves. The universe is a self-organizing, self-correcting, and self-rightening process. All systems are self-organizing, self-correcting, and self-rightening—unless something interferes with the self-organizing, self-correcting, and self-rightening process.

—Avatar Adi Da Samraj
"Reality-Humanity",
Not-Two Is Peace

As with the individual human system, the principal obstruction in the human collective system is ego, manifesting in collective forms—demonstrated in a variety of patterns and habits of disunity, separateness, and conflict. To describe the ego's obstructing

---

3. During His Lifetime, Avatar Adi Da worked not only for the sake of establishing the Reality-Way of Adidam, He was also always (and, perpetually is) intensively involved in a constant Blessing-Work with the entire world. See *The Avatar of What Is* by Carolyn Lee for an account of Avatar Adi Da's World-Blessing-Work.

effect on systems, Avatar Adi Da uses the analogy of sticking a large pole, or "stave", into the wheel of a moving cart. If you do so, you interrupt the wheel's ability to do what it is built to do—and the cycling of the cart wheel comes to an immediate halt. The removal of this "stave" of egoity for the world as a whole requires responsibility at the individual level.

Systems are self-correcting. The universe, or the "world", is self-correcting. What are the "problems" of humankind all over the "world" the result of? Humankind's "problems" are the result of not allowing the system to work. All kinds of other interim decisions are made, and those decisions hold patterns in place, like the stave in the wheel, which will not allow the system to correct itself.

There are "problems" all over the "world"—political and environmental, and all the rest—that can be allowed to self-correct. But all the interferences that are in place are preventing that. And people are not equipped with the right understanding or even willing to embrace a right understanding, unless the matter is addressed to everybody.

The same situation is occurring in the rather local situation of the individual body. The body is a system like all other holistic systems. It is part of a holistic (or total) pattern. It is a pattern within a pattern, but it is a system-pattern. As such, the body has many factors, many elements in play, which have to coordinate with one another in order to establish balance.

The right questions to ask are: How do you serve that system? How do you enable the system to work? This, rather than: How do you cure its "problem"?

This systems-based approach is what I am Recommending in all matters of right-life practice—including larger issues of "world" peace, and so forth. All right life for humankind is fundamentally based on this logic of address—which is different than the logic by which people are functioning otherwise. The systems-based approach is different than how the ego works.

The ego is essentially predatory. It looks to focus its attention on something "problematic", and then it attacks it—in order to control it, get rid of it, solve it as a "problem", and so forth. That is "ego-picking"—which perpetually creates more "problems", and then treats them in the same manner.

After a while, you have done that so many times that nothing works any more—and then you die, and everything altogether collapses. The entire system collapses.

This is what is happening with humankind as a whole. This is what is happening with individuals.

—Avatar Adi Da Samraj
September 9, 2008

◆ ◆ ◆

The same issues pertain at the individual level that pertain at the global level. They are about the same pattern. Self-management must be established at the individual scale, just as it must be established at the collective and global scale. Thus, the big picture and the small picture are one picture. They are hand-in-glove with one another, and must be understood as such.

Global imbalances are a reflection of individuals. At the global scale, everyone is aware of pollution and climate change and extreme weather patterns, and so forth. However, people are less aware of how such global issues are a reflection of what human beings are doing individually and how the system is controlling people negatively. The same system is producing both pollution of the Earth-world and pollution of the individual body. It is all one pattern.

—Avatar Adi Da Samraj
"The Big Picture and The Small Picture",
Prior Unity

In the broadest understanding, then, "conductivity"-healing practice is part of a life that is purposed toward going beyond, or transcending, ego-based patterns—in other words, removing the stave in the wheels—and thereby supporting the collective matter-and-energy system in its natural movement toward balance.

Avatar Adi Da Calls Everyone to Assume Responsibility for the Total Human Structure

Avatar Adi Da points out that we must understand how the human system really works, and ultimately understand and participate in the great Context in which the human system is arising, if we are to be free to grow and purify and heal. And He offers His instruction and Help in this matter—for the sake of bodily well-being, and for the sake of True Freedom.

The human psycho-physical system is not merely a gross phenomenon. Rather, the human psycho-physical system is a participant in a Universal Field (with gross, subtle, and causal dimensions). However, because human beings tend to be so "bogged down" by the influence of their life-histories, their patterned habits, and their habitual associations, they (characteristically) are thoroughly desensitized to the actualities of their own conditionally manifested existence. Thus, especially in this "late-time" (or "dark" epoch), human beings tend to (mistakenly) presume that the entire cosmic domain (including their own body-minds) is merely gross (or merely physical, or merely material)—and, because of this overriding presumption, human beings also tend to (mistakenly) perceive the cosmic domain (including their own body-minds) as merely gross (or merely physical, or merely material).

When the human being is "ruled" by this materialistic presumption, it becomes impossible for real and true purification of the individual body-mind-complex to take place. Because much psycho-physical toxicity relates to the subtle (emotional, mental, psychic, and mystical) dimension of existence (and even, at the "root"-level, to the causal dimension of existence), the psycho-physical toxins cannot pass through and out of the human psycho-physical system if the reigning paradigm is that all of Reality is merely gross (or merely physical, or merely material)—and, therefore, those toxins merely accumulate in the body-mind-complex.

Such accumulation of psycho-physical toxins gives rise, over time, to the particular signs of human character exhibited by any individual—even the physical signs. Whatever is in the mind and the emotions registers in the body as well—because the human being is a single mechanism (and systematic sign). The fact that mental and emotional toxicity also displays itself in the physical body gives you an opportunity to notice that there is something about your habits of living that you must correct. If you do not (thus) correct yourself, then your life becomes an ever-increasing accumulation of distress and limitations.

Such is the characteristic life of the usual human being. Every egoically functioning person (or body-mind-"self") progressively accumulates more and more mental, emotional, and physical toxicity. I Am here to Teach you—and to Reveal to you, and to Give to you, and to Draw you into—the Real Process of becoming Utterly (and Eternally) Free of all psycho-physical limitations, by Means of Transcendental, Inherently Spiritual, and Self-Evidently Divine Real-God-Realization.

—Avatar Adi Da Samraj
"The Necessary Foundation of Right Life",
The Aletheon

Avatar Adi Da's instruction is not only for those moved to enter into the process of Divine Realization. In fact, Avatar Adi Da makes an urgent calling to all of humankind—to abandon the false disposition of gross materialism, by taking responsibility for ourselves as energy, existing in indivisible prior unity with all.

Human beings are inherently obliged to realize their humanity as an <u>ego-transcending</u> discipline. Human beings do not, in Reality and in Truth, have the option to renounce their humanity or the universal Unifying Life-Principle (or cosmically extended Pattern of Oneness) that sustains them. Rather, human beings must assume the inherent responsibility of human relationships. Human beings must assume <u>all</u> the structures of the human mechanism (both lower and higher) as real conditions of existence—and human beings must become functionally responsible for positively conducting the life-force in every area of their experience. To the degree that they do all of this, human beings are obliged to be committed to right life in the dimensions of time and space—and only in that case are they *free to carry on the creative developmental and ecstatically ego-transcending Reality-process of their humanly-born lives.*

—Avatar Adi Da Samraj
"Reality-Politics For Ordinary Men and Women",
Not-Two Is Peace

The healing principle of energy, as clarified and elaborated by Avatar Adi Da Samraj, is key to the necessary transformation of humankind, individually and collectively. Anyone who truly listens to what Avatar Adi Da says about the energy structures of existence, and the Fundamental Divine Source-Condition in which they arise, will discover an entirely new way of living.

It is time for everyone to awaken from the spell of childish, subhuman, ego-possessed, "subjective" (mental, emotional, and physical) obsession. It is time to grow up! The Truth can become obvious to human understanding, and the cultural situation of humankind can become harmonious and benign. It is a matter of entering into the yet hidden (or esoteric) domain of awakened intelligence, "self"-restraint, acceptance of life-positive disciplines of physical, emotional, and mental activity, and conversion from the separative and ego-possessed disposition to the truly ecstatic moral and Spiritual disposition of ego-transcending devotional Communion with the Divine Self-Nature, Self-Condition, Source-Condition, and Self-State of all beings and things. Only the life of Divine Communion permits the child to grow into maturity. That Way of life is the ego-transcending Way that is hidden within (or natively built into) the psycho-physical structures of the human being.

—Avatar Adi Da Samraj
"Cultism Is The Beginner's Level of Human Existence",
The Aletheon

Avatar Adi Da Samraj
Adi Da Samrajashram, 2008

The Art of True Healing

by His Divine Presence,
Avatar Adi Da Samraj

Here Avatar Adi Da describes how to take personal responsibility for one's own psycho-physical well-being—through healing practices, through living a disciplined life, and through the sacrifice (or letting go) of the separate "self" in response to the Fundamental Divine Reality.

Healing is an art.
True healing must involve right responsibility on the part of the one being healed—such that, after the healing takes place, he or she enjoys a greater level of responsibility for his or her total psycho-physical life. Any process that does not involve such a responsibility-transformation of the one being healed is not real healing. Some symptoms may be removed for a while, so that the individual can return to the activities of his or her ordinary life—but, unless the individual has realized a greater level of responsibility for bodily well-being, he or she will simply persist in the same patterns as before, and imbalances and negative symptoms will reappear.

A symptom is a condition of disease that has become so acute that one has started to notice it—but the disease exists long before the symptom appears. Obstructions in the organs of the body accumulate long before exaggerated symptoms arise. At what point is one's condition said to be disease? It might as well be said that one is diseased from the first moment one does something that will ultimately have a negative result relative to one's psycho-physical life. That event is, in fact, the onset of the disease. The failure to practice right life is the disease. The failure to fulfill the Law of "self"-surrender is the disease. Once an individual begins to act in violation of that Law, it is merely a matter of time before symptoms appear.

People usually do not even begin to entertain the possibility of taking responsibility for disease until the disease has already manifested as symptoms. Some people who are more sensitive to their psycho-physical systems than others may do something about a symptom as soon as they notice it. Others wait until they are already seriously disabled before they will take any first measures. When such people are finally suffering a terminal ailment, then, all of a sudden, they want a "miracle cure". This childish approach characterizes most people's relationship to the practice of health. Even if something extraordinary were to happen, such that the disease disappeared, the individual would continue in the unconscious, irresponsible, and un-Lawful pattern that originally led to the disease.

Therefore, the "miracle cure" is not even desirable from the perspective of conscious life.

There is a scene in a motion picture that makes this point.[4] A man without hands has gone with a crowd to pay respects to St. Simon Stylites, who stood for years at the top of a pole in the desert. The man, who has come with his children and his wife, is humble and sorrowful. His wife asks the Saint to heal her husband. Simon says, "Well, all I can do is pray." The people kneel and pray with the Saint while the man holds up his stumps. The next thing you know, two hands have appeared at the ends of the man's arms! But what does he do? He pulls down his arms and tells his children, "C'mon, let's go home." He just walks away, ready to go home and watch television!

Extraordinary "miraculous cures" that relieve one of all responsibility also (thereby) bypass all personal responsibility for conscious living, and (thus) bypass personal responsibility to remain in the Fundamental Condition of Communion with the Living Divine Reality-Truth—and, as such, are false cures, hallucinations, and

---

4. Avatar Adi Da is referring to the movie *Simon of the Desert*, written and directed by Luis Buñuel (released August 27, 1965).

hype. Through true healing, the individual becomes responsible, clarified, and intelligent relative to the entire affair of his or her ordinary life. Lawful and True life does not depend on extraordinary "methods" and "experiences" to relieve one of suffering. Rather, Lawful and True life is a process whereby a person becomes more and more responsibly responsive to the Living Divine Reality-Truth.

The devotional (and, in due course, Transcendental Spiritual) relationship with Me influences the approach of My any devotee to physical "problems". In illness, My devotee cannot dramatize the usual strategies, including bodily habits, emotional games, and general life-strategies. In illness, the accumulative, binding activity that the individual tends to engage is frustrated and brought to a crisis, brought to a point of conscious responsibility in the midst of constant devotional "self"-sacrifice in My Company.

By contrast, the conventional practices of medicine—both naturopathic medicine and conventional Western medicine—do not address the fundamental human activity that is ultimately responsible for the lack of well-being. Certainly, how you treat the body, how you manage your diet and your routine of living, affect the state of your health. In any case, you must be responsible for managing these aspects of your life. However, the fundamental ego-activity of "self"-contraction, which I Criticize, is essentially the "root" of every form of disease. The ego is your disease. The ego is suffering. The ego is your most primitive activity, the "self"-defining contraction that creates the constant, separative, isolated sense of "me". Fundamentally, the ego creates all limiting conditions—hence your many colds and other illnesses! The diseases that you suffer are the result of a fundamentally misguided approach to "experiential" life.

One in whom there is no "self"-contraction is essentially free of the limitations of this great machine of "experiential" life. Such a person need not be concerned about the millions of factors that might pattern any momentary disease that comes from without. My devotees—who live the Reality-Way I have Revealed and Given—will not necessarily be immune to all disease, because many influences affect your presence in the "world", regardless of the degree of your "self"-understanding. Nonetheless, one in whom the entire "program" of "subjectivity" is undone also secondarily observes that the conditions of life are not as they seem to the usual person.

Fundamentally, everything that people are doing all the time is killing them. People fear death and feel guilty about death and about their fear. The most fundamental reason death is not acceptable to people, the most fundamental reason that adapting to a "world" in which there is death is difficult for them, is that they have not understood that the principle of life is sacrifice. When life is understood to be endless, vast sacrifice, then life becomes obvious as the life-giving process of ego-death.

To those who do not understand, there is life and there is death, and they are inimical to one another. It is presumed by such people that if you are alive, death is the opposite of your condition. And if you are dying, life is the opposite of your condition. Truly, however, life and death are a single process, which is Real Life— which does not exist apart from "self"-sacrificial activity, or love. Therefore, when death is viewed in Truth, then the life-drama lived by the usual person is already undermined.

You must become a sacrifice while alive. ∎

From "True Healing Requires You To Change Your Action",
in *The Eating Gorilla Comes In Peace.*

PART TWO

THE FUNDAMENTALS OF "CONDUCTIVITY" HEALING

CHAPTER 4

The Sacred Context
of "Conductivity" Healing

mprovement Of the individual ego-"self" Is Not "Radical" Healing. Only Liberation From the Separate and Separative "self" Allows Perfectly "Radical" Healing and True Joy.

—Avatar Adi Da Samraj
The Dawn Horse Testament

"Conductivity"-healing practices—which are the specific forms of energy healing given by His Divine Presence Avatar Adi Da Samraj—magnify the flow of natural life-energy in the yellow-red conjunction, bringing balance to the physical and etheric dimensions of the being. Therefore, the laying on of hands and Yogic "conductivity" massage (as the principal forms of "conductivity" healing), as well as all the supplemental practices included in this book, necessarily serve health and well-being. However, these practices are given by Avatar Adi Da principally to support the process by which human beings may transcend the body, mind, and "self" and Realize unobstructed feeling-participation in the Fundamental Divine Reality. This reorientation of life—from the ego's search to Communion with the Divine—is the sacred context of "conductivity" healing for those who have responded to Avatar Adi Da as His devotees.

When Avatar Adi Da is recognized as the Divine Reality Incarnate in human Form, the individual enters into the living process of direct relationship to Him. This relationship manifests as a life of devotion and ego-transcending discipline, enacted within a culture of others living likewise—and intended, ultimately, for the Perfect Realization of Avatar Adi Da's Divine Reality-State.

The Transformative Relationship to the Reality-Revealer, Avatar Adi Da Samraj

*I*n *The . . . "Radical" Reality-Way Of Adidam . . . , The Truly Holistic (and Truly "Radical") Approach To psycho-physical Healing (and, Altogether, To psycho-physical Well-being) Is, Fundamentally, The Cultivation Of The Devotional . . . Relationship To Me.*

—Avatar Adi Da Samraj
The Dawn Horse Testament

As a form of "radical" healing, "conductivity" healing addresses not only the contractions in the physical and etheric dimensions but also the root-contraction of "self". As described in chapter 3, a human being's right relationship to the Fundamental Divine Reality in which he or she is arising is what enables such root-level healing. Only through unguarded participation in what is utterly Free is ego undone at its root. Because Avatar Adi Da is the Manifestation of the Fundamental (egoless) Divine Reality, He gives the means to enter into right (and responsive, or devotional) relationship with that Reality.

I Am the Man of "Radical" Understanding. I Exist and Live as the Communication of That Which makes it possible for people to open, uncurl, be turned to relationship.

. . . Until you become capable of existence in this apparent (human) form, open in relationship, you tend to reject the force of existence in a continuously repeated ritual activity, like vomiting. The force of life is abandoned constantly. Even laughter is a form of this ritual abandonment. Non-regenerative sexual activity is a form of it. Ordinary perception is a form of it. It is to throw off, to fail to conduct, the force of life. It is unconsciousness, sleep, the refusal to be born. And its symptom is a life that is not in relationship, that is not whole, that is full of dis-ease, confusion. Such a life cannot function. It only forever seeks its own release—as if release from life were the goal of life.

In devotional Communion with Me, this rejection of the force of life, this rejection of birth, tends to become quieted—such that, more and more, the life-form conducts the force of life rather than rejecting it. The subtle form of the human structure is something like a Sphere, in Which the Current of natural life-energy (and also of the Divine Transcendental Spiritual Energy) continually descends in the frontal line, and then turns at the bodily base and ascends in the spinal line. In devotional Communion with Me, that Current is not rejected—It is conducted.

The force of life rounds the heart, like the planets round the Sun. And the True Divine Heart Is the "Sun" of the living human form. The Fullness that people begin to feel in devotional Communion with Me is this Circle of natural life-force (and, eventually, also My Avatarically Self-Transmitted Divine Transcendental Spiritual Energy), allowed to be conducted in descent (down the frontal line), and allowed to be conducted in ascent (up the spinal line). When that Fullness is felt, there is no more rejection (or "ritual vomiting") of the Current of Energy. Rather, by means of spontaneous "conductivity", the Current (of natural life-energy and, in the case of My by-Me-Transcendentally-Spiritually-Initiated devotees, of My Avatarically Self-Transmitted Divine Transcendental Spiritual Energy) is turned and re-turned—in a spherical Cycle that is completely at ease, without dilemma.

—Avatar Adi Da Samraj
"Relationship and Association",
My "Bright" Word

This responsive Communion (or whole bodily participation) with Avatar Adi Da unfolds from the "Place" that is Prior to the presumption of "self" in the causal dimension. In other words, devotion to Avatar Adi Da "happens" in the egoless Position, Prior to all levels of the human structure. And Standing in that Prior Place is also what truly heals the human being.

In the . . . Reality-Way of Adidam, you Stand in the Divine Self-Position, and the body-mind-complex is Transformed by That Stand. . . .

The changes in the psycho-physical conditions of individuals practicing the Reality-Way of Adidam come about because of profound "root"-devotion and "conductivity"-Communion with Me— the real process of tacitly Standing Prior in the Realization-Disposition, from the beginning. That Realization-Disposition (in and of Itself) Purifies and Transforms the whole body, and Conforms the whole body to Itself.

—Avatar Adi Da Samraj
"The End of The Path Is The Way From the Beginning",
The Aletheon

Such root-devotion spontaneously awakens when there is tacit recognition of Avatar Adi Da's Divine Reality-State. When such recognition occurs, the "conductivity" response to Avatar Adi Da comes alive.

Right relationship to Me is a devotional relationship to Me based on recognition-response to Me As I Am. If you recognize Me As I Am, you are aware of My egoless Reality-State (bodily Incarnate here)— and you feel Me, you feel with Me, you feel in total coincidence with Me—so that you forget your "self" in the midst of your activity, and in all of the happening of the living faculties of the total body-mind. That is devotion to Me. . . .

The Reality-Way of Adidam is a feeling-coincident-with-Me process—or a "conductivity" process. That process cannot be engaged merely by rote. That process requires that you feel coincident with Me—rather than feeling coincident with the separate ego-"I".

—Avatar Adi Da Samraj
"As I Am—and In Plain Sight",
The Aletheon

Forgetting "self" is, in effect, removing "the stave in the wheels" of the human system (as discussed in chapter 3). Therefore, in "self"-forgetting devotional Communion with Avatar Adi Da, the human system shows the signs of moving toward its natural state of equilibrium.

In the anxious ego, there is always an effort to animate body, emotion, mind, and breath for the sake of survival. Based on anxiety, there are all kinds of seeking, and so on. But when there is surrender of heart—when there is true "self"-surrender in Communion with Me, all the faculties turned to Me—the agitations of body, emotion, mind, and breath relax. This relaxation is a characteristic, then, of devotional Communion with Me.

If there is true surrender to Me, forgetting "self", surrender of all the faculties, then Yogic signs appear, in Communion with Me. Basic ones are a calming of the physical, a calming of emotion, a calming of mind, and (likewise) a calming of breath. Thus, a Yogic state of equanimity is realized in the practice of devotional Communion with Me.

—Avatar Adi Da Samraj
July 23, 1995

As Avatar Adi Da indicates in the quotation above, the devotee actively participates in devotional Communion with Him by turning, or yielding, all four of the principal faculties—of body, emotion, mind, and breath—to Him. This turning is responsive, integrated, and ego-transcending.

Through the practice of feeling and breathing in Communion with Beloved Adi Da, I often experience natural life-energy as a living process that can be breathed in and around the physical body and felt radiating from the heart and chest area. This doesn't require any forceful breathing or strategic technique of trying to feel energy—when I am sensitized to Beloved Adi Da's Presence and State and Blessing, the whole body feels naturally aligned to the universal field of life-energy without any effort. There is simply a noticing of equanimity and calm, felt physically and from the heart via the breath.

—Devotee of Avatar Adi Da Samraj

In the Reality-Way of Adidam, the total-body-all-at-once is responsively participating in Communion with Me. There are no exercises of zones, parts, functions, or aspects of the body-mind-complex that are to be strategically manipulated in the practice of the Reality-Way of Adidam.

This does not mean that there is no psycho-physical responsibility, but (rather) that all the disciplines occur merely responsively and with the body-mind-complex as a whole, or all at once.

The practice is an integrated, indivisible totality. Thus, there is no strategic means to be applied. It is simply whole bodily response to Me. In whole bodily response to Me, there is intrinsic transcending of egoity.

—Avatar Adi Da Samraj
April 27, 2008

Avatar Adi Da calls this responsive turning a "Yoga" of devotion. In this Yoga, the devotee is available to Avatar Adi Da's Transmission—of Blessing, and, in due course, of Transcendental Spiritual Energy.

It is only when you stay connected to Me—through the living Means of devotion—that I have the connectedness whereby My Response to you can be conducted.

That is how devotion "causes" My Blessing and gives It room, gives It a conductor.

Therefore, you must make room for Me.

If you do not maintain the connectedness to Me by turning to Me, then the lines of connection fall apart, and you fall back on yourself. . . .

Therefore, . . . you must make the living connection to Me. When you are truly devotionally turned to Me, there is a living connection wherein I can Transmit My Blessing, such that It is tangibly "Known" by you.

All the disciplines in the sphere of psycho-physical life simply turn the mechanism of the body-mind-complex to Me and connect it to Me, so that a means of "conductivity" is established.

—Avatar Adi Da Samraj
"A Living Connection To Me",
The Sacred Space of Finding Me

This living Yoga of devotion to Avatar Adi Da is, thus, the context of all healing in the Reality-Way of Adidam.

Yoga/Yogic

In the ancient language of Sanskrit, the word "yoga" means "yoking", or "union", and has been used to refer to any discipline or process whereby an aspirant seeks to achieve union with God (or the Divine, however conceived). Avatar Adi Da acknowledges this traditional use of the term, but also, in reference to the Divine Yoga of Adidam, employs it in a "radical" sense, indicating a process that is free of the usual presumption of the separate "self" and its search for union with the Divine (or anything at all). The Yogic process of response to Avatar Adi Da is moment to moment devotional Communion with Him, whereby the whole bodily being lives its inherent connectedness to the Divine Reality.

To be My devotee is to be in the "healing Circle" of the relationship to Me and within the circle of the gathering of My devotees, and within the sphere of intimacies, human-scale, that you live every day.

I am not talking about merely "building Me in" to the ceremony of a healing game. I am Recommending <u>actual</u> turning to Me, <u>actual</u> devotional Communion with Me—that actually happening, and being extended into a useful healing practice that works directly and basically just simply on the etheric level.

Therefore, this matter of "conductivity", or energy-sensitivity, energy-responsibility, is a primary responsibility in the Reality-Way of Adidam. You must live the Reality-Way of Adidam for real. It is only interesting if you participate in everything as an actual Yogic process—the Yoga of devotional turning to Me, moment to moment— truly integrated with whatever the circumstance or function is being engaged at the moment.

—Avatar Adi Da Samraj
May 6, 1996

The offering of sacred arts to the Guru is an ancient tradition that exemplifies the relationship between Guru and devotee. The devotee making the following statement is speaking about an occasion in which she offered Avatar Adi Da a performance of Bharata Natyam (a form of classical Indian dance, the movements of which were developed in response to the Divine), and experienced the inherently transformative effects of the Guru's Blessing.

As the dance began, I allowed my mind and therefore my body to be focused on Avatar Adi Da. I adjusted the traditional form of this dance by taking every opportunity to regard Beloved Adi Da and give the dance to Him. As the dance offering continued, the muscular tensions throughout the body softened and the electrical energies could flow throughout, unobstructed, enlivening my body-mind more and more. I became ecstatic in the recognition of Avatar Adi Da Samraj as the very Divine Being.

I knew the principle of the Guru-devotee relationship, one of giving and receiving, but this was the first time that I understood it viscerally and felt it in my entire body-mind. Each time I offered myself to Beloved Bhagavan I felt the Force of His Transmission in my body. It felt like the body would open, the hard top of the head melting so there was no difference between my head and infinity, dissolving the sense of where I began and ended. I had the sense of an individual separate self dissolving, and that there was only a Single Divine Event, only One "Thing" Happening—and yet I was a responsive living part of It. The cycle of giving and receiving continued throughout the entire set of dances.

This understanding of the cycle of giving and receiving was the Gift I received that day, and it has been the basis of my relationship to Beloved Bhagavan Adi Da Samraj ever since.

—Devotee of Avatar Adi Da Samraj

Faith-Full Resort Is the Basis of Healing

T*he All-Pervading Divine Life Itself lives as the individual body-mind-complex and sustains it. If only the body-mind-complex will open into the Current of Radiant Life, with full feeling and without thought, it will be liberated from the ego-possessed games of tension and release of tension. Then there is only Fullness of Life. Such psycho-physical opening into the Current of Life is faith, in the highest sense. It is the bodily confession of dependence on the Living Divine, Prior to both fear and mere belief. It is bodily cooperation with Reality Itself, prior to all "subjectivity" and "problem"-centered efforts.*

—Avatar Adi Da Samraj
"The Transcendental Diet of Man",
The Enlightenment of the Whole Body

The devotional relationship to Avatar Adi Da as principal healing means is intentionally expressed in any healing practice as the "faith presumption". With the word "faith", Avatar Adi Da is not pointing to any form of belief, or fear-based hopefulness, as He indicates in the quotation above. Rather, the "faith presumption" is based upon true examination of the human condition and devotional recognition of Avatar Adi Da's Reality-State. The devotee understands that the body-mind-complex inheres in the Divine Reality—which is Always Already Free, Perfect, Prior to all forms of contraction—and recognizes that turning the faculties to Avatar Adi Da is the means to participate in the transformative Power of His Divine Reality-State.

As My Devotee, You Are Never (In Truth) A "Problem" (or A "Disease") To Be "Cured" (or a "hopeless sinner" To Be "Saved"). Rather, As My Devotee, You Are Called (By Me) To Always Act In An Appropriate and Responsible Manner, To Always Live On The Basis Of Inherently Faith-Full Resort To Me, and (Thus and Thereby) To Always Allow My Perfectly egoless All-Accomplishing Power Of Divine Transcendental Spiritual Conscious Light To Manifest Itself In The "Play" Of (Apparent) "experience".

Such Faith-Full Resort To Me (or The Exercise Of Constant Intrinsically ego-Surrendering Resort To My Prior Perfection and Perfectly egoless All-Accomplishing Power) Is The Fundamental Basis Of General Health and Well-being, and All Healing, In The Only-By-Me Revealed and Given "Radical" Reality-Way Of The Heart. If You Are My Devotee, That Constant Whole-bodily-Surrendering (and Intrinsically ego-Transcending) Devotional Resort To Me Must Be Your Really Practiced Disposition If You Are To Fulfill The Necessary Conditions Of The Process Of "Radical" Healing and Live In Real Devotional Communion With Me. All ordinary "Cures" (or changes of psycho-physical conditions, Produced As the "effects" of "causes" Exercised, Apart From The "Root"-Exercise Of The "Faith Presumption" In The Context Of Intrinsically ego-Transcending Devotional Resort To Me) Are Merely Superficial (or limited and ordinary), At Best Compassionately Intended, and Even Potentially Deluding.

—Avatar Adi Da Samraj
The Dawn Horse Testament

You could say that the "faith presumption" is the first healing "practice"—because (as an expression of devotional Communion with Avatar Adi Da) it undermines the otherwise automatic tendency to turn any healing practice into a form of seeking.

The principal healing "method" is the individual's presumption of health and life (not cure, but well-being prior to disease or cure). This presumption should be made with great intensity and supplemented by health practices such as changing the diet, fasting, laying on of hands by others, Yogic "conductivity" massage, and so on. The "patient" must be free of the "self"-image of disease and remain in devotional Communion with Me.

—Avatar Adi Da Samraj
The Eating Gorilla Comes In Peace

◆ ◆ ◆

The "faith presumption" is not supernatural magic. The "faith presumption" is a way of living the integrity of the whole body (and, thus, of living the integrity of the "world", as "universe"). It is not a matter of believing in the help of an "objective" Deity, but it is a matter of presuming the integrity of the whole body in the Divine Reality and Truth.

The principal "method" of "radical" healing is faith—or the presumption of infinite life, infinitely available life-energy, and health and well-being.

—Avatar Adi Da Samraj
The Eating Gorilla Comes In Peace

"Conductivity" practice—as a form of presuming "infinitely available life-energy"—is integral to the "faith presumption". In fact, Avatar Adi Da indicates that participation in the universal field of natural life-energy is actually a basic form of faith.

I have Spoken about faith in the sense of conscious participation in the great force and field of existence, in which even the body is arising. There is a kind of "faith principle" exhibited through participation in the great force, or field—the universal field—in which natural events are occurring. That is one dimension of faith, which is fundamental even to the Reality-Way of Adidam.

Without a clear understanding of the reality of this great field in which natural forms appear, you cannot really practice that participatory disposition. It would be just an idea, something you are "trying out". And, if it is just something you are "trying out", it would not prove itself to be true—because it can only prove itself to be true if participation is real. It is only in real participation that you "get" the certainty of this great field, or force.

—Avatar Adi Da Samraj
August 16, 1987

Searchless Right Life
Supports Reality-Realization

R ight life, maximum well-being, and the maintaining of a discipline throughout life that keeps the body consistently pure
and balanced and vitalized and able to participate in the
Way of Realization for which right life is the support—such is essential to right and true practice of the Reality-Way of Adidam.

—Avatar Adi Da Samraj
"The Right-Life Discipline of Searchless Raw Diet and Fasting",
Green Gorilla

As stated earlier, devotional recognition of Avatar Adi Da "happens" Prior to the body-mind-"self". However, the devotional
response to Avatar Adi Da requires the participation of every
dimension of the body-mind-complex. To participate profoundly
in the Yoga of devotion to Avatar Adi Da Samraj, the total body-
mind-complex must be available.

*The . . . Reality-Way of Adidam is about Realization of Reality
Itself, or Truth Itself, or Real (Acausal) God—and such Realization
Requires, as Its foundation, the real process of purifying what you
have accumulated through your dis-ease (or "self"-contraction).
That purifying process necessarily involves participation in the field
of existence beyond the gross physical. Therefore, in due course,
that purifying process necessarily becomes a Transcendental
Spiritual Process. Such must be the case, because much that has
been accumulated as a result of the "self"-contracted life is in the
dimensions of energy that are beyond the gross physical. Until all
of that is purified and gone beyond, there can be no Real-God-
Realization. . . .*

*The . . . Reality-Way of Adidam is not merely a philosophical
address to Truth. Rather, the . . . Reality-Way of Adidam is a thoroughly practical process, a practice that is effective throughout the
entire range of conditionally manifested existence (from gross to
subtle to causal), the entire spectrum of the conditional apparatus*

(which is, most fundamentally, a Unity—functioning hierarchically, but altogether). There must be this relinquishment of the "self"-contracted orientation, and of everything that has been egoically accumulated (as a result of that orientation). . . .

All the patterning of ego-bondage—which is the patterning due to the exercise of "self"-contraction—must be gone beyond. It is not that you will achieve some kind of idealized human perfection as a prerequisite for Divine Self-Realization—but there is fundamental purification (and, as a result, a fundamental freedom from the egoically patterned obstruction of energy and attention) that, <u>necessarily</u>, must be the case.

—Avatar Adi Da Samraj
"The Necessary Foundation of Right Life",
The Aletheon

Therefore, Avatar Adi Da gives His devotees practices that enable this purification and reorientation of the total psychophysical being. These practices fall into two categories: "conductivity" practice (related to the energy dimensions of the being) and the "conscious process" (related to the awareness dimension of the being). The entire body-mind-"self" is engaged through these two forms, which reflect the principal Reality-characteristics of Consciousness and Energy.

The "Conscious Process" Is To-Me-Responsive Practice Related To The Faculty Of attention (and To Consciousness Itself). "Conductivity" Practice . . . Is To-Me-Responsive Practice Related To The Energy-Sensitive Faculties Of feeling, body, and breath (or All The Faculties That "Follow" The Faculty Of attention). In The Total Practice Of The Only-By-Me Revealed and Given "Radical" Reality-Way Of The Heart, The Artfully Combined (and, Altogether, To-Me-Responsive) Practice Of The "Conscious Process" <u>and</u> "Conductivity" Is A <u>Perpetual</u> ego-Transcending Discipline.

—Avatar Adi Da Samraj
The Dawn Horse Testament

The "conscious process" is the devotional turning of attention to Avatar Adi Da, and it takes various forms as practice matures. It is an essential and ongoing practice that coincides with and is equally as necessary as "conductivity" practice. Avatar Adi Da even describes them (in *The Dawn Horse Testament*) as "The Combined (and, Thus, Effectively, Single) Practice Of The 'Conscious Process' and 'Conductivity'". As such, this single practice of "conscious process" and "conductivity" demonstrates Avatar Adi Da's Revelation that Consciousness and Energy are Indivisibly One.

the "conscious process"

In *The Dawn Horse Testament*, Avatar Adi Da defines the "conscious process" as "The Devotional Turning Of attention To Me, Such That attention Is, Thus and Thereby, Absorbed—and, Ultimately, Dissolved, or Utterly Transcended—In Me".

The most basic (and ongoing) form of the "conscious process" is **Name-Invocation of Avatar Adi Da**. Name-Invocation is associated with a verbal-mental exercise that turns attention to Avatar Adi Da. (See pp. 161–64 for a description of simple Name-Invocation of Avatar Adi Da, as it is engaged in "conductivity"-healing practice, as well as in daily life and meditation.)

The "conscious process" is also engaged through the consideration and establishment of the **"Perfect Knowledge"** of Avatar Adi Da's egoless Divine State (or Reality Itself).

This is practiced first via a preliminary Listening-practice (and, ultimately, for mature practitioners, via a "Perfect Practice") of "Perfect Knowledge".*

By means of listening to and intensive consideration of Avatar Adi Da's "Perfect Knowledge" Teachings,† the

* The "Perfect Practice" of "Perfect Knowledge" (also called "Radical Self-Abiding") is demonstrated by those who have perfectly transcended egoic "self"-identification with the body and the mind. See *The Aletheon* and *The Dawn Horse Testament* for more on "Radical Self-Abiding".

† See "The Teaching Manual of Perfect Summaries" in *The Aletheon*, *The Gnosticon*, and *Notice This*.

preliminary Listening-practice of "Perfect Knowledge" tacitly "Locates" Avatar Adi Da's State, Prior to all the faculties and functions and experiences of the body-mind-"self".

The preliminary Listening-practice of "Perfect Knowledge" is the establishing of the Intrinsic Prior Self-Position, rather than the body-mind-"self" (or ego-"I"), as the basis for moment to moment practice of "radical" devotion and right life in devotional recognition-response to Me.

—Avatar Adi Da Samraj
"The Way That I Teach The Dog In My House",
The Aletheon

Thus, the "conscious process" is essential to establishing the non-seeking disposition of "conductivity" healing and of practice of the Reality-Way of Adidam altogether. And, as a process that undermines identification with ego at its root, the "conscious process" is essential to "radical" healing.

The "conscious process" is engaged in coincidence with "conductivity" practice. Together, they are a co-equal process that supports the fundamental root-practice of devotional turning to Avatar Adi Da. In the maturing stages of practice-demonstration, the true nature of these (apparently) two practices becomes self-evident.

In The Context Of The Fully Established Devotional and Transcendental Spiritual Practice Of The . . . "Radical" Reality-Way Of The Heart . . . , The Two Essential Responsive Practices (Of The "Conscious Process" and Of "Conductivity") Are Always Merely The Two Evident Aspects Of An Inherent Unity (or The Two Sides Of An Inherently Single Exercise)—Because They Both Arise Responsively From The Always Primary (or First, and Inherently Single)

(continued on next page)

> *Practice Of The Searchless Devotional and Transcendental Spiritual Beholding Of Me (Exercised By Means Of The Whole bodily, or Total psycho-physical, and Inherently Coincident and Single, Turning Of All Four Of The Primary, or Essential and Characteristic, Faculties Of the body-mind-complex To Me).*
>
> —Avatar Adi Da Samraj
> *The Dawn Horse Testament*

"Conductivity" practice is exercised through a comprehensive body of ego-transcending practices that Avatar Adi Da characterizes as "right life". All of the right-life disciplines—"conductivity"-healing practices among them—either directly or indirectly magnify the flow of natural life-energy in the yellow-red conjunction, and (therefore) inevitably support health and well-being.[1] However, neither "conductivity"-healing practice nor any of the disciplines of right life are fundamentally oriented toward improving the experience—bodily or otherwise—of the apparently individual "self". Rather, these practices principally serve the observation, understanding, and transcending of every form of "self"-contraction. That process purifies the "self"-contracted orientation toward gross existence, thereby allowing attention and energy to be steadily focused in What Is Beyond and Prior to all forms of conditional existence.

One could say that, altogether, ego-transcending practice is basically "self"-purification. It is not the Divine that must be found. It is the things that you are deluding yourself with that must be released. The Divine Is the Very Context of existence. The "self"-contraction has taken on all kinds of forms, the summary of which is non-awareness of the Divine Self-Condition.

Ego-transcending practice is basically purification from these forms of "self"-contraction. Thus, ego-transcending practice is not about what people commonly call "the good life"—the Western idea

---

1. See appendix D for brief descriptions of how the disciplines of diet, exercise, and emotional-sexual practice specifically support the yellow-red conjunction.

of "self"-fulfillment, and so on. It is not that at all. However, the person who embraces ego-transcending practice can (and, rightly, should), in general, maintain positive life-signs, healthful signs, positive relational signs, and so forth. All these are simply expressions of the disposition of right practice. The right-life disciplines are not about pursuing "self"-fulfillment, glorification of "self", or clinging to qualities of life, relationships, "experiences", limitations, and so forth, for their own sake. The daily qualities of life may, in accordance with your intentions, be generally whole and positive, but you must still do the practice of transcending egoity.

Fundamentally, ego-transcending practice is about the Process of Outshining all forms of limitation by magnifying the Force of Consciousness Itself, the Force of Love-Bliss Itself. This Process purifies. This Process releases. That Virtue is what you are coming into contact with in the devotional (and, in due course, Transcendental Spiritual) relationship to Me. And, as you mature, you become a more and more responsible participant in this Process of "self"-purification (or, most ultimately, Outshining).

—Avatar Adi Da Samraj
December 11, 1988

❖ ❖ ❖

Healthfulness is one of the signs that most likely will come with right health practice in the Reality-Way of Adidam. Nevertheless, the primary significance of the practice of health in the Reality-Way of Adidam is that it permits "self"-observation and disciplining of the patterns of egoity, in the context of devotional turning to Me. Such is the fundamental significance of the practice of health in the Reality-Way of Adidam.

Maximizing one's potential for good health is a good thing to do. But good health is not an absolute in any case. People become unhealthy for all kinds of reasons, and at various times. For some people, conditions persist regardless of their practice of healthful discipline. Nonetheless, anyone can practice the by-Me-Given disciplines relative to health in an ego-transcending manner, in a manner that goes against the grain of egoity. Such practice is counter-egoic, whether or not it produces perfect health.

Perfect health is not the goal of the discipline in the Reality-Way of Adidam. Good health—or, at least, maximally good health, generally speaking—is certainly a part of such a life of "self"-discipline. But the practice of health in the Reality-Way of Adidam cannot be reduced to such a purpose. Its fundamental purpose is the devotional turning of the faculties to Me and the counter-egoic practice of "self"-discipline.

—Avatar Adi Da Samraj
September 8, 2004

In other words, improving or developing the apparently individual "self" is neither the purpose nor the measure of "conductivity" healing. The process of transcending identification with "self" in devotional Communion with Avatar Adi Da is the principal purpose. And this is demonstrated by freedom from the motive of seeking for any changes of experience or state.

In and Of Themselves, All Manipulations and Exercises Of A psycho-physical Kind Are "cause-and-effect" Devices For Stimulating (or Otherwise Achieving) Some Kind Of conditional Result. However, The By-Me-Given Right-Life Disciplines Of The "Radical" Reality-Way Of The Heart Are Not, In Fundamental Principle, Search-Purposed (or Effort-Bound) To "cause" Any Result. Rather, The Right-Life Disciplines Of The "Radical" Reality-Way Of The Heart Are, Fundamentally, Simply The Intrinsically Searchless Right-Life Demonstration Of <u>Always</u> <u>Prior</u> (or Always Already Existing) Devotional Communion With Me and <u>Always</u> <u>Prior</u> (or Always Already Existing) "Conductivity"-Communion With Me, In Always Whole bodily (or Total psycho-physical) Devotional Recognition-Response To Me.

—Avatar Adi Da Samraj
The Dawn Horse Testament

All the right-life disciplines Avatar Adi Da gives are engaged in this "searchless" manner. He Reveals that Perfection is Always Already (or Priorly) the Case. And (therefore) the perfection of any condition—bodily or otherwise—is not only impossible but also unnecessary.

I n a recent occasion of meditation, as I engaged the practice of three-part "conductivity",* there was suddenly a realization that, at the core, the egoic being does not really allow (or somehow shuts down) the heart-radiating of Bhagavan Adi Da's Divine Self-Transmission. I felt a kind of refusal of the utter heart-Happiness of giving myself over to Bhagavan Adi Da and allowing that Happiness to expand to Infinity. In an instant, the refusal fell away entirely, or shifted by Grace, and there was a free and full participation in Bhagavan Adi Da's Divine Radiance and the conducting of that Radiance in, through, and beyond the body-mind. Immediately, there was the sense of the body opening out into its true spherical form, with no boundaries, no point of reference, no mind in control—no "one" there! The intensity of Freedom, Love-Bliss, and Happiness was overwhelming—and, yet, the body-mind was not receiving that intensity, because the body-mind had ceased to exist as a "thing". It was "pushed out" beyond itself, as an ever-expanding, formless sphere, arising in Bhagavan Adi Da. These were all His Qualities. It was all the recognition of Who He Is when one is gone, when "conductivity" of Bhagavan becomes a Fullness of the dissolution of "self".

—Devotee of Avatar Adi Da Samraj

* See pp. 169–75 for a description of three-part "conductivity" practice.

The search to perfect the body-mind-complex (or even any form of conditional existence) is based on egoic (or "self"-contracted) "self"-identification with the body-mind-complex (and with conditional existence, altogether). Thus bound to the body-mind-complex and to conditional existence, the egoic individual wants the body-mind-complex itself, and conditional existence itself, to prove to be (in and of itself) perfect, or to be (in and of itself) a condition that is characterized by unchanging permanence and unchallenged "self"-fulfillment. . . .

The body-mind-complex is merely a pattern—always temporary, and always (in any moment) based on past adaptation and conditioning. Therefore, the body-mind-complex will never (and cannot ever) demonstrate perfection. The body-mind-complex is to be transcended—not perfected.

—Avatar Adi Da Samraj
"The 'Radical' Divine Way of Adidam",
The Only Complete Way To Realize The Unbroken Light of Real God

While the purposes of the body-mind-"self" are renounced in "conductivity" healing, Avatar Adi Da clarifies that the physical body is absolutely not negated or denied in this practice, or in any of the right-life practices.

The by-Me-Given foundation disciplines of the Reality-Way of Adidam are not ascetical. They are not at all a matter of dissociating from the body-mind-"self" or of disconnecting the body-mind-"self" from its environment of participation. Rather, the by-Me-Given foundation disciplines are entirely life-positive—and entirely a matter of establishing the right (and necessary) equanimity of the whole body (or the total psycho-physical complex of the individual being) through disciplines of basic right life (understood not in moralistic, or puritanical, or merely behavioral terms, but understood in Spiritual, Transcendental, and Divine terms). These by-Me-Given foundation disciplines are, most fundamentally, a matter of participating in devotional and (in due course) Transcendental Spiritual Communion with Me, by bringing the body-mind-"self" into the Condition (and Disposition) of Utter Non-separation. . . .

Right practice of the by-Me-Given foundation disciplines of the Reality-Way of Adidam is simply the living of right life, through the establishment of participatory equanimity, for the sake of devotional and (in due course) Transcendental Spiritual Communion with Me (and, Ultimately, Most Perfect Realization of Me)—not in the mode of a seeker, but in the mode of a non-contracted participant.

—Avatar Adi Da Samraj
"The Necessary Foundation of Right Life",
The Aletheon

❖ ❖ ❖

The Reality-Way of Adidam is not about dissociation from the physical domain or any domain that is presently arising. The Reality-Way of Adidam is a matter of devotional surrender as that structure, as that gathering of faculties in Communion with Me—entering into this Communion more and more profoundly, the process growing by My direct Transcendental Spiritual Blessing Invading the body-mind-complex, Circulating in the body-mind-complex, transcending it without destroying it or dissociating from it.

—Avatar Adi Da Samraj
May 13, 1997

In summary, "conductivity" healing, and right-life discipline altogether, purify the "self"-contracted orientation toward gross existence, thereby freeing the faculties for fuller participation in the Yoga of devotional Communion with Avatar Adi Da. In that Yoga, the healing process, and all of daily life, are no longer purposed toward improving the separate "self" but, instead, become an ecstatic surrender-response to What Is Beyond and Prior.

All Of The By-Me-Revealed and By-Me-Given functional, practical, and relational Disciplines Are Forms Of "Conductivity" Practice—and (As Such) They (All) Serve To Constantly Bring the body-mind-complex Into The Condition Of Energy, Relieving My Devotee Of The Presumption That the body-mind-complex Is Merely "self"-Contracted matter (fleshy, anxious, and Inevitably Suffering). And The Primary and Constant By-Me-Revealed and By-Me-Given Means For Bringing (or Yielding) the body-mind-complex To The Condition Of Energy Is To Yield the body-mind-complex To The Condition Of Ecstasy In Devotionally Me-Recognizing and Devotionally To-Me-Responsive Communion With Me (Divinely Self-Revealed, By All My Avataric Means).

—Avatar Adi Da Samraj
"Cosmic Spiritual Baptism Versus
Divine Transcendental Spiritual Baptism",
The Pneumaton

The Sacred Domain and the Participatory Culture of Touch

*T*raditionally, *it is said that the best thing that one can do is to spend time in the Company of the Realizer, the Master, and to live within the Master's Sphere—in other words, to live in the good company of those who practice devotion, right life, and Spiritual practice in the Company of the Master. Not only is the Master's Company the place of Spiritual Transmission, of Which the Master is the Source, but also in the Master's Sphere everyone exemplifies the Way of right life and encourages one another in the Way of right life and responds to one another's signs, thereby keeping one another accountable for the Way of right life that is Given by the Master. In the "worldly" circumstance, on the other hand, no such process of good company exists, even though the notion of the "good life" may be proposed and offered with smiles.*

—Avatar Adi Da Samraj
"Searchless, Lawful Management of The Body",
Green Gorilla

As is evident everywhere, global human culture is not presently oriented toward Realization of the Divine Reality. Therefore, Avatar Adi Da calls His devotees to establish a cooperative culture through which they may always live devotion and right life in relationship to Him. Such a culture is a means to establish what He calls the "sacred domain".[2] In the sacred domain of the Reality-Way of Adidam, all life-activities simply serve and magnify devotional Communion with Avatar Adi Da. Well-being frees attention and energy to participate in Communion with Avatar Adi Da—and, therefore, practices that establish well-being and equanimity are embraced and integrated into the sacred domain.

The sacred domain should include a positive orientation toward a "psycho-physical well-being" approach to Divine Communion

2. Avatar Adi Da also calls for the restoration of the sacred domain in the global culture of humankind as a whole. He defines "sacred domain" in this broadest sense as "the place where the truly human (and humanizing) culture of ecstasy is truly practiced, . . . assisted by cooperative association between people". See the essay "The Fundamental Domain At The Center of Life" in *Prior Unity* (Is Peace 723, 2015).

146

and Divine Realization—rather than something that is negative with respect to the conditions of existence, or "problematic" about it. Your orientation to the fundamental conditions of existence should be to have them be conformed to the pattern of Divine Communion, of Love-Bliss, of well-being altogether (in the most profound sense).

The common "world" is not like that. You must be skillful in your practice and stay well and achieve what you must achieve in the "world". But you must also stay balanced in terms of your association with the common "world" and be attentive to the requirements of the sacred domain. Do not regard the activities of the sacred domain to be merely a kind of "confection" to be added to life. The activities of the sacred domain are, instead, fundamental to life. If you pattern your life along the lines of the common "world", you tend not to change profoundly. And the "world" will not change profoundly in that case, either.

Therefore, you must take profoundly seriously this obligation to provide the sacred domain of life every day. And you must provide it not only with respect to your own life and "experience" but for My devotees altogether. You should be cooperating with one another to generate this sacred domain, as well as handling all your other business. You should fully, creatively, and happily do so. Because if something is a matter of well-being, it is also a matter of "art"— and it is (therefore) a matter of "fun" (in the most positive sense). And such well-being should not be a luxury.

Well-being should be the core of life. Why should you choose otherwise? If it is otherwise, you complain about it. Well-being is obviously what you prefer—so why not choose it and establish it?

—Avatar Adi Da Samraj
April 13, 1998

As a place of well-being and Divine Communion, the sacred domain is characterized by deep equanimity, by the fullness of both feeling and breath, and by full "conductivity" of natural life-energy in the body-mind-complex. "Conductivity"-healing practices are therefore integral to establishing and maintaining the sacred domain—particularly the principal forms, which involve healing touch. In fact, healing touch is so essential to the sacred domain of the Reality-Way of Adidam that Avatar Adi Da calls His devotees to integrate Yogic "conductivity" massage and the laying on of hands into their lives on a regular basis. Avatar Adi Da calls this aspect of the sacred domain the "participatory culture of 'touch'".

Since Ancient times, Massage (or Mutual "Touch" On The Basis Of an Innate "knowledge" Of the body's Structure and System Of Energy) Has Been A Part Of The Sphere Of everyday life.

Just So, The Participatory Culture Of "Touch" (Through Both Massage and The Laying On Of Hands) Is Fundamental To Right Life For My Devotees, As A Support To The life-Positive Feeling Of Connectedness and The Heart-Certainty That the body Is Part Of A Universal Continuum Of Natural Life-Energy That Includes every one and every thing.

Therefore, My Devotees (Within The Context Of The Natural human Sphere Of Relatedness) Should Offer To each other The Service Of Massage—For The Sake Of The bodily "Conductivity" Of Natural Life-Energy (and, As The Case May Be, My Divinely Avatarically Self-Transmitted Transcendental Spiritual Energy), and (In physical Terms) To Maintain the Contact-life, or "Touch"-life— Doing So (In Each Case) As My Devotee who Is Invoking Me, Feeling Me, Breathing Me, and Serving Me.

—Avatar Adi Da Samraj
The Dawn Horse Testament

Healing touch—through Yogic "conductivity" massage, the laying on of hands, and also what Avatar Adi Da calls "touch-by-water"—allows the individual to feel beyond the presumption of "separate self", into the domain of universal energy. (See Part Four for more on the healing practice of "touch-by-water".)

Massage Is An Aspect Of Right Responsibility For the body. Rightly Administered Massage Breaks The Apparent Isolation Of the body-sensation—"Reminding" the one Being Massaged That the body Is Not a Separate "something", but (Rather) Part Of An Indivisible Energy-Field. "Touch"-Association and (Also) Association With water—Both Of Which Should Be Engaged By My Any Devotee

148

With Significant Frequency (For Relatively Extended periods of time, and, Also, For brief periods of time)—Break Down The Tendency For people To Become physically Isolated and Shut Down, and Serve To Magnify Whole bodily Energy-"Conductivity". . . .

Both "Touch"-By-Massage and "Touch"-By-water Restore the body To Its Natural Condition Of Non-"Difference" From The Universal Energy Of Which it Is Inherently A Part. Therefore, Practices Involving "Touch"-By-Massage and Practices Involving "Touch"-By-water Are Both Basic (and Even Necessary) To The Maintenance Of bodily Health and Well-being.

—Avatar Adi Da Samraj
The Dawn Horse Testament

Without these regular reminders of the body's inherent continuity with the universal field of energy, the tendency to contract into separateness will habitually reassert itself.

Activities such as the laying on of hands and massage should be done as basic health practices. But they are also to be done within the context of a culture of "touch"—a culture where the body is not simply left to be an isolated, separate something or someone, but is instead participatory.

People tend to think of themselves as a kind of a box with a mind inside it, a steel box—something that is not touched, something that is dissociated, something that is a "something" in and of itself (in a separate sense).

Therefore, people characteristically do not allow the body to relax, because the disposition and activity that is egoity is always counter-participatory, always separative, always re-entering the mind and the disposition of separateness. The activity that is egoity is an unrelenting automaticity—and even (in its collective form) a terrible machine that generates the evidence of the "daily news".

For this reason, there must be an equally unrelenting Instruction every moment that counters the egoic disposition that would make a "separate something" out of everything that arises to its view.

—Avatar Adi Da Samraj
May 18, 2006

In order to support frequent practice of healing touch, Avatar Adi Da recommends that it be built in to the intimate circumstance of one's daily life, as is demonstrated in some traditional settings.

Yogic "conductivity" massage is something people should be doing in their contact-life naturally, day to day. There must be a very direct, healing approach by My devotees with one another and the people they are intimate with, in which there is natural, regular physical association. You are the ones who naturally come into physical association with one another, so you are in the position to serve one another's right practice. You should massage one another and (thus) maintain the contact-life, the "touch"-life, through right knowledge of massage as My devotee—Invoking Me, feeling Me, breathing Me, and serving Me.

In the Asian Indian tradition associated with the book Ancient Indian Massage,[3] *this is how massage practice is described. Within families, people massage one another daily. They do not do so merely because it feels good in the muscles. Massage is part of a culture in which there are Spiritual presumptions about how things work, and that understanding is served by this kind of service people provide for one another in the intimate sphere.*

Preventive right practice includes right diet, right emotional-sexual practice, right exercise, and right massage, or "contact-life" upheld in the right and positive form. You should not have to go elsewhere to find that—you should have it right there in your day-to-day circumstance, in the sphere of your intimate friendships, intimate relations, bodily relations. I do not mean sexual relations necessarily—but natural bodily relations, the people with whom you associate intimately day to day.

—Avatar Adi Da Samraj
May 6, 1996

Avatar Adi Da even recommends <u>daily</u> practice of massage for His devotees, if possible, in order to bring the body into the pattern of well-being every day.

---

3. Harish Johari, *Ancient Indian Massage: Traditional Massage Techniques Based on the Ayurveda* (Delhi: Munshiram Manoharlal, 1984). (Quoted on p. 238.)

Optimally, everybody would be massaged every day—there would be some period of time when you are physically given over to another who contacts and massages the body completely, relaxing it into its general feeling of well-being. If you cannot manage it every day, at least know that every day would be optimum, and see how often you can do it. It should be often enough to have massage be basic to your physical "experience". Your disposition should involve being certain that the body is put at ease for a significant part of every day, not only during sleep.

Usually, massage would happen in some kind of intimate circumstance—in other words, with people you know and relate to on a daily basis. I am not talking about just sitting down for a moment while somebody rubs your shoulders—although that is something, of course. Rather, I am Speaking about a whole-body massage, what you could call "sensuous" massage, or a massage that puts you into pleasurable association with the physical as an integrated, whole disposition. Sympathetic "sensuous" massage, or general regular massage, relaxes the body into the habit of being "straightened out".

Of course, there should be some people who are trained in massage in all of its technical details, to be applied to people with different conditions, or even to massage anybody in the gathering of My devotees. In other words, people could periodically receive a massage from somebody whose training is exceptional.

Massage serves the "conductivity" of the general physical body— not only the energy-"conductivity" but the "conductivity" of flows in the body, such as the lymphatic flows. Every day's associations contend to influence the physical into a pattern by reaction. Therefore, massage is a way of putting the body in touch with the pattern of well-being, even in the musculature.

—Avatar Adi Da Samraj
April 13, 1998

Touch and the Transcendental Spiritual Process

The participatory "culture of touch" has implications even beyond well-being and Divine Communion in the sacred domain. As noted in chapter 2, Avatar Adi Da says that touch, as an extension of the faculty of feeling, is the primary sensory mechanism of the Transcendental Spiritual process in His Company. The dimension (or circuit) of feeling-touch is "where" Avatar Adi Da's Transcendental Spiritual Presence is discovered and conducted, by Grace.

Touch, in fact, is the primary perception. It is senior to the other perceptions, because skin covers the whole body. The perceptual organs—sight and audition and smell and taste—are merely holes in the skin. The skin—or touch—is everywhere on the body. Touch is the circuit. Therefore, to enter deeply into that sense of touch in feeling-Communion with Me is the most immediate mode of the Transcendental Spiritual Process in devotional relationship to Me. The other modes of perception are secondary to that of touch, in the order of "experiences" in the growing by reaching to Beyond (while not strategically dissociating, or "self"-contracting, from) the gross physical.

—Avatar Adi Da Samraj
"The Tree of Light Is <u>Above</u> The Head,
and I Shine Forever In The Sky Beyond It",
Hridaya Rosary

❖   ❖   ❖

The principal sense in the human form is touch. The principal form of Transcendental Spiritual perception of Me, then, is simply to feel Me, tangibly. You may also, secondary to that, exercise the other senses, in gross or subtle ways, in association with that feeling of Me. Some people may enjoy a visual kind of perception of Me through Touch, through a kind of connectedness. But a visual perception is not necessary. It simply may occur in some cases.

The principal form of the feeling of contact with Me is through feeling and through this tangible but inexplicable Touch. It even

*has a kind of form to it that may be sensed in a touch-like manner,
subtly, not otherwise being perceived by any of the senses. It may be
seen, but maybe not. There may be some sort of audition (or hearing of sound) associated with it. There may be some taste, some sort
of scent or smell. These are all secondary to the Touch.*

*I Call My Own Divine Body "the 'Bright'". That does not mean
you will necessarily see It visually as "Brightness", but you might see
It in some light-form. But even if you are simply feeling Me, "experiencing" My tangible Touch, you still know what I mean when I
Call It "the 'Bright'", because it is Full and Radiant, Love-Blissful,
Infinitely Expansive. It has all the qualities of brightness, even
though you are not "experiencing" Me in some visual manner at
the moment. That is the "experience" of My Divine Body, then.*

—Avatar Adi Da Samraj
August 11, 1995

Avatar Adi Da thus describes His "Tangible Touch" as the
knowledge of His Divine Body of "Brightness". Reception of His
Touch, which occurs only by Grace, initiates profound healing of
the body-mind-complex, even at the subtlest levels of energy—
and, in fact, is the means whereby freedom from identification
with the body-mind-complex is given.

M*ost Supreme Divine Incarnation, Eternal Master
of my heart, Divine Liberator of all beings in all
worlds, I bow down.*

*I am thrilled to feel the head open as You Acquire this
body-mind through the Beholding of Your Divine Form.
Your Divine Touch, Your Ruchira Shaktipat, clearly originates from Beyond and has the most profound purifying
effect, while Revealing That Which Is Prior to identification
with body and mind. This Awakening beyond body and
mind is always a process of Your Intervention or Touch. The
process of receiving You is deepest Nectar, in which You
connect me to Your Divine Light.*

(continued on next page)

*I felt again Your direct Transmission as an intense, pro-
found Invasion from Above, Descending deep into the very
root of the body. This is not just a process of Descent into the
body. This is simultaneously a process of Descent to the root
of attention. The pressure became overwhelming. I felt Your
Divine Transcendental Spiritual Body Acquire me, and
nothing felt solid. The mind vanished, as You Penetrated
the heart, and this vastly opened the emotional core of the
being to You. I felt the entire psycho-physical being opened
and turned to You and sublimed and released in the feeling of Your Spherical Form of Divine Love-Bliss.*

*The Intoxication feels deep, moving through the frontal
line and passing up the spinal line, but then shattering the
whole thing via the central axis of the entire body. In this
Infusion, there is strong rotation forward, down from the
crown of the head, and up from the base to the crown. The
rotation creates a sudden release, and the body becomes an
egoless Sphere, which is boundless and centerless, not a self-
body. Ordinary references of mind and body do not make
any sense, and I feel myself swooning by Your tangible
Touch and Penetration.*

*I feel deep immersion in Your Divine Body. . . . Da Is
everyone and everything.*

—Ruchiradama Quandra Sukhapur Rani Naitauba,
senior renunciate devotee of Avatar Adi Da Samraj,
from a letter written after an Initiatory Sitting with Him

Avatar Adi Da explains that, as a general rule, healing-touch
practices and "conductivity" practices do not directly lead to or
cause "Transcendental Spirit-Conductivity", but they do activate
and enliven the same sensory mechanisms and energy-circuits that
are activated in the Transcendental Spiritual process. In describing
the structures revealed in the process of "conductivity" of His
Transcendental Spiritual Force, Avatar Adi Da says "It is the same

structure being revealed by energy sensation."[4] In this sense, Yogic "conductivity" massage and the laying on of hands can be regarded as preparatory for and supportive of the Graceful process that becomes sensitivity to and "conductivity" of Avatar Adi Da's Transcendental Spiritual Transmission.[5]

The various practices presented in the remaining chapters of this book are described as they are engaged in the context of "conductivity" of natural life-energy—but they are part of the foundation of the great process of "radical" healing and Divine Realization in Avatar Adi Da's Company and fundamental to the sacred domain of His devotees.

---

4. From spoken instruction given on March 28, 1996.

5. In fact, consistent and full practice of all of the right-life disciplines is a necessary foundation for Transcendentally Spiritually Awakened practice. As Avatar Adi Da describes (in *The Pneumaton*), "The Transcendentally Spiritually Awakened life of My devotee cannot begin until the rightening of the . . . life-conditions is sufficient to allow . . . the unobstructed 'conductivity' of My Avatarically Descending Divine Transcendental Spiritual Presence. This rightening must be done first."

Avatar Adi Da Samraj
Adi Da Samrajashram, 2008

Let My Sign Show Itself

by His Divine Presence,
Avatar Adi Da Samraj

You must discover that healing is not merely about bodily perfection. The body is a sacrifice. The entire cosmic domain is a sacrifice. The real disease to be healed is egoity. The body cannot be healed merely by the transmission of energies, the flowing of energies in the body. You can deal with some physical things in that manner—but you cannot deal with all karma, and you cannot deal with ego, which is the real dis-ease.

My Blessing-Work is a Great Struggle because of this fact. If healing were simply a matter of My Projecting Force (or Energy), everybody would already be healed—and there would not be any healing work to do. But healing does not work that way, because the disease is egoity itself. Even arising conditions are themselves— in some sense, as used by the ego—the disease.

Therefore, you cannot perfect the "world" by any mere healing gesture. The "world" is a complex pattern of karmic design, and the "root" of it is separateness, ego. Thus, true healing is, ultimately, a Transcendental Spiritual matter. The ego cannot be "cured" without sacrifice, nor can it be "cured" without the profound Yoga That I Do.

The energy-healing work that My devotees do is associated with My Blessing-Transmission, but it is working at the etheric level—without psychic content, without the deeper (or subtler) levels operative. It is simply etheric. You cannot heal all beings by an etheric gesture. You can do something, of course—but it is a cooperative matter with the person you are addressing, and there are all kinds of imperfections in it. Therefore, you must actually get beyond the ego's "point of view" about healing, and simply surrender in devotion to Me, and let that process work as it should.

Your disposition should always be in the right pattern of "conductivity" of energy—descending in front, ascending in back. Even though the body you are serving is showing some other tendency at the moment, this flow is what you must serve by your disposition. To see how this works is not a matter of expecting some sort of perfection from the body, because the body is here to be thrown away. Ultimately, the body is a sacrifice. The body does not become a final, perfect "something". The body is always in process.

My Work is completely fluid and beyond bodies altogether, but It enters into both the bodily sphere and the Pattern Beyond. Whenever that conjunction occurs, with My Blessing comes a process, in everyone, in which difficulties, disease, struggle, and all kinds of things must be purified. It is not simply a matter of My Blessing people and everybody feels good forever. This place is not paradise, and it is not intended to be "forever".

People "experience" healings, and so forth, in the Work I Do with them, but the process still goes on. There is karma, there is egoity that must be transcended. Likewise, there are all kinds of laws operative relative to healing and well-being that are far beyond the etheric and the whole display of physical patterns. That is why you will observe that "conductivity" healing does not necessarily work with every kind of issue, nor does it have "final success" with people, because the problems are beyond the etheric. Additionally, the being is "self"-contracted—it is doing the "self"-contraction, even while you are doing healing work, even though you have the most positive disposition toward people feeling well. The counter-struggle occurs in ego-based beings. Therefore, healing is never "perfect", in the final sense. Rather, healing is a constant, continuous, so-to-speak "forever" process.

My devotee must be surrendered and let My Sign Show Itself as It will. The same with treating anyone. As My devotee, this should be your disposition: surrendered, knowing the laws, the right pattern. Invest yourself in this positive, loving, intimate, unproblematic association with anyone you are serving. But always Invoke Me, always be free to let Me Work As I Will. And learn more than this "ideal of perfection" disposition. Healing is much more complex than that.

The re-establishment of right "conductivity" can be very purifying, very healing for many people. Whether it is long-term or not is to be observed, but this "conductivity" is part of it. Beneath "conductivity" is this [Avatar Adi Da makes a fist]—the "self"-contraction. And prior to the etheric, there are more patterns that are governing what is happening in the body. So you cannot simply deal with imbalance at the etheric level and expect it all to disappear, because there is another structure beyond the etheric. And there is ego at the core. So the process of ultimate transformation is a great "play" and drama.

In healing work, My devotee is constantly going beyond egoity. In healing work, practice devotional turning of the faculties to Me and do not own the energy, do not identify with the healing process. You are assisting the healing process in a devotional and surrendered disposition. Always approach healing in that manner, Invoking Me. Always practice with the right attitude. But, ultimately, let it be however it works out. You will see something more than perfection—something more profound. ∎

From instruction given by Avatar Adi Da Samraj to a devotee-healer on April 22, 1996.

CHAPTER 5

Foundation Practices
Used in "Conductivity" Healing

T*he important matters in "conductivity" healing are: the link to
Me (or constant Communion with Me), etheric sensitivity, right
"conductivity" practice, and the Devotional Prayer of Changes
(in disposition and in practice). Anyone practicing "conductivity"
healing must make use of Me in that practice, and presume the
integrity of all of these matters, rather than presume a "problem" to
be dealt with.*
—Avatar Adi Da Samraj
May 5, 1996

His Divine Presence Avatar Adi Da Samraj has given His devotees a number of basic practices that are foundational elements of
"conductivity" healing. These include a devotional discipline specific
to attention (Name-Invocation of Him), instruction relative to right
breathing, technical practices for conducting natural life-energy
(three-part "conductivity" practice and bodily locks), and an ego-
transcending form of prayer (the Devotional Prayer of Changes).[1]

Name-Invocation of Avatar Adi Da Samraj

D*a is not merely a physical sound. . . .
Da Is the Prior-Unity-Force That Always Priorly and
Totally Dissolves all dis-unity, all non-unity, all "difference".*
—Avatar Adi Da Samraj
"Atma Nadi Shakti Yoga",
The Aletheon

1. This chapter focuses on practice of the Devotional Prayer of Changes in the context of health and
healing, but it is also engaged by Avatar Adi Da's devotees for the sake of making positive changes in
circumstances of all kinds. For Avatar Adi Da's full instruction on the Devotional Prayer of Changes in
general, see *The Sacred Space of Finding Me*, pp. 219–51.

161

During any occasion of "conductivity"-healing practice, Communion with Avatar Adi Da is supported by simple Name-Invocation of Him, which is engaged by calling upon Him via His principal Divine Name "Da" or any of the other Names and descriptive Titles given by Him for this purpose. Generally, this is done silently, although outward vocalization is an option when circumstances allow and the devotee is so moved. Simple Name-Invocation is means for turning the faculty of mind (or attention) to Avatar Adi Da, recognized as the Divine Reality in Person. It is the most basic form of the "conscious process"—His technical term for disciplines associated specifically with the faculty of attention.[2] Although it is a discipline principally associated with the faculty of mind, Avatar Adi Da clarifies that Name-Invocation of Him is a feeling-process of heart-invocation. He instructs (in *The Dawn Horse Testament*) that the recitation of His Name "Should Be Made (and Felt, or Radiated) By, From, and At The Heart (and, Thus, Even Via the Total body-mind)".

When performed as a whole bodily feeling-practice, Name-Invocation of Avatar Adi Da supports the devotional process of turning body, emotion, mind, and breath to Him. Thus, Name-Invocation of Avatar Adi Da, as He describes here, is essentially a gesture of renouncing identification with the illusion of the separate "self" and its purposes and, instead, entering into His "Bright" Divine State.

All the apparently "objective" sacred Means I have Given—including Simple Name-Invocation of Me, and the Beholding of My "Representation"-Form—are simply Means for turning from the imagined (or "objectified") ego-"I" and its drama, and turning to Me, and (thereby) entering into My "Bright" Divine State, the Field of My Transcendentally Spiritually Self-Transmitted Perfectly Prior Self-Nature, Self-Condition, and Self-State. In the process of truly profoundly engaging this by-Me-Given practice, the ego-pattern is released—and replaced by true renunciation.

—Avatar Adi Da Samraj
"The Reality-Practice",
The Aletheon

2. See pp. 137–40 for a summary of the other forms of the "conscious process" and the co-equal nature of the "conscious process" and "conductivity" practice.

Forms of Simple Name-Invocation of Avatar Adi Da Samraj

Following are the Names and descriptive Titles which Avatar Adi Da gives to be engaged in the practice of simple Name-Invocation of Him:*

Da
Adi Da
Adi Da Samraj
Samraj Adi Da
Da Parama-Sapta-Na
Adi Da Parama-Sapta-Na
Parama-Sapta-Na Adi Da
Parama-Sapta-Na Adi Da Samraj
Avatar Da
Avatar Adi Da
Avatar Adi Da Samraj
Ruchira Da
Ruchira Adi Da
Ruchira Avatar Da
Ruchira Avatar Adi Da
Adi-Guru Da
Adi-Guru Adi Da
Adi-Guru Adi Da Samraj
Da Hridayam
Adi Da Hridayam
Da Love-Ananda
Adi Da Love-Ananda
Adi Da Love-Ananda Samraj
Love-Ananda Da
Love-Ananda Adi Da
Love-Ananda Adi Da Samraj

or, in Fiji:
Dau Loloma
Turaga Dau Loloma
Turaga Dau Loloma Vunirarama

Each of these Names may be either begun or ended with one of the following descriptive references:

Divine
Bhagavan
Heart-Master
Master
Lord
Beloved
Sri
Hridayam

or (if not already contained in the Name):
Parama-Sapta-Na
Avatar
Ruchira Avatar
Adi-Avatar
Adi-Guru
Ruchira-Guru
Parama-Guru
Samraj

or, in Fiji:
Turaga

* For the meanings of the various Names and descriptive Titles, see *The Dawn Horse Testament* or *The Sacred Space of Finding Me*.

The Practice of Name-Invocation

Instruction from *The Dawn Horse Testament*

Feel Me and Direct the thinking mind

When Engaging In Simple Name-Invocation Of Me, . . . Feel (and Thereby Commune With) Me, While Using The silent (or, Otherwise, vocal, but Always Heart-Felt) verbal Recitation Simply As A Means To Direct and Concentrate and Release the thinking mind.

Indeed, Simple Name-Invocation Of Me (Like Every Form Of The "Conscious Process" In The "Radical" Reality-Way Of The Heart) Is A Direct (Technical and Responsive) Means (By Resort To Me) For Controlling, Purifying, Converting, Relaxing, and Transcending "self"-Contraction (or all the forms and results of egoity, Including All The Tendencies Of thought, emotion, and desire).

Be Feelingly Attracted Beyond egoic limitations

Therefore, Rather Than Casually Allowing (and, Otherwise, Seeking or Suffering) Random "self"-Contraction (including thoughts, emotional states or reactions, and desires) To arise (and To Control attention and the actions or states of the body-mind-complex), Constantly (By Random Intention) Practice Random Name-Invocation Of Me . . . , and Thereby—and By Every Means Given In Devotional Communion With Me, and (Principally) By The Exercise Of "Radical" Devotion To Me, or By Non-Strategically (Effortlessly, Receptively, and Merely By Turning The Natural Faculties Of perceptual body, emotional feeling, mental attention, and cycling breath To Me) Communing With Me—Constantly Feel (or Be Feelingly Attracted) Beyond the egoic (and, Otherwise, conditional) limitations Of psycho-physical Existence. ∎

Right Breathing

A vatar Adi Da gives a basic exercise of right breathing to be engaged in "conductivity"-healing practice, and in all the activities of daily life. This practice can be summarized (based on His words) as follows:

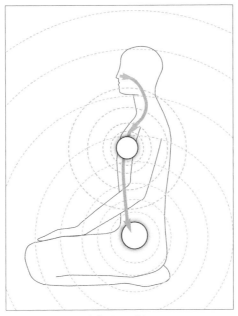

Right Breathing

• Breathe via the nose—initiating the breath, with feeling, from the heart.

• On inhalation, draw in, relax into, and conduct the natural life-energy with the whole bodily being. Inhale fully, to the vital center, completely filling the lungs with air and the whole body with natural life-energy.

• On exhalation, release all hold on the energy of the breath, allowing it to radiate out from the vital center (and the whole body). Exhale fully, with deep feeling, allowing the energy to pervade the body and the universe, and releasing all conditions.

---

vital center / vital region / bodily "battery"

These terms all refer to the region where "vital energy"—
or the natural life-energy that pervades and animates the
physical body—is centered. Also known as the "hara" in
Japanese culture, Avatar Adi Da defines the vital region as
extending from the diaphragm to the bodily base (or perineum), with its focal point, or "felt center", being the
crown of the lower abdomen (approximately 2 inches, or
3–4 finger breadths, below the umbilical scar).

Breathing consciously, in this feeling-manner, brings balance
to the emotional being, and therefore to the etheric body, supporting the integration and balance of the yellow-red conjunction.

*The breath should, in most moments, be full, easy, naturally
open, pleasurable, and equal—equal relative to inhalation and
exhalation, as well as equalizing relative to the necessary har-
monies internal to the body and expressed in human relationships.
You should constantly enjoy natural feeling-awareness (emotional
and physical) of the whole feeling-body, both tacitly and intentionally. Mind should be free as attention, usable to initiate or enjoy
right action as well as right concentration, thought, and intuition.
You should be able to respond, with full attention, feeling, breath,
and body, to the events of life, but always from a disposition of Prior
Fullness that exceeds all the possibilities that would otherwise empty
or suppress you.*

*Of course, full realization of a natural and true pattern of
breath and feeling depends on many factors, and an entire life of
right responsibility in the truest Spiritual sense. Diet and other
habits of life are also constantly tending to determine conditions of
mind, feeling, breath, and body. But the matter of breathing is a
very direct sign as well as a controlling mechanism relative to the
entire cycle of reactivity and reactive emotions. Therefore, if the
process of breathing is consciously exercised, and you become
aware of it as a constant process of energy and feeling (rather than*

mere huffing and puffing), economization and control of emotional reactivity will become more and more natural to you in daily life.

—Avatar Adi Da Samraj
"Emotions and Breathing",
Conscious Exercise and The Transcendental Sun

Integrating right breathing into daily life and "conductivity" healing is a matter of the devotional practice of turning the faculties to Avatar Adi Da. In that turning, the real Substance of breath is discovered to be His "Bright" Divine Presence.

The ego-surrendering, ego-forgetting heart is given over to Me, and the body-mind-complex follows. Sometimes it is just that way. At other times, that same heart-disposition is also conjoined with the breath-process.

Sometimes the breath is full and free. Sometimes obstructions may be felt. Sometimes there is attention to breathing-"conductivity", sometimes not. There are all kinds of permutations of this.

One thing you should understand relative to breathing-"conductivity": It is not really a matter of breathing Me in. It is a matter of breathing in Me. I am All-Pervading. Therefore, inside the body and outside the body, what you are doing with the breathing, founded in the heart-disposition, is allowing the body to move into a state of equanimity in Me.

—Avatar Adi Da Samraj
July 23, 1995

I *was sitting in meditation, turning my feeling-attention to Bhagavan Adi Da—when it was suddenly noticeable that my body was being breathed. My attention was focused on regarding Bhagavan Adi Da's Murti and feeling His Blissful Presence. And then the energy of feeling Him would initiate a full, expansive breath. In this movement of energy, I felt my body to be continuous with its surroundings. There was no sense of separate personal energy. There was a circuit of living energy, and it moved through my body as well. The full breaths moved easily in a circle through my body. The entire feeling-space felt sacred.* —Devotee of Avatar Adi Da Samraj

The Practice of Right Breathing

Instruction from The Dawn Horse Testament

Initiate the Breath From the heart

Breathe Via the nose, Characteristically with the mouth closed.

Initiate the breath From the heart—The Conscious, Feeling, psychic Core Of the bodily being. That Is To Say, Initiate the breath With The Force Of Whole bodily Feeling—Through and With the throat, To the navel.

Inhale With the Whole bodily being

When inhaling, Draw In, Relax Into, and Conduct The Natural Life-Energy Of The Universe (and, As The Case May Be, My Avatarically Self-Transmitted Divine Transcendental Spiritual Energy), With the Whole bodily being, Even Through the entire skin-surface of the physical body (head to toe).

Thus, inhale Into the vital center, or The Great life-Region—the felt center Of Which Is "Rooted" In the lower abdomen, three to four finger-breadths below the umbilical scar and immediately under the skin.

Inhale Fully, With Deep Feeling Of heart and body—Completely Filling the lungs With air and the entire body With Natural Life-Energy.

Exhale With Deep Feeling Of heart and body

When exhaling, Do Not Discard The Energy Itself or Allow It To Dissipate, but Release and Relax All Hold On It, Allowing It To Radiate From the vital center (and the Whole body).

Allow The Pleasurable Feeling Of the heart's Circulation Of Energy Throughout the entire body (the limbs, the belly, the sex organs, the head, the teeth and hair and nails, and so forth) and Even (Tacitly) Throughout The Universe.

Exhale Fully, and With Deep Feeling Of heart and body. Let The Energy Pervade the entire body and The Universe To Infinity, and Release (Via That Radiating and Expansive Energy) all Accumulated conditions, Whether Positive Or Negative—So That inhalation May Bring What Is New and (Thus) Become An Instrument Of Change and Refreshment. ∎

Three-Part "Conductivity"

T he Three-Part Devotional Exercise Of The "General" Form Of "Conductivity" Practice Is Specifically and Simply One Of "Conductivity" Of The (Pervasive and "Objective") Natural (etheric, or pranic, and bodily-"experienced") Energy.

—Avatar Adi Da Samraj
The Dawn Horse Testament

Avatar Adi Da describes the most basic general form of "conductivity" as simply breathing and feeling the universal life-energy, in a cycle of reception and release. This general orientation and practice, which is discussed fully in chapter 2, is fundamental to "conductivity" healing.

Avatar Adi Da also gives a technical (yet still simple) form of general "conductivity", which is to be practiced by all His devotees at random in any occasion of "conductivity" healing—and throughout daily life, regardless of the activity. This practice magnifies the flow of natural life-energy in the Circle of the body-mind-complex, and is therefore integral to "conductivity" healing (and to maintaining health and well-being in general). It is a three-part process, which can be summarized (based on His words) as follows:

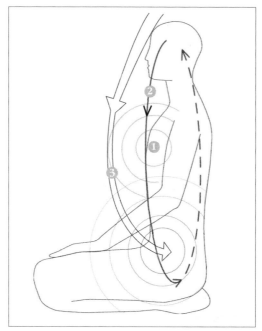

Three-Part "Conductivity"

1. Radiation from the heart. Persistent whole bodily turning to Avatar Adi Da, demonstrated as whole-body feeling-radiation in all directions, generated from the heart.

2. Relaxation of the frontal line. Persistent relaxation of the frontal line of the body from the crown of the head to the bodily base (and even to the toes) for the sake of right natural polarization.[3]

3. Lung-breathing "conductivity"

- **Inhalation-reception**—down the frontal line to the bodily "battery" (just below and behind the umbilical scar).

- **Exhalation-release**—radiated diffusely, in all directions, within the entire body (or radiated either upward in the spinal line or downward via the legs to the soles of the feet, but not beyond the soles of the feet).

---

3. This relaxation of the frontal line should be engaged in an intentional and systematic manner, similar to how it is exercised in the dead pose (described on p. 343).

From the moment I learned about Bhagavan Adi Da's Teaching on "conductivity" practice and "conscious exercise" in the 1970s, I have gratefully applied His straightforward and simple instructions. The beauty of "conductivity" practice is that it can be practiced in any moment—the instruction allows the being to enter any activity as a form of Divine Communion. The body is given to the Divine, and its activities reflect this in an economical and graceful manner. By engaging the body-mind in this simple exercise under all circumstances, there is a sense of letting go of separation from others and things, and, instead, being part of a great unity. The same is true for the three-part "conductivity", where, in Communion with Bhagavan Adi Da, the heart radiates to Infinity and the body is relaxed crown to toe, while the cyclic breathing process allows participation in the universal play of reception-release.

I feel deeply grateful to have received this Teaching from Bhagavan Adi Da, and to be able to apply it in real life. It is an ongoing learning process, since the body-mind itself is a dynamic process and requires constant adjustments of one or another kind. That does not make it self-conscious, but, rather, it is a participatory process that is sensitive to the body's particular state and needs and that makes adjustments as needed. Simultaneously, this living process also has an uninterrupted, universal quality that I have noticed through all the years of my practice, both before and after Bhagavan Adi Da's Lifetime. Apart from obvious health benefits, such as having more energy and being less prone to seasonal ailments, I have also noticed how engaging "conductivity" practice frees up energy and attention for ego-transcending practice in Beloved Adi Da's Company.

—Devotee of Avatar Adi Da Samraj

In addition to intensive application of three-part "conductivity" during any formal occasion of "conductivity" healing, Avatar Adi Da also recommends practice of three-part "conductivity" in a more concentrated manner in these circumstances:

- At the beginning of any formal period of meditation
- If the onset of illness is imminent
- When you are feeling dull, enervated, or lethargic
- When reactivity is tending to be overwhelming
- When you are under stress

It is not necessary or recommended to tie application of the three parts of this "conductivity" exercise to any particular pattern or fixed sequence. For example, radiating from the heart and relaxing the frontal line are not tied to the breath cycle in any specific manner. Similarly, the cycle of the breath is not to be tied or timed to any other external event, like measures of time, or even any internal event, like a certain number of heartbeats. Rather, the entire three-part exercise should be applied consistently but artfully, in any moment in which it is useful to do so.

In order to engage the three-part "conductivity" practice artfully, both in "conductivity"-healing practice and in any daily-life activity, each person must experiment with how to apply it in his or her own case. As Avatar Adi Da once described, there is a "science" (or intensive technical application) to all the right-life disciplines He gives, but they must ultimately become an art— "a living, spontaneous, free, intuitive exercise"[4] based in devotional recognition-response to Him. Thus, by persisting in the devotional response to Avatar Adi Da, the "secret" of "conductivity" practice will be discovered.

When you read My Description of the three parts of the "conductivity" practice in Communion with Me, you can see that the three parts are about the maintenance of this disposition in Communion with Me, but it is such that it coincides with well-being otherwise. It serves well-being altogether. And it is about well-being established at the profound

---

4. From *"I" Is the Body of Life.*

heart-level of your disposition, in Communion with Me, but then with regard to right balance in the domain of the human scale.

—Avatar Adi Da Samraj
May 6, 1996

❖ ❖ ❖

I am Telling you that the "conductivity" in the frontal line must be full all the way down to the base of the body. That means you must be released of your anxiety. And that requires great force of practice and Great Grace (Which is Freely Given to you). It requires great force of practice in response to That Grace.

—Avatar Adi Da Samraj
"Surrender Without Limitation",
My "Bright" Sight

W*hen I first heard Avatar Adi Da's teachings and instructions on "conductivity", I practiced three-part "conductivity" intensively, regularly, and diligently. Because of that foundation of practice, now the "conductivity" process happens in my body-mind spontaneously, without any particular intention on my part. This spontaneous practice of "conductivity" is becoming part of the Transcendental Spiritual process. When there is recognition of Bhagavan Adi Da and attraction to Him, His Transmission of Love-Bliss enters my body-mind and Comes down in the frontal line, and my entire body is pleasurably energized and becomes full of His Transmission. At times when I feel weak or sick, His Radiant Love-Bliss-Light is intentionally but naturally directed to the "conductivity"-blockage in the body and I feel the Healing-Power of His Transmission. When there is saturation with His Love-Bliss-Transmission in the circuit of "conductivity", that Fullness is naturally radiated to relations, friends, and all beings. It is, altogether, a simple and ecstatic practice.*

—Devotee of Avatar Adi Da Samraj

The Practice of Three-Part "Conductivity"

Instruction from *The Dawn Horse Testament*

1. The First Part Is Whole bodily Turning To Me—Actively Demonstrated As Feeling-Radiation From The Heart

The First Part (or Exercise) Of The Three-Part Exercise Of The "General" Form Of The Yoga Of "Conductivity" Is Persistent (Devotionally Me-Recognizing and Devotionally To-Me-Responding) Whole bodily Turning To Me—Actively Demonstrated As ego-Surrendering, ego-Forgetting, and ego-Transcending Heart-Feeling (or Feeling-Radiation), Transcending all conventional and Reactive emotions, and Generated Whole bodily (or In A Total psycho-physical Manner), From The Heart, In all directions (Boundlessly, or To Infinity).

Such Is The Natural (and The Original and Unobstructed) Heart-Attitude, Which Is To Be Practiced By Means Of Devotionally Responsive Communion With My Avatarically-Born Bodily (Human) Divine Form . . . , and Which Is (By Random Application) To Be Constantly Practiced, At all times and In all places, In Formal Meditation and In daily life.

2. The Second Part Is Relaxation Of The Frontal Line

The Second Part (or Exercise) Of The "General" Form Of The Yoga Of "Conductivity" . . . Is Persistent (Devotionally Me-Recognizing and Devotionally To-Me-Responding) Relaxation Of The Frontal Line Of the body (From The Crown Of the head To the bodily base—and Even To the toes).

And This Exercise Is To Be Practiced Toward The Principal Result Of Right Natural Polarization Of The Frontal Line (From

The Crown Of the head, Toward and To the bodily base), and (As A Naturally Coincident and Spontaneous Accompaniment) With Right Natural Polarization Of The Spinal Line (From the bodily base, Toward and To The Crown Of the head).

3. The Third Part Is lung-breathing Exercises

And The Third Part (or Exercise) Of The "General" Form Of The Yoga Of "Conductivity" . . . Is Devotionally Me-Recognizing and Devotionally To-Me-Responding "Conductivity" Via lung-breathing Exercises Of Feeling and breath, or The "Conscious Exercise" Of

- inhalation-Reception (In Descent, Via The Frontal Line Of the body, To The bodily "Battery"), Assisted By Easy Upward Tensing Of the bodily base,*

- Followed By exhalation-Release, Likewise Assisted By Easy Upward Tensing Of the bodily base (and, By Easy Inward and Upward Pulling Of the crown of the lower abdomen)—and, As A General Rule, With the feeling-breath-exhalation Released From The bodily "Battery" and Radiated Diffusely (In all directions) Within the entire body or, Otherwise (but, In General, Less Frequently, or Only Occasionally, As Appropriate), With the feeling-breath-exhalation Released From The bodily "Battery" and Radiated Into The General Pattern (or Line) Of Ascent, Via The Spinal Line Of the body. . . .

And, On Occasion, As Necessary, In Order To Re-Vitalize the body, or, In General, To Serve The General Health Of the body, or In Order To Re-Balance A Too Upward Tendency In the body, the feeling-breath May, Via Both inhalation and exhalation, Be Intensively Pressed Down Into The bodily "Battery", and Then Released Downward From The bodily "Battery", and, Thus, Radiated, Via the legs, Into the soles of the feet—but, Always, or As A Consistent General Rule, Without <u>Any</u> Intentional Concentration Of attention In any part or Any Station In or Above the head. ■

---

* See "Bodily Locks" section on pp. 176–78.

Bodily Locks

he Yogic locks are to be artfully applied as required in order to maintain the integrity (or continuity) of the Circuit of "conductivity"—frontal and spinal.

—Avatar Adi Da Samraj
May 28, 1997

There are various places in the body-mind-complex where energy tends to "leak out" of the "conductivity" circuit. The "bodily locks" or "Yogic locks" are a means of exercising these points in the body in a manner that retains and supports the flow of the energy in the Circle. As Avatar Adi Da describes in *The Dawn Horse Testament*, exercising the Yogic locks "'Reminds' The 'Conductivity' Pattern To Be Present In the body".

The bodily locks that are specifically relevant to "conductivity"-healing practice are the lock of the bodily base and the lock of the tongue, chin, and throat.

• **The Lock of the Bodily Base.** The bodily base (or perineum) is a turning point in the Circle of the body-mind-complex and is thus a place where energy often leaks out. It can also be a place where there is a knot, or contraction of energy. Therefore, the lock at the bodily base is key to the art of keeping the circuit of energy in the body-mind-complex continuous.

The Yogic Lock Of the bodily base . . . Is An Internal Upward Tensing (Either Brief and Constant Or, Otherwise, Brief and Repetitive) Applied To the bodily base, By Drawing In, Back, and Up, Via the genitals, the perineum, and the anus, and Toward The Spinal Line, and With the crown of the lower abdomen Simultaneously, and Lightly, Drawn In and Up— Such That An Unbroken Line (or Continuous Circuit) Of "Conductivity" Is Maintained Between The Frontal Line and The Spinal Line, Via the bodily base.

—Avatar Adi Da Samraj
The Dawn Horse Testament

• **The Lock of the Tongue, Chin, and Throat.** You can assist "conductivity" practice during any energy-healing practice (and at any time) by occasionally using the Yogic lock of the tongue, chin, and throat. This is done by pressing the tongue lightly to the roof of the mouth, and pulling the chin down slightly.

The Yogic Lock Of the tongue and chin and throat . . . Is A Pressing Of the tongue Lightly To the roof of the mouth, With the chin Pulled Down Somewhat (and, Generally, With the mouth closed, and With all breathing Exercised Via the nostrils), In Order To Rightly Conduct The breath-Energy and (As The Case May Be) My Avatarically Self-Transmitted Current Of Divine Transcendental Spiritual Presence Via the head and throat, and (When Necessary) To Lock The breath-Energy and (As The Case May Be) My Avatarically Self-Transmitted Current Of Divine Transcendental Spiritual Presence Below the throat.
—Avatar Adi Da Samraj
The Dawn Horse Testament

Over time, with consistent practice, sensitivity to when and how to engage these locks will develop such that they become an effective support to "conductivity" in the Circle.

These locks are natural forms of control of the physical body and the nervous system in association with breathing, or the sense of relative emptiness or fullness of bodily energy. You should adapt them yourself to the inhalation-exhalation pattern of formal "conscious exercise" . . . and to random moments of ordinary life.

The locks are a secondary practice, to be used when and if you will. The primary practice is the simple one of reception-release in whole bodily feeling. The locks only serve to counter some of the secondary side effects (or accompaniments) of the feeling-cycle of the breath, wherein it is felt that energy is being channeled and lost through a single area of the body, rather than expressed constantly and radiantly via the whole body.

The primary practice is the present and "radical" Stand As Unobstructed and Full Feeling, Which is Love-Bliss (or Self-Radiance), and breathing from the prior position of limitless Life

(or Fullness). (Previous to . . . true Realization of this Fullness as Divine Presence or Reality, you should simply exercise and breathe with full, whole bodily feeling rather than merely mental intention.)
—Avatar Adi Da Samraj
"The Internal Locks of The Whole Body",
Conscious Exercise and The Transcendental Sun

The Devotional Prayer of Changes

The Devotional Prayer of Changes is a participatory process that has a real basis in the psycho-physics of the universe. It is a means for participating in the real universe, and in Reality Itself, in such a manner as to release the characteristics in the human body-mind-complex which are holding certain conditions in place, and to animate the characteristics in the human body-mind-complex which can be exercised so as *not* to hold those conditions in place.

—Avatar Adi Da Samraj
"The Devotional Prayer of Changes Is A Disposition
That Can Actually Affect Phenomena",
The Sacred Space of Finding Me

Fundamental to "conductivity" healing is a unique practice of ego-transcending prayer that Avatar Adi Da gives to His devotees called "the Devotional Prayer of Changes". The Devotional Prayer of Changes is, primarily, devotional Communion with Avatar Adi Da and, secondarily, conscious participation in conditional existence as an indivisible unity. As a direct extension of the "faith presumption"—of inherence in the Divine Reality and of infinitely available life-energy—the Devotional Prayer of Changes is an essential healing practice in and of itself, which supports the balance and integration of the yellow-red conjunction. Therefore, an extended discussion of Avatar Adi Da's instructions on this practice is presented here.

The Devotional Prayer of Changes
Is a Transformed Disposition

First and foremost, the Devotional Prayer of Changes is a transformed disposition at the deepest level of the being. Ingrained,
unconscious presumptions—such as "I am a patient who needs
to be cured" or "the world and the body are physical-only"—
profoundly impact one's health and well-being, as well as the
circumstances of life. But if such unconscious presumptions are
positively transformed, conditions will necessarily be positively
transformed.

*It may appear, from the outward "point of view", that you are
generating conditions because of activities you are performing outwardly, and so on. And, certainly, that is the case in some ordinary
sense. But, more fundamentally, the reason you are doing the
actions in that form—having the random thoughts and reactions,
and so forth—is because of fundamental presumptions that are
manifesting constantly.*

*If you can get at the seat of the presumptions, change them, and
consistently and deeply maintain a different kind of disposition,
then that will not only change your behaviors and your mind, and
so forth—it also brings about different conditions, or brings different conditions into your sphere of presumption.*

*This process is not magic—although it is magical in some gen-
eral sense, you could say, or (otherwise) extraordinary. Rather, this
process occurs based on a law of conditional existence—that all
conditions arising are the product of deep-seated presumptions. If
you can change those presumptions, and (likewise) change your
behaviors (and so on), then conditions change. This is because the
presumptions exist at the level of energy-modification that is the
source of conditions, which can very directly affect the grosser,
more peripheral aspect of "experience".*

*You cannot change conditions to the degree of perfection, as I
have Said. But this principle I am describing can be very readily
demonstrated by changing presumptions through the Devotional
Prayer of Changes.*

Yes! You can prove that this law of conditional existence is the case.

—Avatar Adi Da Samraj
April 28, 1995

The principal deep-seated presumption that is addressed and transformed in the Devotional Prayer of Changes is the presumption of separate "self", the illusion of ego. And the principal means for that transformation is devotional Communion with Avatar Adi Da. In such devotional Communion—turning body, emotion, mind, and breath to His Living Divine Presence—egoic contraction upon "self" is loosened, thereby allowing natural life-energy and the transformative Force of the Divine Reality to influence conditions.

The Devotional Prayer of Changes . . . becomes more and more effective with the growing disappearance of ego-presumption, separateness, ego-possession, "self"-content, and "self"-remembering.

The more profoundly separate "self" is surrendered and forgotten in devotional Communion with Me, the more profound your practice will be and the more profound the Devotional Prayer of Changes will be as part of your practice. . . .

The more there is of such growth in practice, the more you will see that the process is true. You will see how the process works. You will see that cosmic existence is a Unity, and that there is no separateness in it. You will "know" the Divine Basis of it all by Communing with Me.

—Avatar Adi Da Samraj
"I Will Be Incarnated Countlessly Through My Devotees",
My "Bright" Form

A Summary of the Practice
of the Devotional Prayer of Changes

Avatar Adi Da gives a "rudimentary" form of the Devotional Prayer of Changes to all His devotees, as well as a "fully developed" form for those who are awakened to the Transcendental Spiritual dimension of practice.[5] Following is a simple summary (based on Avatar Adi Da's instruction) of the practice of the Devotional Prayer of Changes in its rudimentary form, as it is engaged in the context of the universal field of natural life-energy:

---

5. The fully developed form of the Devotional Prayer of Changes is described in *The Dawn Horse Testament*. Note that Transcendentally Spiritually Awakened devotees also engage the rudimentary form of the Devotional Prayer of Changes, in relation to both natural life-energy and Avatar Adi Da's Transcendental Spiritual Energy.

• **Formulate the prayer.** Account for the specific details about the present circumstance and the desired outcome.

• **Enter into devotional Communion with Avatar Adi Da.** Turn bodily to Avatar Adi Da present before you—invoking, feeling, and breathing His Living Divine Presence.

• **Relinquish identification with all problems and negative conditions or states.** This occurs primarily by Communing with Avatar Adi Da and thereby identifying with and affirming the Divine Self-Condition that always already transcends all conditions.

• **Engage the prayer in the cycle of breathing-"conductivity":**

♦ **Exhale-release** identification with the negative conditions and release all doubt and concern.

♦ **Inhale-receive** the intended positive condition with heart-feeling, presuming and picturing the intended outcome, via mind and emotional disposition.

• **Change your action.** Maintain the affirmation and presumption of the changed condition, and thereafter act in a manner that serves and demonstrates the intended changes.

In and of itself, the above exercise is an extension of ongoing devotional Communion with Avatar Adi Da. As such, every moment of life and practice can be transformed into the Devotional Prayer of Changes. In *The Dawn Horse Testament*, Avatar Adi Da describes true ego-transcending prayer as "The <u>Essential</u> Attitude, or Fundamental Posture, Of the Total body-mind-complex".

The Devotional Prayer of Changes is simply an expression of the right disposition. It is the willingness to be changed in your disposition and your life altogether and to make changes in life.

—Avatar Adi Da Samraj
March 25, 1993

♦ ♦ ♦

In every moment in which you engage the practice I have Given, in effect you are practicing the Devotional Prayer of Changes. You are enforcing a positive (or right) presumption.

—Avatar Adi Da Samraj
April 28, 1995

181

In addition, the Devotional Prayer of Changes should be exercised intensively when there are signs of imbalance and ill health—both in the context of healing treatments and in formal occasions of prayer.

The Devotional Prayer of Changes, which is practiced by My devotees in the Reality-Way of Adidam, is a resort to devotional Communion with Me and the relinquishment of any negative mind and emotion that identifies with the "problem". It is the release of identification with all negative conditions and the assumption of an entirely right disposition, through Divine Communion.

The Devotional Prayer of Changes is the entire relinquishment of identifying with dis-ease or any kind of presumed "problem". It is assuming Divine Communion, affirming a wholly right condition, and allowing that wholly right condition to be fully assumed, felt, breathed, and lived.

Therefore, the Devotional Prayer of Changes is not merely an interior exercise of pleading with Me for Divine changes. Rather, the Devotional Prayer of Changes is devotional Communion with Me, wherein the disposition of the right (or positive) condition is assumed, and then felt, breathed, and lived.

Therefore, if, as My devotee, you are really doing the Devotional Prayer of Changes, you are <u>doing</u> the changes. You are entering into the condition of Divine Communion, such that you are already established in the disposition of the right (or desired) condition—and, therefore, you are effective in implementing that right condition.

The Devotional Prayer of Changes should be practiced regularly by all My devotees, and it may be practiced in conjunction with daily formal meditation (or, as the case may be, "Perfect Contemplation"). It should also be done whenever a healing treatment is given, and in conjunction with the laying on of hands.

The Devotional Prayer of Changes should also be performed regularly by groups of My devotees for the sake of any particular individual or group of individuals. When the Devotional Prayer of Changes is done for someone who is not physically present, it is good practice to view the person's photograph, passing it among those who are performing the Prayer, especially if they do not know the person.

—Avatar Adi Da Samraj
The Incarnation of Love

When learning and applying the practice of the Devotional Prayer of Changes, it is important to follow Avatar Adi Da's exact instructions, as given through His direct Word (presented in this section, and in other sources[6]), and to always refresh your understanding of the practice through ongoing study of Avatar Adi Da's Word.

The Devotional Prayer of Changes Is Whole-Bodily-Participatory Prayer

Avatar Adi Da describes truly ego-transcending prayer as "whole-bodily-participatory" prayer.[7] The practice of the Devotional Prayer of Changes engages all of the four faculties of the body-mind in Communion with Avatar Adi Da, and thereby the intended outcome of the prayer is brought into association with Avatar Adi Da's Living Divine Presence.

In the practice of the Devotional Prayer of Changes, you are not merely saying to Me, "Would you please make this better?" Rather, you are entering into devotional Communion with Me, bringing the contents of the faculties to Me, in the manner of the Devotional Prayer of Changes—releasing the negative view of a something, and affirming a positive view of it. In other words, you <u>present</u> the transformed version in your devotional Communion with Me. . . .

Therefore, by right participation in devotional relationship to Me, you are enabling Me to Do My Divine Avataric Blessing-Work.

—Avatar Adi Da Samraj
"The Devotional Prayer of Changes Is Your Participation In My Divine Avataric Blessing-Work",
The Sacred Space of Finding Me

Whether the prayer is for one's own well-being, or another's, the key to releasing any negative view is for there to be a transformation of emotional presumptions on the part of the one offering the prayer.

---

6. For a full collection of Avatar Adi Da's instruction on the rudimentary form of the Devotional Prayer of Changes, see *The Sacred Space of Finding Me*.

7. From "Real Ecstasy", in *The Aletheon*.

In the right practice of the Devotional Prayer of Changes, rather than thinking of somebody and their illness, and merely feeling sympathetic and crying out, "Oh, Whoever, won't You make XYZ healthy again?", there is a transformation of such emotional presumptions—even picturing and viewing the individual in a positive, healthy disposition or state—and you <u>hold</u> to that transformed disposition in devotional Communion with Me, rather than presuming anything else, rather than presuming negative conditions in that person's state of health, and so forth.

—Avatar Adi Da Samraj
"The Devotional Prayer of Changes Is A Disposition
That Can Actually Affect Phenomena",
The Sacred Space of Finding Me

As Avatar Adi Da indicates above, visualization in the Devotional Prayer of Changes is associated with transformed emotional presumptions. The visualization is primarily a matter of feeling—and not a mental technique for seeking change.

The Devotional Prayer of Changes is simply a matter of presuming the intended outcome to be the case—not merely picturing a change that you want to have happen, but (instead) actually presuming something to be the case and functioning accordingly.

You tend to picture a change tentatively in order to get a result to happen. There is an element of doubt or effort or seeking in that approach. When you practice the Devotional Prayer of Changes, you simply maintain your right presumption—presume the intended outcome to be the case, rather than merely making an effort to hold the picture in order to make a change happen, to produce a result.

There is no seeking involved, no doing it tentatively and seeing if there will be a change. The Devotional Prayer of Changes is simply presuming the outcome—without any other psychological baggage or "self"-contraction, or falling back from the presumption.

—Avatar Adi Da Samraj
April 28, 1995

Breathing-feeling "conductivity" is also integral to truly effective prayer. In fact, one of Avatar Adi Da's principal Teaching-admonitions to children—"breathe in the good stuff, breathe out the bad stuff"—

is a way of describing the Devotional Prayer of Changes in simplest terms. By exercising inhalation-reception and exhalation-release in specific association with the prayer, the intended outcome of the prayer is associated with the universal field of life-energy (and, for Avatar Adi Da's Transcendentally Spiritually Awakened devotees, with His Transcendental Spiritual Energy).

By relinquishing presumptions at the mind level, the deeper level that is governing what is outward, you can change the pattern at that subtle level. It is still just pattern patterning, but you can take advantage of the law of replication-shift-change by not using a particular pattern—even a thought or presumption—by just letting it go, exhaling it away, not picturing it. Breathe away the bad stuff. Instead, presume a pattern that is as you would have it be in the context of gross vibratory appearances. Breathe it in at the mind level and the feeling level. Presume it, or "picture" it, so to speak. In this manner, you are associating with the realm of patterns prior to their "congealing" in the gross manner.

—Avatar Adi Da Samraj
January 31, 1996

In this testimonial, a woman describes a turning point that occurred after many years of struggling with recurrent fibroids in her uterus.

A *number of years after having had surgery to remove the fibroids in my uterus, I found out that I had them again. And shortly thereafter I began to have occasional spotting, which was a sign that these growths were affecting the uterus.*

At this point, it was clear that I had to take responsibility for my life and health in an entirely new way. So, one day, while I was on retreat at the Mountain Of Attention Sanctuary, I decided that I was going to just completely resort to Avatar Adi Da—rather than continuing to be eaten alive by my conviction of impending doom.

(continued on next page)

I read Bhagavan Adi Da's instructions on how to practice the Devotional Prayer of Changes and began to do it on the spot, not waiting until I was in a formal circumstance. I turned my feeling-attention to Bhagavan Adi Da and then began to exhale all negativity associated with my body, particularly my reproductive organs. Immediately, I felt how I had not actively been conducting loving energy to this part of my body over the years. And this reminded me that soon after I'd first been diagnosed with fibroids, I had received Communications from Beloved Adi Da in which He indicated that I stored my reactive emotions in my reproductive organs.

So, as Bhagavan Adi Da instructed, I began to presume my uterus and ovaries were in normal condition and shape. I envisioned my uterus, ovaries, and whole lower body to be completely free of any obstructions. As I did this, I felt relieved of the verbal mind and its limitations, and sensitized to an expansive state that was free of fear and concern about health and death. In the submitted, surrendered state, it was clear that I was greater than the body-mind. I was radiant energy, and I no longer had to "buy" any assumed limitations. I felt Bhagavan Adi Da showing me the simple process of granting attention to Him, rather than granting it to my "problem". It soon became clear that whether I continued to have difficulties with my health was not the point. It was clear that Communion with Bhagavan Adi Da, the Radiant One, was the "point".

I began to do the Devotional Prayer of Changes every day, and when I came out of meditation each day my intimate partner would also do the laying on of hands on me. Pretty soon I stopped looking for the symptoms. I simply began to relax into the prayer, trusting that the Divine was healing me. I was beginning to have faith with my mind as well as my heart. The mind was not doubting and undermining this real process. It, too, was being healed—of negative presumptions.

So the symptoms became secondary or incidental to me. As it happened, at the time of the month when they usually would have reappeared, the symptoms did not recur. But that was not the point. I had been shown a superior process of dependence on faith and Grace. In yielding to a principle superior to the egoic dilemma, I was drawn out of myself into direct Communion with the Divine.

—Devotee of Avatar Adi Da Samraj

Even the physical body participates in the Devotional Prayer of Changes, by taking action that supports the intended outcome.

The Devotional Prayer of Changes involves . . . transcending your limitations and embracing a different action. You must involve yourself and not just be looking for magic. You must act differently and fulfill your part in what is necessary to make the changes. If God is just making everything, why would there be the Devotional Prayer of Changes anyway? You are making all these changes. And to make the changes be different, more profound, more Divine, you must relinquish your lesser presumptions and change your act. That is the message of My Instruction to you about the Devotional Prayer of Changes.

—Avatar Adi Da Samraj
March 5, 1993

Of course, the actions to be taken depend on the intended outcome of the prayer, and must be intelligently considered in that context. For example, right action that would affirm a prayer for one's own health and healing might include intensifying any number of right-life disciplines, such as meditation and three-part "conductivity", as well as an appropriate change of diet (or even a period of fasting) and engaging other healing disciplines (like those described in this book).

Regardless of what actions are taken, and regardless of the intentional exercise of feeling and breath and mind, the Devotional Prayer of Changes is never a form of seeking or struggle.

One of the basic secrets of the Devotional Prayer of Changes is that it is not a matter of counter-effort, or struggling against something. The Devotional Prayer of Changes is a matter of realizing an unobstructed condition in devotional relationship to Me, and establishing as a living presumption—through perception and affirmation—a condition as you would have it be. And then it is a matter of living on that basis, in that presumption, and playing your life-role that corresponds to its fulfillment.

—Avatar Adi Da Samraj
April 4, 1988

This searchless approach to the Devotional Prayer of Changes is possible because the practice is established in tangible and present Communion with the Divine.

For My Devotees, True and Positively Effective Prayer Is Not Based On The Un-Happy (or, In Any Manner, egoic) Sense Of Separation From The Divine. For My Devotees, True and Positively Effective Prayer Is The True and Right Esoteric Prayer-Practice . . . Of ego-Transcending Devotional (and, In Due Course, Transcendental Spiritual) Communion With My Avatarically Self-Revealed (and By-My-Divine-Avataric-Grace Heart-Evident, and Self-Evidently Divine) Person. And That True and Positively Effective Esoteric Prayer Of My True Devotees Expresses (and Magnifies) Faithful (or Always-Already-Happy) Affirmation Of psycho-physical Intimacy (or Oneness) With The Inherent Love-Bliss Of My (Avatarically Self-Revealed, and Intrinsically egoless, and Self-Evidently Divine) Person—and, Thus, With The Inherent Completeness, and The Inherent Perfection, Of Self-Existing and Self-Radiant Being (Itself).

—Avatar Adi Da Samraj
The Dawn Horse Testament

The Practice of The Rudimentary Devotional Prayer of Changes

Instruction from *The Dawn Horse Testament*

Participation In What Is Always Already The Case

The Devotional Prayer Of Changes Is, At Its Foundation, ego-Surrendering, ego-Forgetting, and ego-Transcending Devotional Communion With Me.

Thus and Thereby, The Devotional Prayer Of Changes Is True Participation In The Divine Self-Nature, Self-Condition, Source-Condition, and Self-State That Is Always Already The Case (and That Always Already Transcends all conditions).

And, On That Basis, The Devotional Prayer Of Changes Becomes ego-Surrendering, ego-Forgetting, and ego-Transcending Participation In The Active and Directly Effective Relinquishment and Release Of particular (and even all) Negative (or Otherwise Non-Useful) conditions, and (Subsequently) In The Active and Directly Effective Affirmation, Reception, and Enactment Of particular (and even all) Positive (or Otherwise Useful and Right) conditions.

Primarily, The Rudimentary Form Of The Devotional Prayer Of Changes Involves (and Requires) ego-Surrendering, ego-Forgetting, and ego-Transcending Devotional (and, As The Case May Be, Transcendental Spiritual) Communion With Me. . . . Secondarily (or Supportively), The Rudimentary Form Of The Devotional Prayer Of Changes Involves (and Requires) Effective (and Heart-Felt) Release Of particular

(continued on next page)

(and even all) Negative conditions Via exhalation and Effective (and Heart-Felt) Reception Of particular (and even all) Positive conditions Via inhalation. . . .

Begin With The Practice Of Communion With Me

Therefore, Each Occasion Of The Rudimentary Devotional Prayer Of Changes Should Begin With The Practice Of ego-Surrendering, ego-Forgetting, and ego-Transcending Devotional (and, As The Case May Be, Transcendental Spiritual) Communion With Me.

And, As (By Means Of My Avatarically Self-Transmitted Divine Grace) That ego-Surrendering, ego-Forgetting, and ego-Transcending Exercise Becomes Devotional Communion With The One "Bright" (Spiritual, Transcendental, Divine, and Non-conditional) Love-Bliss-Condition (Self-Revealed By Me and <u>As</u> Me), The Rudimentary Devotional Prayer Of Changes Should Be Allowed To Become Effortless Heart-Relinquishment Of All egoic "self"-Identification With, and All Affirmation Of, Any and All "Problems", and any and all Negative conditions or states.

Then The Devotional Prayer Of Changes Should Be Activated Via the breath

Then, On The Foundation Of That Primary Demonstration Of Devotion To Me, The Rudimentary Devotional Prayer Of Changes Should Be Intentionally Activated Via the breath—In Any Number Of Cycles Of exhalation and inhalation (Engaged In The Context Of The Circle Of the body-mind-complex), Performed As breathing-"Conductivity" (In Its "General", or By-Me-Commonly-Given, Form), and Done In The Same Manner In Which (At My Devotee's present-time Stage Of Practice-Demonstration Of The "Radical" Reality-Way Of The Heart) It Is (According To My Instructions Given In This Testament, and In Even All The "Source-Texts" Of My . . . Divine Avataric Reality-Teaching)

Typically To Be Engaged During Meditation (or, As The Case May Be, During "Perfect Contemplation") and In the moments of daily life.

And, In The Context Of The Rudimentary Devotional Prayer Of Changes, The "General" (or By-Me-Commonly-Given) Form Of breathing-"Conductivity" Should Be Performed As Heart-Felt Release (Via any number of exhalations) Of particular (Specially Selected, or, Otherwise, Prominently Apparent) Negative conditions (and Even Of all Possible Negative conditions), and (Subsequently, and More and More) Heart-Felt Reception (Via any number of inhalations) Of particular (Specially Intended and, Altogether, Affirmed and Visualized) Positive conditions (and Even Of all Possible Positive conditions).

Live All That Serves and Demonstrates The Intended Changes

Likewise (Because The Devotional Prayer Of Changes Is Not Merely An "interior" Exercise, but The Actual, and Fully Affirmative, and Truly ego-Surrendering, ego-Forgetting, and ego-Transcending Assumption Of The By-Me-Avatarically-Self-Revealed Condition Of Spiritual, Transcendental, Divine, and Intrinsically Non-conditional Love-Bliss, and, On That Basis, Also Of any number of Positive, and "Problem"-Free, conditions or states), Every Occasion Of The Rudimentary Devotional Prayer Of Changes Is To Be Followed, In The Context Of daily life, By Continued Feeling and breathing and Assuming, and Actual Living (or En-Acting), Of ego-Surrendering, ego-Forgetting, and ego-Transcending Devotional (and, As The Case May Be, Transcendental Spiritual) Communion With Me, and (Also) By The Feeling and breathing Assumption, and The Actual Living (or ego-Surrendering, ego-Forgetting, ego-Transcending, and "self"-Disciplining En-Actment), Of All That Is Required To Serve (and Even To Directly Demonstrate) The Prayerfully Intended Changes. ■

Avatar Adi Da Samraj
Adi Da Samrajashram, 2008

Be Purified
By Right Association
With The Divine

by His Divine Presence,
Avatar Adi Da Samraj

You must be purified through right association with the Divine. Through such purification, each aspect of the being is brought into a condition of balance, or equanimity. You should be open-hearted, open whole bodily, surrendered to Real God, breathing evenly in both nostrils all the time, breathing fully without contractions in any area of the body-mind-complex, without reactive emotions. Characteristic reactive emotions are associated with each level of the body-mind-complex. You must be free of those reactive emotions, which are simply contractions of the nervous system in the total body-mind.

Wherever there is a contraction at any level of the nervous system, certain physical phenomena begin to develop, and a certain chemistry begins to develop in the form of toxins, imbalances of the hormones of the body, and impurities of the bloodstream. Just as each of these centers is impure and contracted, the forms of action whereby you express these centers are likewise impure and obstructed. Yet, if you can enter into whole bodily surrender, then each aspect of this total body-mind is purified physically, emotionally, mentally. The body-mind-complex becomes simply an unobstructed, balanced presentation to the Divine. Then the body-mind-complex is a pure, effective mechanism of association with the Divine and provides the vehicle for the ultimate transcending of egoity, as well as for positive influence in the "world". . . .

Therefore, the liabilities in this mechanism must be understood, and you must practice beyond them. You must turn them to the Divine. You must bring the will of right effort, of skillful means, to the fulfillment of disciplines whereby you purify and harmonize the body-mind-complex and make it a vehicle for ego-transcending practice. The body-mind-complex is the context of practice. Therefore, the body-mind-complex must be in a certain condition if ego-transcending practice is to be effective. Spiritual practice is not just a matter of believing something. You must transform the body-mind-complex altogether.

Likewise, prayer is not just a verbal address to an abstract deity. Prayer is a total surrendering of the entire body-mind—physical, emotional, mental, and psychic—to the Divine Reality. Therefore, you must transform the conditions of the body-mind-complex. You must purify it, relieve it of its obstructions, make it dependable, make it something that is under your control, something that is balanced, something that can practice effectively. . . .

When you enter into True Prayer—in other words, prayer in its fullest sense—then things will work for the good, not because of a "God" who likes people who do this sort of thing and rewards them, but because of the Law, because of the Nature of the Divine, because of the Condition of this phenomenon of human existence. Human existence is a psycho-physical phenomenon. Therefore, it is responsive to psycho-physical changes.

Through the Agency of the Divine, you can definitely have an effect on every aspect of physical existence, every aspect of "experiential" existence. Of course, to have such an effect is not an end in itself. It is simply an extension of the life of Real-God-Communion, which is ego-transcending and which ultimately transcends the "world" altogether. But it certainly is a positive dimension or extension of the life of ecstasy. Thus, seeing that a "little bit of the law" makes positive change and throws out fear, you should be reinforced in your faith and establish more profoundly your commitment to the lawful process through which not only positive changes may occur in your life but (altogether) your life will be positively transformed into another kind of existence than you presume on the basis of your conventional "experiencing" and learning. ∎

From a discourse given by Avatar Adi Da Samraj on October 4, 1980.
Portions of this discourse were adapted by Avatar Adi Da
for inclusion in His essay "Real Ecstasy", in *The Aletheon*.

PART THREE

PRINCIPAL "CONDUCTIVITY"-HEALING PRACTICES

CHAPTER 6

The Laying On of Hands

The laying on of hands is an extension of the Devotional Prayer of Changes, but it makes very direct use of etheric energy for healing—and, ultimately, because those performing the laying on of hands are My devotees, it makes use of Me altogether, and of My Blessing-Force, in the context of healing.

—Avatar Adi Da Samraj
April 26, 1995

The laying on of hands is an ancient practice. It survives to this day in many cultures, having been handed down in the traditional manner—within families, in religious settings, and from master-teacher or shaman to apprentice. And the laying on of hands is even being utilized in the modern medical setting.[1]

Some individuals may be particularly gifted in this form of healing—whether through innate sensitivity, cultural orientation, or training. But empathetic healing service to another through touch is fundamental to the human experience, and thus the laying on of hands can be practiced by anyone.

In the Reality-Way of Adidam, performing the laying on of hands is primarily a matter of turning to Avatar Adi Da as the egoless Divine Reality and thereby allowing His Healing-Force of Blessing to influence conditions. Secondarily, it is a concentrated exercise of feeling-attention and the directing of natural life-energy that also heals (and, otherwise, positively influences) conditions. Regardless of any particular condition being addressed in an occasion of the laying on of hands, it is the receiving of Avatar Adi Da's Healing-Force of Blessing and the magnification of natural life-energy that support the balance and integration of the yellow-red conjunction.

1. Examples of practices that include application of the laying on of hands in the modern medical setting are "Therapeutic Touch", "Healing Touch", and "Touch for Health". Examples of articles and research on this topic include: Avery Comarow, "Top Hospitals Embrace Alternative Medicine", *U.S. News*, accessed March 3, 2018, http://health.usnews.com/health-news/managing-your-healthcare/pain/articles/2008/01/09/embracing-alternative-care; and Diane Swengros, et al, "Promoting Caring-Healing Relationships: Bringing Healing Touch to the Bedside in a Multihospital Health System", *Holistic Nursing Practice* 28 no. 6 (Nov/Dec 2014): 370–75.

Thus, with His detailed description of the laying on of hands, Avatar Adi Da has accounted for the total human structure and its condition, and linked the practice directly to the Divine Reality Itself. And He has indicated that it is—for His devotees, and even for all humankind—the most basic healing-touch practice.

Healing Touch in the Traditions— Ancient and Modern

Life-force flows in a subtle circulatory system throughout the body. Where there is stress because of worry or fear over work or personal problems, the flow of life-force tends to become congested in various places, leaving the rest of the body without sufficient energy to function well. Deep pressure can release the blocked life-force. After the energy is released and flowing freely, light touch and non-touch techniques can polarize the energy—that is, organize and align the life-force along its proper pathways.

—From *Your Healing Hands*, by Richard Gordon*

Jin Shin Jyutsu . . . helps us remember that every one of us possesses the simplest instruments needed to bring about harmonious balance—the breath and hands. It reminds us that these instruments are all that we need to enhance our physical and mental vitality, which in turn help illuminate the cause underlying disease or disharmony. Most importantly, it reawakens our awareness of the life energy that permeates the universe. This renewed awareness enables us to send life-giving energy through various locations on the body.

—From *The Touch of Healing*, by Alice Burmeister†

* *Your Healing Hands: The Polarity Experience*, by Richard Gordon (Oakland, CA: Wingbow Press, 1978), 32.

† *The Touch of Healing: Energizing Body, Mind, and Spirit with the Art of Jin Shin Jyutsu*, by Alice Burmeister (New York: Bantam Books, 1997), 12.

On one occasion—I complained about pains in my cheek—I had an infection in the left oral cavity. John lifted his hand, pointed it at my cheek, and regarded it with a resolute determination. Then he quickly lowered his hand and touched my cheek. He held it there some second [sic], and then, swift as lightning, he drew it back again. It was my impression that he had mobilized a great amount of psychic energy.

—From *Shamanic Healing and Ritual Drama*, by Ake Hultkrantz*

The physician primarily uses concentration and relaxation in his body to make his own qi *flow in the direction he desires. He can transport it outside his own body to make it enter the patient's body, transmitting the* qi *directly or by touching the person. Chinese scientists have discovered that when this is done, magnetic and bio-electrical reactions occur, as well as hormonal and molecular changes. The greatest changes seem to occur within the body cells.*

—From *Oriental Medicine: An Illustrated Guide to the Asian Arts of Healing*†

One of the ministers of the Yellow Emperor (the founder of Chinese medicine) was a Wu Yi doctor named Zhu You. Zhu You practiced an ancient form of Qi emission combined with sacred prayer while treating his patients. So effective was this method of treatment that the Yellow Emperor's Classic of Internal Medicine states that in ancient times most illnesses were treated according to Zhu You's healing methods. Practitioners of this method were known as professional "prayer healers," and were once widespread throughout ancient China.

—From *The Secret Teachings of Chinese Energetic Medicine*, Volume One‡

---

* *Shamanic Healing and Ritual Drama: Health and Medicine in Native North American Religious Traditions*, by Ake Hultkrantz (New York: Crossroad Publishing, 1992), 91. The author is referring to John Trehero, a Shoshone medicine man.

† *Oriental Medicine: An Illustrated Guide to the Asian Arts of Healing*, edited by Jan Van Alphen and Anthony Aris (London: Serindia, 1995), 190.

‡ *The Secret Teachings of Chinese Energetic Medicine*, vol. 1, by Jerry Alan Johnson (Pacific Grove, CA: The International Institute of Medical Qigong, 2005), 16.

How to Practice the Laying On of Hands— A Summary

I Am The Power That Heals and Blesses My Devotee. By Virtue Of Devotional Communion With Me, My Devotee who Is Rightly Administering The Laying On Of Hands Is Conformed To Me and (Thus and Thereby) Is Able To Function As A Conduit For My Divinely Avatarically Self-Transmitted Healing-Power.

—Avatar Adi Da Samraj
The Dawn Horse Testament

The following is a summary of Avatar Adi Da's instructions on the laying on of hands, drawn principally from *The Dawn Horse Testament*. It is offered as a basic orientation to the expanded discussion of the practice presented in this chapter.

When learning and applying the practice of the laying on of hands, it is important to follow Avatar Adi Da's detailed instructions, as given in His direct Word (throughout this chapter, and in other sources). Once you have adapted to the practice based on Avatar Adi Da's detailed instruction, you can use the summary below as a guide to ongoing practice of the laying on of hands (while also always refreshing your understanding of the practice through study of Avatar Adi Da's Word).

For the One Receiving the Laying On of Hands

• Relax and close your eyes. Generally, you should lie on your back to support full relaxation, but the laying on of hands can also be received in other positions.

• Turn the faculties to Avatar Adi Da, entering into whole bodily Communion with His Living Divine Presence. Intend full receptivity of His Healing-Force of Blessing.

• Consider, accept, and affirm necessary changes in your life-patterns.

• Breathe in a relaxed manner, receiving the pervasive, universal life-energy on inhalation and releasing all negative or toxic patterns on exhalation.

For the One Performing the Laying On of Hands

• Before the occasion begins, discuss with the recipient what areas of his or her body should be addressed in the laying on of hands occasion.

• Regard Avatar Adi Da's Murti-Form. See and feel Him present before you—and allow yourself to be heart-moved to Him. Invoke Him via the Name "Da" (or any one of His other Divine Names), both audibly and silently.

• Relax into the all-pervading and universal field of life-energy. Feel and breathe the life-energy throughout the body.

• Engage "conductivity"-breathing coordinated with the cycle of healing-touch in the precise manner as follows:

Inhalation Phase

♦ Inhale, feeling Avatar Adi Da at heart, and <u>either</u>:
  ○ raise the hands to His Murti-Form in the gesture of Invocation and Beholding*
  <u>or</u>

(continued on next page)

---

* The gesture of Invocation and Beholding is performed by facing Avatar Adi Da's Murti-Form and (as Avatar Adi Da describes in *The Dawn Horse Testament*) "Raising the hands, head-high and shoulder-wide, With the hands Opened Forward".

○ place the hands near the area of the body you will serve on the person receiving the laying on of hands.

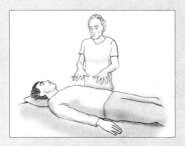

Note: Do not touch the person receiving the laying on of hands during the inhalation.

♦ Throughout the inhalation, invoke Avatar Adi Da and magnify the reception of His Healing-Force of Blessing.

♦ Inhale the energy downward to your vital region, and perhaps retain it there via the locks of the bodily base and the throat.*

♦ Fill the bodily "battery"† and the whole body with energy, and concentrate the energy as love (or free feeling-attention) and as the affirmation and visualization of positive change.

Exhalation Phase

♦ On exhalation, either touch the recipient's physical body or etheric body (a few inches beyond the surface of the physical body) at the area to be healed.

---

* See pp. 176–78 for a description of the bodily locks.

† The region of the body extending from the diaphragm to the bodily base, with a focal point at the crown of the lower abdomen approximately 2 inches, or 3–4 finger breadths, below the umbilical scar.

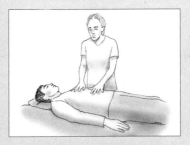

◆ Let the healing-force pervade that area.

◆ Maintain right polarization of the body (crown to base) via relaxation, exercise the disposition of turning to Avatar Adi Da, and affirm healing.

◆ Exhalation may be accompanied by a light upward tensing of the bodily base.

◆ Toward the end of the exhalation, remove the hands from the body and shake them with the fingers and wrists relaxed, thus intending the release of all negative energies and conditions.

• Repeat the inhalation/exhalation process until there is a sense that the healing cycle is complete.

• Throughout the occasion, Commune with Avatar Adi Da through sighting of His Murti-Form and/or simple Name-Invocation of Him.

• To complete the occasion, audibly invoke Avatar Adi Da by Name, and engage several cycles of the breath with the feeling that all negative conditions have been completely released.

• After the occasion, run water over your hands, or take a shower or a walk, to further release any accumulated energies.

Elements of the Practice of the Laying On of Hands

O*f all possible practical disciplines of healing, the by-Me-Given Devotional Prayer of Changes is the most auspicious practice, and the by-Me-Given (and anciently known) practice of the laying on of hands is the most pure, potent, direct, and effective physical expression of the intention that is affirmed in that prayer in devotional recognition-response to Me.*

—Avatar Adi Da Samraj
The Eating Gorilla Comes In Peace

The following subsections explore Avatar Adi Da's instruction about the fundamentals of the practice of the laying on of hands. Because the laying on of hands is an extension of the Devotional Prayer of Changes, Avatar Adi Da's instruction given here expands and builds upon the instruction given on that practice in chapter 5 (pp. 178–91).

Allow Reality to Enter the Sphere of Patterns

The principal disposition of the laying on of hands is ego-transcending devotional Communion with Avatar Adi Da. In fact, in order for the laying on of hands to be effective, the practice must genuinely "link up" with Avatar Adi Da's Healing-Force of Blessing. Natural life-energy and a loving disposition toward another are healing forces, but the truly transformative power of the laying on of hands is Avatar Adi Da's Living Divine Presence. When that connection is made in real terms, then Avatar Adi Da's Blessing-Force can influence conditions, through the etheric "fluid" of your feeling-relationship to the one receiving the laying on of hands.

My Blessing-Work with you is Real. You must understand it in its own terms, and not merely through imaginative childish thinking. It is not a fairy tale—it is a matter of right Yogic address to Me, right bringing of the body-mind-complex to Me.

My Blessing of that one for whom you feel sympathy—if you are calling on Me for it—needs to work through your own body. You bring

206

*Me into that pattern of your relationship. If you understand it, then
it is a profound Yogic matter, and not merely some sort of wishful
thinking or conventional praying. It is a literal Yogic, devotional, and
(in due course) Transcendental Spiritual matter. You must truly
Invoke Me, breathe Me, feel Me, and serve Me—allow Me to enter not
only into your body but into the entire sphere of the pattern of your
existing sympathies. It is the "Devotional Prayer of Changes use" of
Me, in which, through your own sympathy mechanism, My Blessing
can then pass to that one with whom you have the connection in this
stick-with-glue kind of connection that friendship contacts make.*

—Avatar Adi Da Samraj

May 13, 1997

In the late 1980s, a devotee of Avatar Adi Da went to
visit his father in an English country hospital, where his
father was staying after suffering a minor stroke. It soon
became clear that his father was ready to die.

T*he nurses just drew curtains around us, so the lively
noise of families visiting was quite audible in the
background.*

*Then, as my mother and I sat on either side of my dying
father, Beloved Adi Da "Showed up" in this hospital in the
English countryside—remarkably, tangibly Present, a great
descending Force Pouring down on us in this humble medical "nowhere" place. I had spent time in His Company and
His environments when He was traveling in Europe in
1986, and now His Presence was as unmistakable as if He
had walked into the room.*

*Beloved Adi Da Served my father in his death transition
very evidently. Beloved Adi Da also greatly eased my lifelong fear of death at what could have been a very disturb-
ing time. He made an "Easy Death"* for my dad and made
it easeful for me to simply serve my mother that day, and
other family members over the next few days.*

(continued on next page)

* This is a reference to the book *Easy Death*, Avatar Adi Da's principal text on the death and
dying process.

Many years later, in 1995, I spoke to Beloved Adi Da about my family, praising Him for His Service to them and describing His "appearance" at my father's death.

Beloved Adi Da said in reply, "Yes, I have 'sticky connec- tions' to all your family members."

He then repeated the phrase "sticky connections"—and, at the time, it seemed obvious that He meant He had an actual, tangible connection to all His devotees' family members.

In later years, I understood that all this signified Bhaga- van Adi Da's Great Compassion, surely, but also His Ultimacy, His Prior Connectedness with all beings.

—Devotee of Avatar Adi Da Samraj

In the laying on of hands, the healing process is assisted by affirmation and visualization of the desired changes. As in the Devotional Prayer of Changes, affirming and visualizing in the lay- ing on of hands are not mental techniques, but natural expressions of a transformed emotional disposition.[2] In other words, affirma- tion and visualization—and the laying on of hands altogether— are matters of deep feeling, and resting in the sense of well-being prior to all conditions. As an extension of the Devotional Prayer of Changes, the laying on of hands is an enactment of the "faith presumption"—presuming infinitely available life-energy, and inherence in the Divine Reality Prior to all conditions (whether apparently positive or apparently negative).

The open heart is inherently characterized by faith, not by belief in this or that. Faith is not a "thing" in mind. Faith is a disposition, a feeling of trust. . . . Trust is another way of describing true feeling, then—"self"-surrendered, "self"-forgetting. True feeling is a funda- mental sense of trust, and that is faith. Faith is not the feeling that you can escape death, or that the body need not suffer, or that

2. See p. 184 for further instruction on visualization in the Devotional Prayer of Changes.

nothing bad will happen in life—those things happen anyway, one way or another. Even when such things do happen, the truly Spiritually awakened person enjoys the feeling of trust—and trust is at the "root" (or the core) of the being. Trust is not the superficial gesture of mind, not "I read this—therefore, I believe that." Rather, trust is a core disposition of faith, well-being, integrity.

The "root" of trust is no-"self", the separate "self" surrendered and forgotten in the embracing of Reality altogether. Even though you cannot comprehend Reality with your mind, you embrace It in the disposition of "self"-sacrifice—which shows itself in the human being as a sign of true sanity and well-being, in the midst of all the mortal display that bodily manifested beings suffer.

—Avatar Adi Da Samraj
"The Grace of Trust",
My "Bright" Form

The Radiant Force of Avatar Adi Da's Living Divine Presence can also transform conditions. When an opening is made for the Force of Conscious Light—by means of the "self"-surrendering disposition in devotional Communion with Avatar Adi Da—then the laying on of hands becomes an effective extension of the Devotional Prayer of Changes. In that opening, Avatar Adi Da's Healing-Force of Blessing can Do Its Work.

The Devotional Prayer of Changes . . . is the turning of all the faculties to Me—being steady, Invoking Me, devotionally Communing with Me.

Thus, that process is a turning out from (or away from) ego-patterning.

When there is such Invocation of Me, and when it is more and more constant, the Prior-Unity-Force of My Person—Reality Itself— is allowed to enter into the sphere of patterns.

If people are devotionally turning to Me, they will notice that things loosen up and changes happen.

Sometimes there are purifications, sometimes there are break-throughs.

All kinds of pattern-changes occur—even without necessarily uttering anything in the formal manner of the Devotional Prayer of Changes, and even without necessarily focusing on something in particular that you want to be changed.

Such changes will always be a reflection of the Prior-Unity-Force of Reality Itself in Its egoless Self-Nature.

My Own Force of Person—when Invoked by this perpetual Invocation of Me and whole bodily turning to Me—displaces ego-patterns. . . .

Such Invocation of Me simply allows That Which Is of the Nature of Prior Unity to replace the fragmented ego-"world"-pattern.

Thus, it is intrinsic to the devotional turning to Me that changes occur, that things open up, that people open up.

Change inevitably follows the process of ego-transcending whole bodily Invocation of Me.

—Avatar Adi Da Samraj
"Invoking The Prior-Unity-Force of My Person",
The Sacred Space of Finding Me

*I*n April 1998 I received word that my mother was physically failing and I should fly from Fiji to California to visit her in order to be sure to see her again before the end of her life. When I first saw her, I could see that she was in a state of despair—completely unlike her usual bright disposition. I also discovered that she was having a lot of difficulty sleeping. She could not lie down or her breathing would become too labored. Even sleeping in a recliner chair was fitful.

Her main health issue was a heart-condition—a result of having contracted rheumatic fever as a child. So when she was resting outside in the sun in a chaise longue, I did the laying on of hands over her heart-region, just placing my hands in that position and silently invoking Avatar Adi Da Samraj as I did so. When I finally lifted my hands from her heart, she said, "That felt so good. Please do it again." So I immediately started again.

After that laying on of hands, my mother returned to the house and immediately lay down in her recliner chair— and slept straight through for eight hours. For the remaining days of my time in California, she never had trouble sleeping again. And, more importantly, she was her usual happy and radiant self again.

—Devotee of Avatar Adi Da Samraj

The Healing Cycle: Magnifying Healing Life-Energy and Releasing Negative Energy

The laying on of hands is an intensive "conductivity" practice. Full "conductivity" magnifies natural life-energy in the body of the one performing the laying on of hands so that it may be directed into the body of the recipient. Therefore, the one performing the laying on of hands practices "conductivity" breathing in the Circle of his or her body-mind with great energy and intention—thereby supporting the balance and integration of the yellow-red conjunction.

The magnification of natural life-energy is coordinated with the affirmation of positive changes and appropriate healing via the breath cycle. Although Avatar Adi Da gives a specific sequence of actions associated with the breath cycle, it is important to remember that devotional Communion with Him is the principal guide to effective exercise of the breathing-feeling process in the laying on of hands—just as in all other circumstances.

The practice of turning the faculty of the breath to Me is not about observing breaths, counting breaths, noticing breaths in any technical fashion. It is about entering into relationship with Me via the breath, Communing with Me via the breath. The breath is not the subject of your practice. I Am! All the faculties of the body-mind-complex must be devoted to Me—and, since breath is a principal

211

faculty, you must exercise yourself in relation to Me via the breath. The practice is not to get very curious about the breaths themselves, or finicky about breathing. Rather, the practice is to devote yourself to Me completely, and to use the leading faculties of the body-mind-complex as the principal mechanisms for that practice. The ego-transcending practice in My Divine Avataric Company is a devotional practice, then—not merely a functional one.

—Avatar Adi Da Samraj
"The Devotional Yoga of The Breath",
My "Bright" Form

In *The Dawn Horse Testament*, Avatar Adi Da describes how the one performing the laying on of hands coordinates hand positions and "conductivity" practice with the inhalation-exhalation cycle. This cyclical pattern assists the magnification and directing of energy to the recipient, and also minimizes potential contact with negative energies:

During inhalation, energy is magnified in the body of the one performing the laying on of hands, and the hands do not touch the one receiving the laying on of hands:

As You Invoke Me, Feel Me At Heart, and

> • *inhale The Natural Life-Energy Downward Into Your Own vital Region.*

> • *Retain The Natural Life-Energy There—Perhaps Locking the bodily base, and Even Applying A Downward Pressure In The Region Of the throat.*

As You inhale,

> • *Concentrate and Focus The Natural Life-Energy As Love and As The Affirmation and The Visualization Of All Desired Changes.*

During the inhalation, You May Either

> • *Raise Your hands To Me In The Gesture Of Invocation and Beholding or (Otherwise)*

> • *Place the open palms Near the area To Be Served On the individual (Without Actually Touching his or her body).*

During exhalation, energy is directed toward the recipient through intensified "conductivity" and by placing the hands on (or near) the recipient's body:

During exhalation,

- *the hands Can Touch Either the physical body Or (Otherwise) Simply the etheric body (which Extends a few inches Beyond The Surface Of the physical body) at the area To Be Healed.*

During exhalation,

- *Let The Accumulated Living Healing-Force Pervade the areas To Be Healed, and*
- *Continue To Relax the Whole body (Thus Establishing Right Polarization Of the body),*
- *and To Engage The Process Of Heart-Radiating (In The Constant Disposition Of Whole bodily Turning To Me) and Of Affirming Right, Appropriate, and Positive Healing.*

In Addition, exhalation

- *May Be Accompanied By A Light Upward Tensing Of the bodily base.*

The end of exhalation is associated with releasing any negative energies:

As the exhalation Nears Completion,

- *Withdraw the hands From the body of the individual, and*
- *Shake Your hands Toward the ground, or Into space, With the wrists and fingers limp,*
- *and With The Feeling That all Negative energies or conditions that Have Come Into the hands From the person Being Treated Are Being Shaken Off and Naturally Released Into The Domain Of Cosmic Nature.*

Repeat this inhalation-exhalation process "Until There Is A Feeling-Sense That The Healing Cycle Is Complete". The one performing the laying on of hands can then take further steps to complete the process of releasing negative energies:

At The End Of Any Period Of The Laying On Of Hands,

- *audibly Invoke Me By Name, and*

- *inhale and exhale The Natural Life-Energy Via Several Cycles Of the breath,*

- *With The Feeling That all Negative conditions that Have (In Any Manner) Become Associated With Your Own body-mind-complex During The Laying On Of Hands Are Being Completely Released Through exhalation (Via the entire body-mind-complex).*

It May Also Be Useful To

- *Hold Your hands Under running water In Order To Wash them and Complete The Cycle Of Releasing any Negative energies (and Also For Basic Hygiene, If the person Receiving The Laying On Of Hands is ill).*

- *Alternatively, You May Take a shower or a walk, Releasing any energies that Were Accumulated Via the hands During The Laying On Of Hands.*

Change of Action

As "the most . . . effective physical expression" of the Devotional Prayer of Changes, the physical dimension of the laying on of hands also continues beyond any specific healing occasion. Change of action in daily life is an essential follow-up because, for the prayer expressed in the laying on of hands to truly be effective, "the Total body-mind-complex Must Positively Change"—and this includes the physical and emotional patterns of one's daily life.

The Devotional Prayer Of Changes Is Not A Matter Of Merely Sitting Around Exercising mind-forms. When You Truly Practice The Devotional Prayer Of Changes, You Have To Get Off Your backside and Act.

—Avatar Adi Da Samraj
The Dawn Horse Testament

Therefore, the laying on of hands begins with the recipient's acknowledgment of this principle and obligation.

The individual who Is Administering The Laying On Of Hands Asks the individual who Is Receiving The Laying On Of Hands To Relax, To Close the eyes, To Turn The Faculties To Me, To Fully Receive My Healing-Force Of Blessing (bodily, and Altogether)— and, Then, To "Consider", Accept, and Affirm The Necessity Of Right and Appropriate Changes In his or her conditions of life and Habits Of Action, and To Take Responsibility For Enacting Those Changes.

—Avatar Adi Da Samraj
The Dawn Horse Testament

After any occasion of the laying on of hands, the one who received the healing is called by Avatar Adi Da to follow through on this affirmation of right action, as means to fully participate in the prayer initiated in that healing occasion.

In addition to holding to a rightly positive disposition, you must also animate your life in further whole bodily participation in the change, as you would have it. . . . You do not just sit around and wait for the change to occur. You have to do something about it. On different occasions, there will be different implications relative to your activity . . . —but taking the necessary action is fundamental.

—Avatar Adi Da Samraj
"The Devotional Prayer of Changes Is A Disposition
That Can Actually Affect Phenomena",
The Sacred Space of Finding Me

Such change of action involves persisting in devotional Communion with Avatar Adi Da, and in the "faith presumption" (of health and well-being prior to disease or cure), and practically and consistently demonstrating the intended outcome in daily life.

True and sustainable change and positive, mature human adaptation are not made on the basis of any "self"-conscious reaction-resistance to old, degenerative, and immature habits.

True and positive change is not a matter of not doing something.

True and positive change is always a matter of doing something else—something that is inherently right, free, pure and purifying, balanced and re-balancing, truly regenerative, and (altogether) a matter of functional equanimity.

True and positive change is always a matter of both right principle (based on right understanding, and, especially, right "self"-understanding) and right (and consistently applied) "self"-management.

Therefore, you must be intrinsically open and free to always feel and participate in modes of "self"-managing life-functioning that are new and right. . . .

Always Stand Intrinsically Prior to all negative judgements about what you have done and what you tend to do.

Always intensively engage the happy ordeal of habit-transcending new adaptation in ecstatic devotional Communion with Me, the Divine Avataric Master.

—Avatar Adi Da Samraj
"Right Principle and Right Self-Management:
The Secrets of How To Change",
The Aletheon

Be a Conduit, Not a Healer

The one performing the laying on of hands is responsible to bring his or her own practice of Divine Communion, "conductivity", and energy-sensitivity to the healing occasion. In fact, the greater someone's understanding, sensitivity, and responsibility relative to the etheric-energy dimension of existence, the more effective that individual can be in the laying on of hands, and even in any circumstance of healing. This is a principle that

Avatar Adi Da calls all those who perform healing services to understand and embrace.

Through your own etheric influence, you can also aid another by raising the level of life-force available to the individual. That, among other things, is what a healer does to reduce the gross physical obstructions that prevent an individual's integration with the energy body and the Divine Radiance of Life. The healer knows that the etheric body heals when it is integrated properly with the physical body. Thus, the healer must have a right relationship to the life-force and know the secret of well-being. When the healer has renounced his or her own obsession with the gross physical level of existence and has abandoned the dogmas of cure, unconsciousness, and irresponsibility for life, then the healer knows very well that his or her presence or quality of relationship and attention to an individual has a primary influence on the ultimate healing process.

The more potent the healer—the more healthy, the more whole, the more mature in devotional and Spiritual practice he or she is— the more the healer's own etheric body is expanded and opened to its Divine Source. Thus, obviously, there are people who are better healers than others. Many can have responsibility for healing, but there will be degrees of difference between them. Likewise, any individual will have times when he or she is better at healing. Over time, any person may become a healer—because, through the practice of true Spiritual life, that one is set free of all his or her own obstructions. The law of the laying on of hands, for instance, is completely obvious to such a one—straightforward, no more mysterious than prescribing an aspirin. The healer is certain of the healing, and has a great deal of strength and confidence in this practice.

—Avatar Adi Da Samraj
"The Doctor Is A Healing Presence",
The Eating Gorilla Comes In Peace

However, Avatar Adi Da emphasizes that the person performing the laying on of hands is not "doing" or "causing" the healing. By means of the ego-transcending gestures of devotional

Communion with Avatar Adi Da and whole-bodily participation in the universal field of natural life-energy, the one performing the laying on of hands simply serves as a searchless conduit in the healing process.

The trouble with the laying on of hands is that people think of themselves as "me" putting some force out to "this guy". The "me" has to get out of the way for the laying on of hands to be workable in any remarkable sense. Those who perform the laying on of hands must be a channel for the process of life-energy and be very sensitive to it. But people are full of mind and full of "self", and think of themselves as healers and all the rest of it—and they thereby obstruct the process of "radical" healing. In that case, there is only a minimal kind of influence going on through them—or perhaps some influence occurs in spite of them!

—Avatar Adi Da Samraj
Da Prana Ratha

I n 1992, I went on my first retreat to Beloved Adi Da's Hermitage in Fiji. I had only been a devotee for six months, so I was really surprised when I was suddenly invited to do my professional form of body-work on Beloved Adi Da. I had not expected anything like this and had no reference for what it would be like to be in such a circumstance with Avatar Adi Da—in fact, I was completely petrified! But later, when I first went in to see Beloved Adi Da, I was only a couple of feet away from Him and I looked into His Eyes and it was like looking into Infinity. He did not say anything. I prostrated,* and then I started to do body-work on Him.

During the treatment session, I was still nervous, but I also felt there was a lot going on that I had no idea about. Afterward, nothing was said about the body-work.

A week later, I was called to work on Beloved Adi Da again. This time I felt a little more confident. I started working

* Prostration is a traditional form of approach to the Realizer, signifying and embodying the surrender of the "self" to the Divine.

on Him, and then about halfway through the occasion, this stray thought flitted into my mind: "Maybe I can help this man." As soon as I thought it, I instantly recognized it was the ego designating itself as "the healer" and approaching Him as an "ordinary man".

Two nights later, I was told that there were Communications from Beloved Adi Da for me. Instantly, I knew what they were about. It was an extensive Communication, in which Beloved Adi Da directly Addressed my presumptions about being "a healer". I've always resisted being called a healer, because I really don't see myself that way, but obviously part of me had some kind of feeling that I was! So I felt that Beloved Adi Da was reading things about me that I was hiding from myself. His Communications repeatedly referred to "healer-types", and His basic Criticism was that I was self-guruing, thinking that I could heal. And it was very obvious to me He was responding to this apparently stray thought I had.

I immediately understood what He was talking about and I was moved to respond to Him in writing, having received personal instruction from the Guru. I cannot remember the details of what I wrote, but I made clear that I understood what He was Communicating, and that I felt I was obviously being healed by Him on some level from this ego-stance.

I thought that would be it and I would never be invited to work on Beloved Adi Da again. But the next week came around, and He asked me to work on Him again. I worked on Beloved Adi Da two or three more times during my retreat. I guess partly because of the healing, cleansing— whatever you want to call it—that He had done with me, the later sessions felt more natural and easy, and I began to much more feel Him instead of being so nervous. In a way it is impossible to describe, but it just felt like I was in a field of energy, where there were huge waves of energy. I lost that

(continued on next page)

feeling of separateness that is usually part of my point of view. I felt like I was simply in His Field of Energy. And interestingly, I could see that, on one level, His Body was a conditional body like everyone else's, but I also felt that He had no psychic guarding whatsoever. I felt like, on some kind of level, I could put my hand right through Him with no resistance. I had not felt that before, with anyone, even very young babies. And I have never felt that on anyone else but Him.

—Devotee of Avatar Adi Da Samraj

The Yogic whole bodily turning to Avatar Adi Da is what enables the "self" to "get out of the way"—and it magnifies the sensitivity to etheric energy, and, most significantly, allows Avatar Adi Da's Healing-Force to influence conditions. Thus, Communion with Avatar Adi Da is always the primary responsibility of the one performing the laying on of hands.

The healing process is a matter of adjusting and serving the "conductivity" of the body, but it requires the ability to Invoke Me and Commune with Me. It requires the one performing the healing not to be egoically involved in the healing "business", but to participate as My devotee, to do healing work based on the sensitivity that arises in Communion with Me. Etheric sensitivity is a likely beginning to such sensitivity because the etheric energy is so close to the physical.

—Avatar Adi Da Samraj
May 6, 1996

❖ ❖ ❖

If the laying on of hands becomes a thing in itself, or if the one performing the laying on of hands gets "self"-involved in it—that is when it becomes aberrated. The laying on of hands is not about "self"—it is about Me.

—Avatar Adi Da Samraj
April 20, 1996

One becomes more effective in performing the laying on of hands, and the Devotional Prayer of Changes in general, by regularly practicing it, by magnifying "conductivity" in the Circle altogether, and by deepening Communion with Avatar Adi Da. As Avatar Adi Da says about the Devotional Prayer of Changes (in *The Sacred Space of Finding Me*), "the strength of your devotional resort to Me, the loudness of your silent Communion with Me, has something to do with the outcome".

M y friend and fellow devotee Jeff, who was in the last days of his life, asked me and my intimate partner to do the laying on of hands with him each day. This was a special time when we could bring him our energy.

We would sit on his bed and each focus on a different area of Jeff's body. He had an altar with a Murti of Beloved Adi Da Samraj near his bed, and the room felt full with Divine Presence. I could feel Jeff's one-pointed attention on his Guru. I would invoke Beloved Adi Da in my heart, and then place my hands above Jeff's heart, head, navel, or feet. Immediately I would feel a current of energy running through me and into Jeff and then, in this particular circumstance, felt the current of healing energy returning from him and moving back through my body. I envisioned light and blessing with each breath. The breath was a part of the process of reception and release.

I felt a deep love for Jeff, beyond what I had felt in our everyday encounters. It was a love that came from beyond me, and that was all about bringing him this love through healing energy. I could feel his body (which was often in much pain) relax, and I could feel him moving into a peaceful state that was just about feeling and breathing.

What was most amazing about these sessions of the laying on of hands was that I did not feel like I had to do any kind of procedure, or even think about what I was

(continued on next page)

doing. As soon as I would begin, it was like I was just a vehicle for the healing work. It was as if I had been plugged into a circuit of infinite light, love, and energy, and I was just a means to help that wash over and through Jeff's physical and etheric bodies. This was the simplest experience of the laying on of hands that I have ever had.

When we would leave the room, we would remark about what a gift the session had been for us. It was just like sitting in Darshan with Beloved Adi Da Samraj. It was a forgetting of myself, a forgetting of all of my concerns for Jeff, and a most precious chance to Commune with What is Greater than all of us. I was instructed in a non-verbal, feeling manner about how to engage in the Sacrament of Universal Sacrifice.* Giving and receiving, breathing and feeling, with the heart open wide. Instead of being like a knotted ball of twine inside myself, the thread was being unraveled. The threads were numerous—light-and-energy connections, with no limitation.

—Devotee of Avatar Adi Da Samraj

* The constant and real exchange between the devotee and Avatar Adi Da: the devotee is always offering the gift of the surrender of egoic "self" to Avatar Adi Da, and always receiving Avatar Adi Da's Gift of Divine Blessing in return.

This depth of Communion with Avatar Adi Da matures, by Grace, into sensitivity to His Transcendental Spiritual Transmission—and in this context, the practice of the Devotional Prayer of Changes expressed through the laying on of hands (and altogether) becomes even more potent, as the devotee functions as an egoless conduit for His Transcendental Spiritual Force.[3]

Prayer Becomes <u>Most</u> Effective When the individual psychophysical person Is Transcendentally Spiritually Awakened By Me— Such That the body-mind-complex Is . . . Surrendered (or "Tuned")

3. Details on the Transcendentally Spiritually activated forms of practice are given in *The Dawn Horse Testament.*

To My Avatarically Self-Transmitted (and Perfectly Subjective, and, Thus, Truly all-and-All-Surrounding and all-and-All-Pervading) Divine Transcendental Spiritual Current. . . .
And . . . By Effectively "getting out of the way" (or Removing The mental, and bodily, and, Altogether, egoic Obstacles To My Divine Transcendental Spiritual Infusion Of conditional events), and By Generating Entirely Positive and Intensely Auspicious and Profoundly Felt mind-forms (or Even mind-Transcending bodily Invocations Of Me), My Devotee Can Cooperatively Allow Me To Transcendentally Spiritually Pour Into, and To Directly and Newly and Positively Affect and Change, any particular condition (or conditions) At All.

—Avatar Adi Da Samraj
The Dawn Horse Testament

Of course, practicing the laying on of hands in relation to natural life-energy is also directly associated with Avatar Adi Da's Blessing-Power. As He once said, "If you are participating in Me through the natural-life-energy sign, you are breathing Me, you are giving Me your feeling-attention, and exercising the breath in such Communion with Me. What do you care what level of energy is being 'experienced' in the body in that practice? What difference does it make?"[4] Therefore, whether or not one is sensitive to Avatar Adi Da's Transcendental Spiritual Presence, practice of the laying on of hands is effective. It is simply the devotional love-response to Avatar Adi Da that makes it so. In this intimate exchange of healing-touch, both participants simply come into Avatar Adi Da's Radiant Divine Company—and that alone heals and transforms the being.

The Divine Truth, Reality, and Person is the ultimate Healer. I Am Adi Da Samraj, the Divine Avataric Incarnation of the Divine Truth, Reality, and Person—and, therefore, My Mere Divine Avataric Presence is the most benign healing Influence. Without obstruction or limitation of any kind, I Incarnate the Acausal Divine Being. Therefore, those who enter My Divine Avataric Company enter the Very Presence of the Acausal Divine Person. I

4. From a discourse given on December 6, 1993.

need not perform any special intentional action to heal—though I may, in fact, intentionally exercise healing capabilities of both ordinary and extraordinary kinds. Nevertheless, My Avatarically Self-Transmitted, Self-Existing and Self-Radiant, Divine Transcendental Spiritual Presence Itself spontaneously Purifies, Harmonizes, and Rejuvenates My devotees, whole bodily. It Restores them to the ecstasy of Divine Communion and, ultimately, to Most Perfect Divine Self-Realization.

My Mere and Blessing Divine Avataric Transcendental Spiritual Presence does not merely Heal My devotees of illness, quirks of character, and subhuman (or degenerative) habits. My Mere Presence Heals My devotees of the entire accumulation of their developmental history of embodiment in the "world", and It Draws them into Divine Love-Bliss, Beyond the consolations of future embodiment, high and low. The relationship between Me and My devotees is the greatest and most Sacred Mystery—and, indeed, human beings have been advised, since ancient times, that the most auspicious occupation of humankind is devotion to a living Spiritual Master.

Likewise, the right association of My by-Me-Transcendentally-Spiritually-Awakened devotees with Me magnifies the spontaneously healing mechanism that I bring to My every devotee. That mechanism is love. My Transcendentally Spiritually Awakened devotees conduct My Avatarically Self-Transmitted, Inherently Perfect, and Self-Radiant Transcendental Spiritual Energy, Purifying each one's accumulation of independent, "subjective", and mortal "experience". Through right association with others, My Transcendentally Spiritually Awakened devotees consciously share the qualities and energies of My Divine Transcendental Spiritual Company in a most benign manner, such that the imbalances of each individual are harmonized by the spectrum of qualities radiating from others.

The process of reception-release that is engaged by even My beginning devotees in devotional intimacy with Me is the direct communication of life-energy, providing a circuit for the "conductivity" of energy in the body-mind-complex. Such love (maturing, in due course, as Transcendental Spiritual Communion with Me) Perfectly Enlivens and Rejuvenates the whole-bodily being and (Ultimately) enables My devotee to transcend the entire "world".

The true art of the physician, or the intentional healing practice of any of My devotees in relation to another living being, is a reflection and duplication of the Divinely Healing "politics" that is enacted between Me and My devotee, and that is (likewise) practiced within the culture of all My devotees. Such mutual healing epitomizes the sacred intimacy of right association among human beings. It is a ceremony of mutual sacrifice among My devotees, which demonstrates their understanding and their happy (moment to moment) devotional turning to Me, the Eternal Divine Source-Condition in Which all relationships are arising.

—Avatar Adi Da Samraj
The Eating Gorilla Comes In Peace

From the Radiant Life Clinic: Further Guidelines Based on Avatar Adi Da's Instructions

Where to perform the laying on of hands. Generally, the laying on of hands is performed in an environment in which the person receiving the laying on of hands can lie down comfortably, let go of social consciousness, and magnify devotional Communion with Avatar Adi Da. Avatar Adi Da instructs, as mentioned above, that the laying on of hands should be performed in a setting where the one administering the laying on of hands can regard His Murti-Form, for the sake of invoking His Blessing on behalf of the person being served.

Who should perform the laying on of hands, and for whom. You should perform the laying on of hands only for someone with whom you have a positive connection, and who is open to receive Avatar Adi Da's Blessing via this practice. Therefore, the laying on of hands is generally practiced by a devotee of Avatar Adi Da for another devotee, though it can also be performed for other individuals who are positively disposed to this form of healing practice.

> I was in school to learn a healing system called "BodyTalk". One day I was practicing with one of my fellow students when there was a pause in the session and I started silently invoking Bhagavan Adi Da with my hands still on the lady's stomach. She immediately asked, "What are you doing?" I told her I was invoking Beloved Adi Da and she said, "It feels like the ocean." Ever since then, she and I started calling the laying on of hands "Ocean Hands"—she is very clear that it is Beloved Adi Da's Presence that has that quality, and got to experience Him directly in a way that she could instantly feel and understand.
>
> —Devotee of Avatar Adi Da Samraj

Multiple people offering the laying on of hands. Any occasion of the laying on of hands may be performed by a single person, or by more than one person. The effect of having multiple people perform the laying on of hands on an individual can be very potent and healing.

Communicate with the recipient. Previous to starting the occasion, you should be familiar with the particular form of bodily or emotional difficulty the person receiving the laying on of hands is experiencing. Be clear on what the intended positive outcome is.

Visualization. Visualization in the laying on of hands is not a mental exercise, but a feeling and energetic process associated with the physical body. (See also the description of visualization in the "Devotional Prayer of Changes" section on p. 184.) When a devotee once confessed to Avatar Adi Da that she was having trouble with visualizing while performing the laying on of hands, Avatar Adi Da said to her, "It is not about visualization, it is about feeling."

Different individuals may have different forms of visualization that naturally arise out of the feeling-and-energy process of the laying on of hands. Regardless, the laying on of hands practice is always founded in the turning of all the faculties to Avatar Adi Da, and allowing Him to do the healing.

How long and how often to perform the laying on of hands. The laying on of hands can be performed daily or whenever it is needed. The length of time for an occasion of the laying on of hands depends on the particular circumstance of the person receiving the laying on of hands. There is no set length of time, but an occasion could last from 5–10 minutes, or longer, as needed.

Where to place the hands. Avatar Adi Da did not give specific indications about the placement of the hands in the practice of the laying on of hands. The person offering the laying on of hands should simply remain sensitive to the recipient, the condition being addressed, and the feeling of life-energy associated with the recipient's body. The one performing the laying on of hands should also be open to subtle feeling-impressions that come up and non-verbal communications that might come from the body-mind of the recipient to help guide the placement of the hands.

One can either touch a single area of the recipient's body with both hands next to each other or place one hand on one area of the recipient's body and the other hand on another area, effectively creating an energy "connection" between the two areas. One can also freely sweep one or both hands over the whole body (head to toe), and/or over the arms, as one is moved.

Non-touch Approach. In chapter 7, Avatar Adi Da gives explicit indications about "touch and non-touch" zones of the body in the practice of Yogic "conductivity" massage. Although He did not comment on these specific matters in relation to the laying on of hands, the same basic guidelines can be followed. The person offering the healing treatment should be sensitive to the recipient and where it is appropriate to physically touch that person. If there is a question, one can always simply touch the etheric field of a particular area rather than the physical body itself. Note that

Avatar Adi Da's instructions (presented on pp. 257–61) to not touch the top of another person's head should be followed in the practice of the laying on of hands. If there is an extreme condition in the head region (such as a brain tumor, or severe migraine), then the sides and front and back of the head can be touched (either through touching the physical head or touching the etheric field around the head, depending on what is needed in the individual's case).

Avatar Adi Da Samraj
Adi Da Samrajashram, 2008

The Practice of The Laying On of Hands

Instruction from The Dawn Horse Testament
by His Divine Presence,
Avatar Adi Da Samraj

*Avatar Adi Da's final and complete instruction on the laying
on of hands, as given in* The Dawn Horse Testament *(excerpts of
which are included in the preceding sections of this chapter), is presented here in full.*

The Healing Of others In The Reality-Way Of Adidam

In The Only-By-Me Revealed and Given "Radical" Reality-Way
Of The Heart (or "Radical" Reality-Way Of Adidam), The Healing
Of others Is Served By "Considering" With them My Divine
Avataric Self-Revelation and My Divine Avataric Reality-Teaching,
By Discussing The Specific Practical Changes (Relative To dietary,
emotional-sexual, social-behavioral, Devotional, and, As The Case
May Be, Transcendental Spiritual Matters) That Must Necessarily Be
Made In their daily lives If There Is To Be True Health and Well-
being, and By Engaging The By-Me-Given Practices Of The Devo-
tional Prayer Of Changes and The Laying On Of Hands.

The Laying On Of Hands Is A Form
Of The Devotional Prayer Of Changes

In The "Radical" Reality-Way Of The Heart, The Laying On Of
Hands Is, Essentially, A Matter Of Performing The Devotional

Prayer Of Changes On someone's Behalf While Maintaining physical Contact With that person Via the hands.

In The By-Me-Given Practice Of The Laying On Of Hands, the
individual who Is Administering The Laying On Of Hands Asks the
individual who Is Receiving The Laying On Of Hands To Relax, To
Close the eyes, To Turn The Faculties To Me, To Fully Receive My
Healing-Force Of Blessing (bodily, and Altogether)—and, Then, To
"Consider", Accept, and Affirm The Necessity Of Right and
Appropriate Changes In his or her conditions of life and Habits Of
Action, and To Take Responsibility For Enacting Those Changes.

The one Performing The Laying On Of Hands Familiarizes
himself or herself With the areas of the body where the individual
Is Suffering.

Regard My Form and Invoke Me By Name

When You (As My Devotee) Perform The Laying On Of Hands,
You Should Do So In A Setting Where You Can Regard My
Representation-Form, For The Sake Of Magnifying Invocation Of
Me and Reception Of My Healing-Force Of Blessing.

Invoke Me By Name, Both audibly and With "the tongue of the
mind", Using Any Of The By-Me-Given Forms Of Simple Name-
Invocation Of Me.

Inhale The Natural Life-Energy

As You Invoke Me, Feel Me At Heart, and inhale The Natural
Life-Energy Downward Into Your Own vital Region.

Retain The Natural Life-Energy There—Perhaps Locking the
bodily base, and Even Applying A Downward Pressure In The
Region Of the throat. The inhalation Is Always A Matter Of Magni-
fying The Invocation Of Me, and A Matter Of Magnifying Recep-
tion Of The Natural Life-Energy (and, In The Case Of My By-Me-
Transcendentally-Spiritually-Awakened Devotees, The "Locating"
Of My Divine Transcendental Spiritual Energy), and (Thus and
Thereby) Filling The bodily "Battery", and the body Altogether,
Including the hands.

As You inhale, Concentrate and Focus The Natural Life-Energy As Love and As The Affirmation and The Visualization Of All Desired Changes.

During the inhalation, You May Either Raise Your hands To Me In The Gesture Of Invocation and Beholding or (Otherwise) Place the open palms Near the area To Be Served On the individual (Without Actually Touching his or her body).

The Reason Why, During The inhalation Cycle, the hands Are Not Brought Into physical Contact With the body of the individual Being Served Is In Order To Avoid Taking On Negative conditions From the individual Being Served.

During Exhalation, Let The Healing-Force Pervade the areas To Be Healed

During exhalation, the hands Can Touch Either the physical body Or (Otherwise) Simply the etheric body (which Extends a few inches Beyond The Surface Of the physical body) at the area To Be Healed.

During exhalation, Let The Accumulated Living Healing-Force Pervade the areas To Be Healed, and Continue To Relax the Whole body (Thus Establishing Right Polarization Of the body), and To Engage The Process Of Heart-Radiating (In The Constant Disposition Of Whole bodily Turning To Me) and Of Affirming Right, Appropriate, and Positive Healing. (In Addition, exhalation May Be Accompanied By A Light Upward Tensing Of the bodily base.)

As the exhalation Nears Completion, Withdraw the hands From the body of the individual, and Shake Your hands Toward the ground, or Into space, With the wrists and fingers limp, and With The Feeling That all Negative energies or conditions that Have Come Into the hands From the person Being Treated Are Being Shaken Off and Naturally Released Into The Domain Of Cosmic Nature.

Repeat The inhalation-exhalation Process Until There Is A Feeling-Sense That The Healing Cycle Is Complete.

I Am The Power That Heals

I Am The Power That Heals and Blesses My Devotee. By Virtue Of Devotional Communion With Me, My Devotee who Is Rightly Administering The Laying On Of Hands Is Conformed To Me and (Thus and Thereby) Is Able To Function As A Conduit For My Divinely Avatarically Self-Transmitted Healing-Power.

Release All Negative Conditions

At The End Of Any Period Of The Laying On Of Hands, audibly Invoke Me By Name, and inhale and exhale The Natural Life-Energy Via Several Cycles Of the breath, With The Feeling That all Negative conditions that Have (In Any Manner) Become Associated With Your Own body-mind-complex During The Laying On Of Hands Are Being Completely Released Through exhalation (Via the entire body-mind-complex).

It May Also Be Useful To Hold Your hands Under running water In Order To Wash them and Complete The Cycle Of Releasing any Negative energies (and Also For Basic Hygiene, If the person Receiving The Laying On Of Hands is ill).

Alternatively, You May Take a shower or a walk, Releasing any energies that Were Accumulated Via the hands During The Laying On Of Hands.

When, How, and With Whom To Engage
The Laying On Of Hands

The Cycle Of The Laying On Of Hands May Be Engaged any number of times, For As long a period As Desired, and As Often As Desired.

The Laying On Of Hands Should Be Practiced As A Form Of "Conscious Exercise" and As A Form Of The Devotional Prayer Of Changes.

In General, The Laying On Of Hands Should Not Be Performed Casually—That Is To Say, With people For whom one Feels No Real Sympathy, or With people who Have Made No

Feeling-Response To My Divine Avataric Reality-Teaching, or To The Only-By-Me Revealed and Given "Radical" Reality-Way Of The Heart Altogether, or To My Avatarically Self-Revealed Divine Person. The Laying On Of Hands Is Most Effective When Performed By My Devotees In Relation To one another. However, The Laying On Of Hands May Also Be Engaged By My Devotee In Relation To anyone With whom My Devotee Feels True Sympathy and who Is Also (himself or herself) Positively Disposed To Receive This Form Of Healing Practice From Me Via My Devotee. ■

CHAPTER 7

Yogic "Conductivity" Massage

*M*assage is not merely a matter of getting the muscles to relax *so that you feel better. Of course, that is a dimension of the purpose of massage. However, the form of massage that I Recommend is a systematic approach, which is important for the sake of constantly regenerating the flows of energy in the body. Such massage is a principal aspect of basic well-being.*

—Avatar Adi Da Samraj
May 28, 1997

Massage is an ancient healing modality, practiced in many cultures for its benefits to human well-being. The technical forms and purposes of massage vary widely across traditions, ranging from those intended to simply relax the physical body to those that stimulate and circulate subtle energies. Some traditions of massage are based in an esoteric understanding of the human structure and work with the underlying energy circuitry in a Yogic manner.

Avatar Adi Da developed Yogic "conductivity" massage to specifically work with the Circle of the body-mind-complex, the path of natural life-energy (and His Transcendental Spiritual Energy) in the human form. In addition, He introduces the devotional basis of the practice, which makes it a unique form of massage attuned to the ego-transcending process embraced by His devotees.

Thus, Yogic "conductivity" massage is a uniquely oriented but straightforward form of healing touch that directly supports energy flows and balance in the yellow-red conjunction. Through "conductivity"-Communion with Avatar Adi Da Samraj, and full feeling-participation in the universal field of natural life-energy, energy flows are magnified in the Circle of the body-mind-complex, in both the person giving the massage and the person receiving the massage. Yogic "conductivity" massage thus serves the bodily well-being of both participants.

Massage in the Traditions

As food is a necessity for the organism from birth to death, so is massage to the human organism. Food provides nourishment from external sources to the organism, whereas massage excites the internal resources and provides nourishment in the form of proteins, glucose, and other vitalizing chemicals which are within the system. Massage, like a mother, preserves the body energy and saves the organism from decay. It also works as a cleanser and helps the organism in discharging toxins out of the body through sweat, urine and mucous, thus rejuvenating the body.

—From *Ancient Indian Massage*, by Harish Johari*

Perfectly masseed [sic], one feels completely regenerated, a feeling of extreme comfort pervades the whole system, the chest expands, and we breathe with pleasure; the blood circulates with ease, and we have a sensation as if freed from an enormous load; we experience a suppleness and lightness till then unknown. It seems as if we truly lived for the first time. There is a lively feeling of existence which radiates to the extremities of the body, whilst the whole is given over to the most delightful sensations.

—From *The History of Massage*, quoting Claude-Étienne Savary[†]

---

* *Ancient Indian Massage*, by Harish Johari (Delhi: Munshiram Manoharlal, 1984), vii.

† *The History of Massage: An Illustrated Survey from Around the World*, by Robert Noah Calvert (Rochester, VT: Healing Arts Press, 2002), 33. Savary, a Frenchman, is describing his experience receiving massage in Egypt in 1785.

Chinese massage is commonly called Qigong massage, because it is based on affecting the energetic (Qi) system, as well as the circulatory systems of blood and lymph. (. . . Chinese medicine holds that imbalances or blockages in the Qi circulation system are the root of the body's illnesses.) Therefore, in order to effectively use massage to help the patient recover from sickness, the physician must study Qi, understand the Qi circulatory system in the body, train their own Qi, and learn how to use their Qi while massaging in order to help the patient to regain Qi balance. Massage is classified as one of the major fields of Qigong in China, and requires a long period of concentrated study. You can see that Chinese Qigong massage was developed for healing, rather than just relaxation and enjoyment.

—From *Chinese Qigong Massage,* by Dr. Jwin-Ming Yang*

"Aches and pains" and especially a general "tiredness" can also call for a massage. The healing massage involves forceful manipulation of large areas of the body, concentrating on the shoulders, back, and stomach. The massagers rub their sweat onto the one being healed and periodically shake their hands off into space, expelling the patient's sickness. . . . As the healer Kana puts it: "We massage each other to get out the sickness. We also massage to make a person ready for the healing num."

—From *Boiling Energy,* by Richard Katz[†]

---

* *Chinese Qigong Massage: General Massage,* by Dr. Jwin-Ming Yang (Jamaica Plain, MA: Yang's Martial Arts Association, 1992), 5.

† *Boiling Energy: Community Healing among the Kalahari Kung,* by Richard Katz (Cambridge, MA: Harvard University Press, 1982), 51–52. The Kung are a Kalahari desert tribe from southern Africa; "num" is their word for spiritual energy.

How to Practice
Yogic "Conductivity" Massage—
A Summary

W*hile Engaged In This Practice (Of Yogic "Con-ductivity" Massage), My Devotees Participate, Whole bodily, In Devotional "Conductivity"-Communion With Me, and (Thus) My Devotees Demonstrate Right "Conductivity" Of Natural Life-Energy (and, As The Case May Be, Of My Avatarically Self-Transmitted Divine Transcendental Spiritual Energy), In A Cycle Of Energy That Moves Up the back (In The Spinal Line) and Down the front (In The Frontal Line).*

—Avatar Adi Da Samraj
The Dawn Horse Testament

The following is a summary of Avatar Adi Da's instructions on Yogic "conductivity" massage, drawn principally from *The Dawn Horse Testament*. It is offered as an orientation to the expanded discussion of the practice presented in this chapter.

When learning and applying the practice of Yogic "conductivity" massage, it is important to follow Avatar Adi Da's detailed instructions, as given in His direct Word (throughout this chapter, and in other sources). Once you have adapted to the practice based on Avatar Adi Da's detailed instruction, you can use the summary below as a guide to ongoing practice of Yogic "conductivity" massage (while also always refreshing your understanding of the practice through study of Avatar Adi Da's Word).

Note: Avatar Adi Da does not prescribe a specific set of physical manipulations, strokes, or techniques for Yogic "conductivity" massage, but simply describes the mode of touch as "feeling-breathing-massaging". Therefore, a wide range of energy-sensitive physical manipulations, strokes, or techniques can be used in the massage. The one performing the massage should take into account the recipient's bodily state and needs, as well as his or her own level of expertise. (See also pp. 273–79.)

For Both Participants in Yogic "Conductivity" Massage

• Throughout the occasion, enter into whole bodily Communion with Avatar Adi Da.

• Intensively practice "conductivity" of energy in the Circle, up the back and down the front.

• Steadily practice this specific form of Yogic "conductivity" breathing:

> With deep, relaxing feeling, engage inhalation and exhalation with the intention to move the breath and energy in the Circle of the body-mind-complex, by alternating between
>
> • inhaling <u>and</u> exhaling upward in the spinal line and
>
> • inhaling <u>and</u> exhaling downward in the frontal line.

For the One Performing Yogic "Conductivity" Massage

• Prepare the environment for the occasion and wear loose, comfortable clothing. (In appropriately intimate and/or body-tolerant contexts, you may also choose to be unclothed.)

• Have the recipient lie down on a table or bed, and stand or kneel to the side of the recipient.

(continued on next page)

• Take into account the degree of polarity and the level of intimacy with the recipient, ensuring appropriate and comfortable touch-contact for both participants.

• Using energy-sensitive touch, follow the pattern of the Circle, by moving up the back of the body and then down the front of the body.

    ♦ First intend and move the energy upward, via feeling-breathing-massaging of the back of the body upward: from the feet and legs, to the buttocks and hips, then the lower, middle, and upper back, to the shoulders, neck, and base of the head.

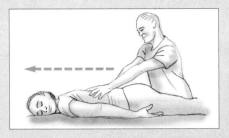

    ♦ Then, intend and move the energy downward, via feeling-breathing-massaging of the front of the body downward: from the head and face (below the brows), down to the neck, shoulders, and arms, chest, abdomen, hips, thighs, legs, and feet.

• Periodically shake your hands in rapid feeling-exhaling-releasing gestures away from the recipient's body, in order to shake away negative energies and patterns in the flow of energy, and to move trapped energy.

• Do not massage the recipient's head above the brows (in other words, above the forehead).

• Include erogenous zones in the massage, using the non-touch approach or, in appropriate circumstances (such as between committed sexual intimates), with direct (and sensitive) touch.

• At the end of the massage, shake your hands toward the ground in a feeling-exhaling-releasing gesture of "throwing off" any negative energies and patterns that may have been contacted during the massage.

For the One Receiving Yogic "Conductivity" Massage

• You may be unclothed or wearing loose clothing.

• Receive the massage in a relaxed and receptive (and passive) manner.*

• If there are signs of arousal of sexual energy during the massage, simply feel and breathe the energy in the circuit of the body or use the specific breath pattern Avatar Adi Da indicates.

• If there are signs of spontaneous reveries of any kind, simply allow these to arise and pass.

• Persist in this searchless disposition, until the occasion becomes calm and stress-free, and generally free of contents.

---

* Under specific circumstances, some occasions of Yogic "conductivity" massage might include mutual responsiveness and exchange. See pp. 251–52.

A Yogic Practice of Conducting Energy

While the laying on of hands is primarily a form of the Devotional Prayer of Changes, Yogic "conductivity" massage is, as its name indicates, primarily a form of "conductivity" practice—assisted through physical touch of the recipient's body.

The By-Me-Given Practice Of Yogic "Conductivity" Massage Is An Energy-"Conductivity" Practice Of Whole bodily "Touch". . . .

By Right Practice Of Yogic "Conductivity" Massage, The Yogic (or Altogether Right) Energy-"Conductivity" Of the Whole and Total body of the recipient (and, Coincidently, but Secondarily, the Whole and Total body of the Administering-individual) Is—By A Natural Means That Simply Uses, Supports, and Is Supported By The Energy-Pattern That Is Always Already An Inherent Characteristic Of the Natural physical body—Systematically Re-Asserted, Regenerated, and Kept Right.

—Avatar Adi Da Samraj
The Dawn Horse Testament

"Conductivity" in the Circle of the Body-Mind-Complex

Yogic "conductivity" massage is founded in the body's inherent circuitry. It simply works in the Circle, loosening knots of contraction and magnifying natural life-energy in the yellow-red conjunction. Thereby, Yogic "conductivity" massage supports the self-correcting system, allowing the body-mind-complex to heal itself, or to otherwise maintain its natural state of well-being and equanimity.

Yogic "conductivity" massage should properly follow the body-circuit and the movement of the body's energy. In other words, the form of the massage should be up the back, from the feet to the head [but not touching the top of the head[1]], and then bringing the energy

---

1. See pp. 257–61 for Avatar Adi Da's instructions about why one should not touch the top of another person's head.

244

down the frontal line through the face and ending with the feet. This is a way of massaging the body, working with the musculature, that also works the natural energy-circuit of the body—up the back to the head, and down the front, starting with the face, all the way to the feet.

—Avatar Adi Da Samraj
November 13, 1996

Yogic *"conductivity" massage is integral to the maintenance of my physical and mental health. About four years ago I began suffering from chronic anxiety. This condition is characterized by a hyper-awareness of the fragility and inherent vulnerability of the physical body, and this induces a fight-or-flight response within it. My heart rate increases, my breathing gets rapid and shallow, and my mind begins to race. The effects of these symptoms can range from low-grade discomfort to full-blown panic attack. Due to their side effects, I have avoided the medications available to treat this condition, and have instead relied upon my practice of the Reality-Way of Adidam. The turning of my faculties to Avatar Adi Da during meditation and throughout daily life is the primary means for establishing equanimity, but, secondarily, Yogic "conductivity" massage has proven to be hugely beneficial. Avatar Adi Da has indicated that the natural energies in the body travel in a circular motion, down the front to the bodily base and up the back. The anxiety tends to reverse this flow and break the circuit, shooting the energies up my frontal line and out of the top of my head, leaving behind a wake of agitated thoughts. Yogic "conductivity" massage reestablishes the natural flow of the bodily energies; my mind is instantly quieted and the impulse to flee the body-mind is quelled. When the massage is finished, I feel a deep and easeful pleasure throughout my entire body, and my attention is freed up and available for the practice given by my Guru.*

—Devotee of Avatar Adi Da Samraj

As with the general "conductivity" practice, the radiant heart-disposition in response to Avatar Adi Da's Living Divine Presence is the foundation for magnifying the flow of natural life-energy in the Circle during any occasion of Yogic "conductivity" massage.

The heart-process is the primary action in Yogic "conductivity" massage. The circuit of the massage is simply relative to "conductivity", the Circle. The origin of the process and the disposition of the process of Yogic "conductivity" massage is at the heart in devotional Communion with Me. The heart is also an area associated with the emotional disposition, bodily registered. Therefore, the heart is an area to be opened through Invocation and Communion with Me, not only by the one performing Yogic "conductivity" massage, but by the person who is receiving the massage.

—Avatar Adi Da Samraj
May 5, 1996

From this disposition of heart-radiance, the natural circuit of the body-mind-complex can be served in a simple and straightforward manner. The one giving the massage knows that the polarized circuit is inherent to the body-mind-complex—and that the body-mind-complex is continuous with the infinite and universal field of life-energy, and inhering in the Divine Reality Prior to all conditions. In other words, the "faith presumption" is brought directly to Yogic "conductivity" massage.

In healing work, you presume wholeness. You simply Invoke Me—entered into real Communion with Me, as you presumably do in your daily practice—and, in that Communion, you relate to the body of the person receiving the healing treatment as being whole, in Communion with Me. The recipient of the healing treatment should be doing the same. That is why this is basically a practice to be done between individuals who are My devotees, so that both the one giving and the one receiving the healing can participate. First of all, healing work is a matter of just that—presuming wholeness and enabling the person to relax—and then being able to serve the person's "conductivity" of energy.

Polarity is a matter of positives and negatives, opposite sides—all that sort of thing. Polarity "techniques" are about that. But, previous

246

to that, there is Invocation of Me, Communion with Me, "conductivity" practice, the disposition of the Devotional Prayer of Changes. That is first. And then you see the body as a whole and relate to the key energy structures. You can see the body as a circuit—descending from above, going through the bodily base, even down to the toes, and ascending through the bodily base and up the spinal line again.

—Avatar Adi Da Samraj
May 5, 1996

Mutual Participation and Polarity

Avatar Adi Da describes Yogic "conductivity" massage as a formal service one individual performs for another. As such, the one administering the massage is active in a specific manner, and the one receiving the massage is passively receptive.[2] However, both participants enjoy the healing effects of the occasion.

It Is Always The bodily Health and The bodily Well-being Of Both Participants—and, As A General Rule, Specifically the (In any moment) recipient Of The Direct Intentional Massage—That Is Being Addressed In Any Specific Occasion Of Right Yogic "Conductivity" Massage.

That Is To Say, Even Though It Is the (In any moment) recipient Of Yogic "Conductivity" Massage whose bodily Health and bodily Well-being Is Being Specifically, Directly, Actively, and Intentionally Served, The Entire Context and Occasion Of Right "Conductivity" Massage Practice Must (Itself) Be Entirely bodily-Health-Positive and bodily-Well-being-Positive For Both Participants (Even If and When Only the Administering-individual Is Active, While the recipient Remains Entirely Passive).

—Avatar Adi Da Samraj
The Dawn Horse Testament

Although there are outwardly "active" and "passive" roles in an occasion of Yogic "conductivity" massage, Avatar Adi Da calls both individuals to be fully participant in the massage.

2. See pp. 251–52 for Avatar Adi Da's instructions on when mutual massage is appropriate and useful.

Yogic "conductivity" massage is not something that is merely done in a formalistic, professional manner by a masseuse on a "passive patient". That is simply the model of conventional professional patient-doctor relationships. That has nothing to do with Yogic "conductivity" massage.

Both participants in Yogic "conductivity" massage are to be fully involved in the "conductivity" process. The manner in which they practice depends on the factors that have to do with "touch"-sensitivity, energy-sensitivity, and the nature of their relationship otherwise. But the process requires "conductivity"-participation by both participants.

Massage is typically thought of as being strictly about a recipient who is supposed to be completely passive, just receiving a treatment. Yogic "conductivity" massage is not a treatment. It is an exercise—not only in touch, but in relationship. It is a mutual participation. It is a practice in relationship, and in the context of a body-positive understanding of life. Those are fundamentals of the practice of Yogic "conductivity" massage.

People who administer Yogic "conductivity" massage must understand they are to be fully engaged in the energy process. That is part of their responsibility. It is full participation, not merely professional detachment. Dissociation is built in to the so-called "doctor-patient relationship" in the Western style. This is because the Western notion of science is about dissociation, not participation. It is detachment and control. The notion is to "objectify" the other.

That is not Adidam. Adidam is participatory. It is not about dissociative introversion. On the other hand, it is about the transcending of egoity at its "root" and transcending ego-based patterning. Therefore, all of that brought together is the context of the practice of Adidam, including Yogic "conductivity" massage.

—Avatar Adi Da Samraj
October 23, 2008

Because of the energies exchanged between participants during Yogic "conductivity" massage, it is important to sensitively consider with whom you practice it.

You must understand that you can only have certain people work on certain people. You must be very sensitive to who works with whom. If you understand that when you do healing work with people it is not just a superficial "technique", that there is actually a transfer of energies and psychic content and everything altogether, then you understand that you must be very sensitive to all of that.

And you must be rightly prepared and in a right disposition to be able to do the massage and be very aware of what you are doing with the person that you are working with and of what his or her particular sensitivities are, because you become involved with the person you are working on.

Traditionally, massage has actually been done by family members, such that it is only an intimate circle of people that you work on, and you do not really have casual, arbitrary contacts with people just coming in and working on you—because it is a very intimate matter, and it is also a matter of energy.

Therefore, if you are selecting someone to massage you, you must have sensitivity and choose someone who will function rightly in relationship to your own body, and also in the moment and altogether. A particular person may be fine working on you in one moment, and then in another moment that same person just does not work at all. So you must begin to be sensitized to such matters as well.

—Avatar Adi Da Samraj
July 1, 1996

Specifically, Avatar Adi Da says that a positive feeling-disposition must exist between the participants in Yogic "conductivity" massage. Such a disposition allows the participants to enter freely into the domain of feeling, thereby magnifying "conductivity" and invocation of Avatar Adi Da. In particular, the one performing Yogic "conductivity" massage should be clear in his or her emotional disposition toward the recipient.

The one performing Yogic "conductivity" massage should be in balance, or certainly in a good disposition and state, rightly practicing devotional Communion with Me. The one performing the massage simply brings the devotional practice, moment to moment—Invoking

Me, feeling Me, breathing Me, and being there to serve Me. Thus, altogether, it is done in My Sphere, and it is done with sensitivity to the energy-evidence of the person you are relating to, for the sake of his or her well-being.

The attitude (or disposition) of heart-feeling is essential to create "Pleasure Dome"³—or to generate and take care of all the factors that are present there (including the human factors), such that it is a place of good feeling and physical comfort. Obviously, relaxation is required, along with the heart-disposition—these are two funda-mental requirements for healing work.

The positive, or flowering, or radiant disposition, the loving disposition, is quite natural to a person in that state serving another. That radiant disposition makes it workable—it is essential.

If all this right practice and this sensibility exists, performing Yogic "conductivity" massage is simply a matter of using your own disposition of attention and "conductivity" to serve the right polar-ization and flow of energy in the Circle of the recipient's body.

—Avatar Adi Da Samraj
May 6, 1996

It is beneficial to the Yogic process of the massage if the partic-ipants have opposite energetic qualities. Such opposite qualities— which can be called "yin" and "yang", "femaleness" and "male-ness", or "ingoing" and "outgoing"—create greater flow of energy between the participants, and thereby assist in the magnification of energy flow in the recipient.⁴

Optimally, Yogic "Conductivity" Massage Is To Be Practiced By My Devotees who Naturally Manifest A Polarity Of bodily Life-Energy Opposite *To one another. This Is Because A Positive "Conductivity"-Exchange (or Transfer) Of Energy (Between Opposite Poles Of Energy, and, Especially From the individual who*

3. The "Pleasure Dome" is a term Avatar Adi Da adopted from the poem *Kubla Khan* by Samuel Taylor Coleridge. Avatar Adi Da uses this term to indicate the fullness and pleasurably participatory nature of the sacred domain of the Reality-Way of Adidam. See chapter 4, pp. 146–48, for more about the sacred domain.

4. For Avatar Adi Da's essential *Dawn Horse Testament* instruction on the manifestation of these opposite qualities in the human being, and the universal Unity and Divine Singleness to which every body-mind-complex belongs, see pp. 217–18 in *Always Enact Fidelity To Me.*

Is Administering The Massage To the individual who Is Receiving The Massage) Is Fundamental To The Yogic Rightness and Effectiveness Of Yogic "Conductivity" Massage.

—Avatar Adi Da Samraj
The Dawn Horse Testament

Avatar Adi Da also points out, however, that the energetic polarity necessary for right Yogic "conductivity" massage is contained within the body of the recipient. These opposite energetic qualities within any (and every) individual are the same qualities that may express themselves between two individuals, and which are activated through the protocol of the massage.

The Practice Of Yogic "Conductivity" Massage Should Always Engage The Intrinsic Bi-Polarity Of the recipient's bodily Life-Energy "Conductivity"—First (and In The "Yin", or Negatively Polarized, or "Feminine", or Ingoing Energy-Mode) Up the back of the body and, Then (and In The "Yang", or Positively Polarized, or "Masculine", or Outgoing Energy-Mode), Down the front of the body.

—Avatar Adi Da Samraj
The Dawn Horse Testament

And, regardless of whether or not there is a strong polarization of energy between the participants, Avatar Adi Da emphasizes:

In Any Case, Yogic "Conductivity" Massage Should Always Be Administered In A Context Of Positive Relatedness and Genuine "Touch"-Sensitivity and Energy-Sensitivity, Wherein Whole bodily "Touch"-Contact Is Both Appropriate and Comfortable To Both Participants.

—Avatar Adi Da Samraj
The Dawn Horse Testament

How the massage is performed depends on the level of intimacy between the participants. Avatar Adi Da describes that, when practiced by individuals who are in a sexually intimate relationship, some occasions of Yogic "conductivity" massage could become "mutually responsive"—instead of being confined to the specific roles of "giver" and "receiver".[5]

In Cases Of Appropriately Intimate (and Uniquely "Touch"-Sensitive and Energy-Sensitive) Association Between The Participants, A Mutually Responsive (and Even Limitlessly Free) physical Interplay Between The Participants May (At Least On Some Occasions) Be Both Appropriate and (In Terms Of Yogic "Conductivity" Itself) Useful.

—Avatar Adi Da Samraj
The Dawn Horse Testament

Touch-Sensitivity and Energy-Sensitivity

As Avatar Adi Da indicates, the person giving a Yogic "conductivity" massage must be sensitive to the impact of his or her touch on another's body and have a basic understanding of the relationship between the physical and the etheric bodies. That person should keep focused on the point of contact with the recipient and pay attention to what level of touch is appropriate and effective.

Yogic "conductivity" massage is not just muscle massage, as I Say in The Dawn Horse Testament. *It is an energy process, and you work the musculature to the degree that is useful relative to the energy-"conductivity" process. A person who has energy-sensitivity or strong "conductivity" can serve the working of the energies in whomever the individual is serving.*

This working of the energies is generally done immediately in the laying on of hands situation. Generally speaking, that is also how it should be done in Yogic "conductivity" massage. People have different degrees of such sensitivity and ability, but it is essentially just that—working the energy in someone physically for the purpose of physical health and well-being.

—Avatar Adi Da Samraj
July 30, 2008

5. See also pp. 265–66 below, clarifying the purposes of Yogic "conductivity" massage relative to conventional sexual motives.

❖ ❖ ❖

Massage is a kind of laying on of hands. You can just manipulate a person's muscles, or you can do it with a feeling-understanding of the life-process in that body and act as a transmitter and conductor of energy in your sensitive approach to the other person.

—Avatar Adi Da Samraj
March 8, 1980

❖ ❖ ❖

Just the grabbing of the muscles can feel good if the muscles are aching—but, beyond that good feeling, not enough is being served by such an approach. In Yogic "conductivity" massage, there must be some basic understanding of the energy-mechanism involved in healing touch and what it is that you are there to serve by (effectively) laying hands on some body—it is called "massage", but it is a laying on of hands. And laying on of hands—done very lightly or (otherwise) very firmly (as it is generally done in massage)—is about working the flows, the physical flows with the energy flows, and (necessarily) the emotional connection of the flows, in the body-mind circuit, front and back.

—Avatar Adi Da Samraj
May 28, 1997

Optimally, the person administering Yogic "conductivity" massage is sensitive to etheric energy. Some individuals are naturally and uniquely sensitive to etheric and other subtle energies, and therefore can be particularly effective at Yogic "conductivity" massage (as well as other forms of energy healing). Avatar Adi Da recommends receiving Yogic "conductivity" massage from such individuals whenever possible. Avatar Adi Da further indicates that such individuals may experience visualizations and feeling-signs associated with the yellow-red fields (or other energy dimensions) of the person he or she is working with.

Direct sensitivity to the etheric can show itself differently in each individual. Some have a visual sense of energy flows in the body, seeing colors, streams of energy, dark areas or light areas, and so on. Sometimes people hear things that are related to the etheric. But, generally speaking, a visual sense of the etheric is typical in cases of such sensitivity.

If there is this kind of sensitivity to the etheric, this sensibility, and it is consistent, then the individual can approach healing in the manner that I am Communicating to you—Invocation of Me, continuous practice of devotional Communion with Me, breathing Me—and (then) allowing such energy-sensibility to be the context of the healing work.

—Avatar Adi Da Samraj
May 6, 1996

❖ ❖ ❖

In The Case Of some individuals, Energy-Sensitivity May Become Spontaneously Accompanied By Energy-Visualization. The Energy-Field Closest To the physical body Corresponds To The Outermost Field-Colors Of The Cosmic Mandala. Thus, The Energy-Field Most Directly Specific To Yogic "Conductivity" Massage Is Of A Radiant Yellow-Red Hue (or A Flame-Like Color-Pattern, Suffused With The Colors Of Yellow, Orange, and Red). If any individual (recipient or Administering-server) Spontaneously (Without Seeking) Sees The Energy-Field Of the body In Such Colors (or, Indeed, Any Color At All, and Especially Either Blue or White), or (Either Simultaneously Or Otherwise) Sees or Feels The Energy-Field Of the body As A body-Surrounding Sphere or Great Oval, he or she Should, Of Course, Freely Participate In Yogic "Conductivity" Massage By "Exercising" The Feeling-Breathing Process In Conjunction With Such Spontaneous Visualizations and Feeling-Signs.

—Avatar Adi Da Samraj
The Dawn Horse Testament

Yogic "conductivity" massage can still be effective and beneficial even if the one giving the massage does not have a well-developed sensitivity to etheric energy (or other subtler energies). As long as there is participation in the universal field of natural life-energy via breathing and feeling, it is still possible to magnify healing life-energy in the yellow-red conjunction.

Whatever other perceptions may be involved (visual, and so forth), the principal perception is touch—the feel of energy, the sense of energy as you regard (or, otherwise, touch or move your hands around in) someone's etheric field.

—Avatar Adi Da Samraj
May 5, 1996

Regardless of the level of sensitivity, Avatar Adi Da clarifies that it is not energy-sensitivity in and of itself that makes Yogic "conductivity" massage effective.

Some people demonstrate an obvious sensitivity to etheric energy. However, in and of itself, such sensitivity has nothing to do with devotion to Me or with the process of fullest healing that I am Describing. Such energy-sensitivity can enable such people to do some kind of effective healing work. If a healer works on the physical body, some effective healing can be done, if the healer has "knowledge" of the body and how it works. The same with working on the etheric level— it can be done in a very secular fashion, just as something in and of itself as a healing profession.

I am not talking about that. I am Talking about something expanded beyond even that kind of potential etheric sensitivity that people might have under any circumstances. I am Talking about bringing that sensitivity fully into My Sphere, practicing healing in the context of Communion with Me—not merely as a "self"-based "technique", a mind-"technique", and so on, but as actual devotional Communion with Me. That requires people who are really My devotees, who know the practice of whole bodily turning to Me, who know what it is to Invoke Me, what it is to Commune with Me—and, therefore, know the difference between healing done in Communion with Me and etheric-energy-sensitivity just by itself.

—Avatar Adi Da Samraj
May 6, 1996

Elements of the Practice of Yogic "Conductivity" Massage

The following subsections present Avatar Adi Da's instruction about the fundamentals of Yogic "conductivity" massage more fully.

Feeling-Breathing-Massaging

Avatar Adi Da describes the form of touch engaged in Yogic "conductivity" massage as "feeling-breathing-massaging". The exact type of physical manipulations are secondary to this "conductivity" disposition in relation to the recipient's body.

By practicing "conductivity" in his or her own body and by intending the movement of energy in the recipient's body—through feeling, breathing, and physical touch—the one performing the massage effectively assists the release of contractions in the Circle of the recipient's body-mind-complex.

Avatar Adi Da's fundamental description of feeling-breathing-massaging is given in *The Dawn Horse Testament*:

The Energy Must, First, Through "Touch"-Manipulation Of the recipient By Means Of Yogic (and, Therefore, Also Feeling and Breathing) "Conductivity" Massage, Be Intended and Moved

> • *Upward (In The Spinal Line) Through Feeling-Breathing-Massaging Of the entire back of the body Upward (Even multiple times),*
>> *From the feet and legs Upward To the buttocks and hips, lower, middle, and upper back, shoulders, neck, and base of the head—*
> *and, Then, The Energy Is To Be Intended and Moved*

> • *Downward In The Frontal Line Of the body of the recipient Through Feeling-Breathing-Massaging Of the entire front of the body Downward (Even multiple times),*
>> *From the head and face (Below the brows) Downward To the neck, shoulders and arms, chest, abdomen, hips, thighs, legs, and feet.*

Altogether, This Is To Be Done In Such A Manner That the entire body of the recipient (and, Simultaneously, and Even Coincidently, the entire body of the Administering-individual) Is A Continuous and Unbroken Circuit (or Circle) Of Right and Optimum Energy-"Conductivity".

Do Not Touch the Top of the Head

Avatar Adi Da indicates that the top of the recipient's head should not be massaged. He explains that the top of the head is, in fact, an organ of feeling-sensitivity to what is beyond gross (physical) existence.

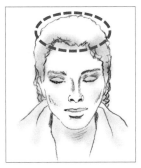

As A General Rule, Yogic "Conductivity" Massage-Practice Should Not Involve Massage Of the recipient Above the brows To the top of the head, Either In Relation To The Spinal Line Or In Relation To The Frontal Line. . . .

The "Conductivity" Of This Area Of the body Can Be Interrupted or Even Reversed By Massage Practice (or By Casual physical Exchanges In General)—and, Therefore, the upper portion of the head (Above the brows) Should, As A General Rule, Not Be "Touched" By others, and (Thus) Not Be "Touched" As Part Of The Specific Practice Of Yogic "Conductivity" Massage.

—Avatar Adi Da Samraj
The Dawn Horse Testament

Because of present-day fixation on the physical dimension of existence, there is minimal or no awareness of this important function of the top of the head.

The characteristic sense of Reality from the Western . . . perspective [is] . . . the perspective of the closed head, or the closed "fontanelle"—which "locates" the "subjective point of view" within the body-mind-complex, and the "objective environment" in the grossly apparent sphere.

—Avatar Adi Da Samraj
"Indivisible Perfect Space",
The Aletheon

However, the top of the head is the principal bodily location by which the human being becomes aware of subtle energies and Spiritual Energy. It is also the bodily location where Avatar Adi Da's descending Transcendental Spiritual and Blessing Force enters the rightly prepared human vehicle—which He describes as "an Intense Invasion of the frontal line by My Avatarically Self-Transmitted Divine Transcendental Spiritual Force of Love-Bliss—Beginning at the crown of the head, and Descending into the lower vital region, to the bodily base".[6]

In the Transcendental Spiritual practice of the Reality-Way of Adidam, in addition to the awareness of the natural energy circulating within the body, there is a constant, tangible, and bodily experience of Avatar Adi Da's Transmitted Transcendental Spiritual Presence of Energy and Love-Bliss—which Itself Reveals His State as the egoless and Indivisible Divine Reality. Avatar Adi Da's Transcendental Spiritual Energy of Love-Bliss can be felt to descend from above into the being via the crown of the head, infusing the whole being with His Love-Bliss. And, yet, there is no sense of a separate self that is "receiving" His Transmission of Love-Bliss.

—Devotee of Avatar Adi Da Samraj

---

6. From "Atma Nadi Shakti Yoga", in *The Aletheon*.

For a number of years, Ren-ai Lindley (a trained practitioner of Hawaiian Kahuna bodywork, Swedish massage, and Polarity Balancing) and Ross Keen (a doctor of osteopathy, naturopathy, and kinesiology, and founder of Spironics bodywork) had as their principal service to Avatar Adi Da the offering of healing body-work. During that time, Avatar Adi Da asked them to help develop the massage form that became Yogic "conductivity" massage.

REN-AI: *We were at the Mountain Of Attention Sanctuary in Northern California, when Beloved Adi Da directed us to a book called* Ancient Indian Massage *by Harish Johari, which is listed on His* Basket of Tolerance *bibliography. He said that we should study it, and then propose forms of massage for the Reality-Way of Adidam.*

One of the things that really struck us about the book—and this was something that Beloved Adi Da mentioned specifically—was that this massage was to be done within families: with your intimates, with children, and even children massaging their parents. It was not something you particularly paid people from outside the family to do—it was just part of everyday relationship.

The book did not present a simple "step 1, step 2, step 3" kind of format, but we extrapolated from the instructions and developed a massage sequence. Beloved Adi Da then asked us to perform the sequence on one of His renunciate devotees. She reported back to Him about the massage, and then He gave further instructions. The instruction I particularly remember was that Beloved Adi Da really wanted the massage to go in a circle, up the back of the body and down the front, because that is the energy-circuit—whereas we had followed the sequence recommended in the book, starting in the middle, with the buttocks and the legs first. That was one of the major corrections that Beloved Adi Da made to our initial proposal. At that time, Beloved Adi Da also

(continued on next page)

said that the person giving the massage should use a shaking-off of the hands to release any negative energies, and to do so always in the context of invocation of Him.

We started to further systematize the sequence, adding other forms of massage, such as elements from Swedish, Hawaiian, polarity balancing, and other modalities. We also developed a sequence for self-massage, which Beloved Adi Da was very keen on, saying that this is a practice that everyone should do for themselves, as a means of own-body responsibility. Beloved Adi Da guided the development of the sequences at the time, most graciously allowing us to try them on Him. However, later He said that Yogic "conduc-tivity" massage did not need to have any specific sequences as such: it was more a matter of what felt right to do, but always keeping that circuit, up the back and down the front. I have found this to be very important guidance from Beloved Adi Da in doing massage, as it has helped me to focus on feeling Him Self-Emerging in every body, rather than on any particular strokes or methods.

When we were developing the original sequence, we had included the Indian head massage, which, according to the book, was very forceful—you actually hit the person's head with the side of your hands, chopping, vigorously rub-bing, and so on. So we were surprised when Beloved Adi Da initially said to include that element.

ROSS: Beloved Adi Da had given us permission to try this forceful head massaging on Him, but I was definitely unsure about doing this, and it felt particularly shocking to me to be doing it on Him. Meanwhile, we were also experi-menting with it with other devotees as well.

It was not long after that that Beloved Adi Da com-municated that the massage was not to be done on the top of His head, and then later on He said not to do it on devo-tees, either, because He said the top of the head is "My Place" and "That is where I Enter."

The top of My Any Devotee's head Should, As A General Rule, Be Reserved For __My__ "Touch"—Either By Direct physical Contact Or (In Any Case) Simply By My Transcendental Spiritual Blessing-Regard—and, Otherwise, As A General Rule (Except In Instances Of Extreme bodily conditions and Extreme physical Emergencies), The Area Of the top of the head Should Not Be "Touched" By anyone Other Than oneself.

The Area Of the top of the head, From Above the brows, Is A Principal Locus Of bodily Connectedness To That Which Is Above and Beyond and Prior To the body and the mind, Both In Terms Of Natural Life-Energy and (As The Case May Be) My Divinely Avatarically Self-Transmitted Transcendental Spiritual Energy.

—Avatar Adi Da Samraj
The Dawn Horse Testament

Yogic "Conductivity" Breathing

In *The Dawn Horse Testament*, Avatar Adi Da describes a specific form of "conductivity" breathing that both participants actively, fully engage throughout an occasion of Yogic "conductivity" massage—alternating cycles of inhalation/exhalation upward in the spinal line and then downward in the frontal line.

During The Entire Occasion, Process, and Event Of Yogic "Conductivity" Massage, __Both__ Participants Should Steadily (and With Deeply Relaxing Feeling) Practice Yogic "Conductivity" Breathing.

Thus, In Random (but Relatively Frequent) moments, __Both__ Participants Should

• *Engage inhalation and exhalation __Intentionally__—and With The Specific Intention To "Move" (or inhale and Draw, and, Alternately, exhale and Release) Both the breath and The Natural Life-Energy (and, As The Case May Be, My Divinely Avatarically Self-Transmitted Transcendental Spiritual Energy)—*

and, Thus and Thereby, Alternate Between

- *inhalation/exhalation Upwards Via The Spinal Line (To The Core Of the brain, and, Ultimately, To Infinitely Above the mind and The Total Crown Of the head) and*

- *inhalation/exhalation Downwards In The Frontal Line (To the bodily base and, From there, To the feet).*

See also p. 267 below for specific instructions on breathing in relation to sexual energy.

How to Address Erogenous Zones and Sexual Energy

By Means Of The Right Practice Of Yogic "Conductivity" Massage, the physical body of (Always Especially and Specifically) the recipient Is Helped To self-Regulate and self-Maintain its Natural Integrity and Equanimity—Such That, Characteristically, There Are No Knots (or Obstructions) In The bodily Flow Of Energy, No bodily Stresses Of Energy (Frontal or Spinal), and No Trapping Of Energy, Whether In the genitals Or In any other bodily part, place, or function.

—Avatar Adi Da Samraj
The Dawn Horse Testament

Avatar Adi Da instructs that Yogic "conductivity" massage should address the total body of the recipient, in a non-puritanical manner. As Avatar Adi Da describes above, Yogic "conductivity" massage is "body-positive"—and, thus, in the practice there is no negative disposition toward or avoidance of any part of the body. The genitals are often a place in the Circle of the body-mind-complex where etheric energy is either built up or constricted. Therefore, including the genitals and other erogenous zones when serving the energy flow in the total Circle of the body is essential.

Right Practice Of Yogic "Conductivity" Massage Is Not A Matter Of puritanically Avoiding the genitals of the recipient, but Of Positive (and Appropriate)— "Touch" or Non-"Touch"—Energy-Stimulation

Of the genitals of the recipient, By Means Of Feeling-Breathing Yogic "Conductivity"-Address To and Via the genitals of the recipient, In The Context Of his or her bodily Totality.

—Avatar Adi Da Samraj
The Dawn Horse Testament

Because of people's tendency to be complicated or suppressed in relation to sexual energy, Avatar Adi Da gives very specific instruction on how to incorporate the genitals and other erogenous zones in Yogic "conductivity" massage.

How one serves the total body of the recipient depends upon the nature of the intimacy between the participants:

• **Non-Touch Approach.** In general, the recipient's genitals (and other erogenous zones) are to be included by using what Avatar Adi Da describes as a "non-touch" form of massage.

In The Non-"Touch" Alternative, the individual who Is Administering The Massage Passes his or her hands Over and Above (Rather Than physically "Touching") the genitals (and other "erogenous" areas of the body of the recipient), With An Effortless Feeling-Breathing-Intention (and A Tacit Feeling-Breathing-Observation) Of Energy Flowing Through those bodily areas (and, Altogether, Within and From the Whole bodily person of the individual who Is Administering The Yogic "Conductivity" Massage and To and Within the Whole bodily person who Is Receiving The Massage).

—Avatar Adi Da Samraj
The Dawn Horse Testament

This non-touch approach takes into account the sensitivity of the genitals, and the tendency to break the circuit of energy at that point in the body.

In Yogic "conductivity" massage, you do not touch the top of the head, and (in general) you do not touch the genitals, either. You do not touch either "end" of the body, for basically the same reason—because to do so tends to upset the balance. Therefore, in Yogic "conductivity" massage, I Instruct people not to massage the top of a person's head, and, likewise (in general), not to massage a person's genitals.

—Avatar Adi Da Samraj
April 27, 2008

• **Touch Approach.** If the participants are in a sexually active intimate relationship,[7] direct touch of the genitals and other erogenous zones can be applied as means to support whole bodily "conductivity".

If Direct "Touch"-Contact Is Appropriate, The Yogic "Conductivity" Massage Of the genitals Should, Characteristically (and As A General Rule), Be Limited To A Positively Energizing Right Address, Which Is Consistently Whole-body-Based (Rather Than genitally-Compartmented), and Which Is Energy-Conserving (and, Thus, As A General Rule, Not Purposed Toward degenerative orgasm), and Which Is Actively and Positively Both Energy-Effective genital "Touch"-Contact and (Altogether) Right True Yogic "Conductivity"-Practice.

—Avatar Adi Da Samraj
The Dawn Horse Testament

The non-puritanical and total-body principle of Yogic "conductivity" massage also applies to the practice of self-massage.[8]

Your genitals are just a part of the body, so why would they not be massaged by you yourself sometimes, if required for your well-being and equanimity? Be straightforward. Transcend your limitations and your inheritance of negativity by fully accepting right and Yogic responsibility for your total body-mind, not allowing any part of it to be taboo. Such is your business.

—Avatar Adi Da Samraj
May 1, 1995

---

7. See *Always Enact Fidelity To Me* for a description of all the forms of emotional-sexual practice in the Reality-Way of Adidam.

8. See pp. 272–73 for a description of the practice of self-massage recommended by Avatar Adi Da.

◆ ◆ ◆

For women, it is very useful for daily self-massage (or, otherwise, massage by another), to include the breasts, rather than avoiding that area of the body as if it were a "negative", somehow separate from the rest of the body. The same is true relative to the genitals, for that matter.

The whole body should be a unity. There should be no "negative" zones, no "zeros". If you mentally take energy away from any part of the body—for puritanical reasons, or for whatever reasons—you may (thereby) psychologically instigate potential disease "problems" in that area of the body. The body must be lived as a whole and treated as a whole, conducting fully all over with no "negative" zones. Some of this is a matter of personal attention to yourself, and some of it can be served by others.

—Avatar Adi Da Samraj
May 7, 1995

Although the genitals are always to be included in Yogic "conductivity" massage, Avatar Adi Da emphasizes that "Right Yogic 'Conductivity' Massage Is Not A Specifically and conventionally sex-Purposed (and, Thus, degenerative-orgasm-Intending) Practice."[9] This is the case even when the massage is engaged by individuals who are emotionally and sexually intimate. The discipline of Yogic "conductivity" massage is not intended to stimulate the impulse to sexual release in either participant.

Rather than intentionally evoking all the mental, emotional, and physical ego-patterns associated with sexual release, Yogic "conductivity" massage is intended to conserve energy for the sake of magnifying and balancing the flow of life-energy in the Circle, and to free energy and attention for devotional Communion with Avatar Adi Da.

The By-Me-Given Practice Of Yogic "Conductivity" Massage Is, Specifically, A Whole bodily Energy-Conserving Yogic "Conductivity" Massage-Practice, In Which the genitals of the recipient . . . Are Simply Part Of The Whole bodily Continuum Of Natural Life-Energy

---

9. From *The Dawn Horse Testament.*

(and, As The Case May Be, My Divinely Avatarically Self-Transmitted Transcendental Spiritual Energy) That Is Being Served By The Process Of The Massage.

—Avatar Adi Da Samraj
The Dawn Horse Testament

If signs of sexual arousal do occur during a session of Yogic "conductivity" massage, Avatar Adi Da instructs that each participant should simply take full personal responsibility for conducting the sexual energy.

Right Yogic "Conductivity" Massage . . . Is—In Principle, and Necessarily—Always A Matter Of The Constant Yogic Discipline and Exercise Of Fundamental own-body Responsibility Relative To the bodily (and Total psycho-physical) domain As A Whole, and (Therefore) Relative To the genitals In Particular, and All The Possibilities Associated With Exercises Of the sex-function, and Any and All Stimulations Of Energy Associated With the genitals and The Possibilities Associated With Exercises Of the sex-function. . . .

If, During The Process Of Yogic "Conductivity" Massage, genital Energy-Stimulation (Whether In The Course Of A genital "Touch" Or A genital Non-"Touch" Approach) Becomes Observable In the recipient To A Significant Degree (Demonstrated, In the male recipient, By Responsive bodily movements, or By One or Another Degree Of penis erection, or, In the female recipient, By Responsive bodily movements, or By vaginal secretions, and so on) It Should Always Be Immediately Understood and Used (By the recipient and By the Administering-individual) As A Positive (or Non-Problematic) Energy-Indicator Of The Process Of Right and Regenerative Yogic "Conductivity".

—Avatar Adi Da Samraj
The Dawn Horse Testament

Avatar Adi Da gives a basic admonition to feel and breathe any aroused sexual energy in the bodily circuit, inhaling down the front and exhaling up the back—with perhaps the use of light upward tensing at the bodily base to assist the turning of the energy—as in general "conductivity" practice. Additionally, Avatar Adi Da gives specific instructions in *The Dawn Horse Testament* on conducting sexual energy into the bodily "battery" in the context of Yogic "conductivity" massage:

The genital-Specific Energy Indicated In the body of the recipient (or In the body of the Administering-individual) May Be Effortlessly and Searchlessly Felt and Breathed (By Both Participants) To Flow (Even Via a single Continuous inhalation)

• *From the genitals, Down Into the bodily base,*

• *Then Upwards, Via The Spinal Line, To A Point Just Below The Level Of the navel,*

• *Then Forward and Slightly Down, In A Spiral-Like Curve, Into The bodily (or abdominal) "Battery" (Just Above the genitals)—*

• *With The Energy Thus Flowed To The bodily "Battery" Constantly Drawn Into Place, and (At Last) Retained In Place, By A Light or Rhythmic Inward-Upward Tensing Of the bodily base.*

When this is engaged, Avatar Adi Da further states (in *The Dawn Horse Testament*) that "conductivity" of the sexual energy "Will, Inevitably and Spontaneously, Regenerate and Strengthen The Vitality Of the recipient (and The Vitality Of the Administering-individual), As Well As Serve his or her General bodily Balance and Well-being".

The principle of responsibility for one's own total body-mind is applicable to anything that arises in the process of the massage, whether sexual in nature or not. Regardless of what arises, each participant is responsible for the energy integrity of his or her own body-mind, and for maintaining the devotional disposition of turning body, emotion, mind, and breath to Avatar Adi Da.

In Order That The Practice Of Yogic "Conductivity" Massage Be Truly and Consistently ego-Transcending and Right, Both The Participants In An Occasion Of Yogic "Conductivity" Massage Should Be Constantly Devotionally (and, Thus, Recognition-Responsively) Turned To Me, In Such A Manner That The psycho-physical Faculties (Of Both Participants) Are Not Contracting Upon the Habit-Patterned ego-"self", and (Instead) My Own and Very (and Intrinsically egoless and Self-Evidently Divine) State Is Directly "Located", In Constant Real Devotional (and, As The Case May Be, Transcendental Spiritual) "Conductivity"-Communion With Me.

—Avatar Adi Da Samraj
The Dawn Horse Testament

Allow Signs of Purification and Take Right Action

During an occasion of Yogic "conductivity" massage, the magnified natural life-energy in the Circle of the body-mind-complex may elicit signs of purification. Avatar Adi Da says all such signs—no matter how uncomfortable or potentially fascinating—should simply be observed, allowed, and released in the context of depthful turning of mind, emotion, body, and breath to Him.

The flow of "conductivity" does not merely affect the physical. It affects the psycho-physical dimension altogether, sometimes creating purifying signs and changes. Sometimes it does not feel so good at first, and then it balances again. All this is to be expected—as a possibility, anyway. Just relax and go about your business. Do not make much of it. Just let the process happen.

—Avatar Adi Da Samraj
May 5, 1996

❖ ❖ ❖

In This Process (Both During and After The Specific Occasions Of Yogic "Conductivity" Massage), the recipient (and, Perhaps, Also the Administering-individual) May "Experience" Spontaneous Deep Reveries (or the arising Of mental, emotional, and physical Memory-Patterns), Even Progressively Passing Backwards In time, "Regressing" Toward and Into An Even embryonic Stage (or, Perhaps, Even Into What Appear To Be past-lifetime Indications).

All Such Occurrences—and, Indeed, All Otherwise or Coincidently "experienced" Energy-phenomena—Should Be Tacitly Accepted, and Freely Allowed To arise and pass As They Will, and Neither Sought Nor Held On To. All Such Happenings Are Merely Modes Of The self-Adjustment (or Spontaneous and Automatic Purification, and Transformation, and Energy-Regeneration) Of The psycho-physical Patterns Associated With human embodiment.

Therefore, Let all such "experiences" (and Even all the phenomena of human "experience" Altogether) arise and (As They Inevitably Will) pass away. And Always Persist In The Searchless Right Practice I Have Revealed and Given To You (Including This Searchless Right Practice Of Yogic "Conductivity" Massage) Until The present-time Event Becomes (and, Indeed, Is) Only A Resonant Equanimity—Calm and Stress-Free, and Free Of all contents Otherwise.

—Avatar Adi Da Samraj
The Dawn Horse Testament

Some of the signs of purification reveal patterns of habitual contraction. Such patterns constrict feeling-participation in the universal field of natural life-energy and in "conductivity"-Communion with Avatar Adi Da. Thus, as with the laying on of hands, Yogic "conductivity" massage should be followed by change of action and a demonstration of right life that addresses these habitual patterns of contraction.

Massage "techniques" can have a useful function in demonstrating to you the signs of your own emotional and physical contraction for which you then must be responsible. There is no real magic in massage. You can urge the physical to relax in various ways—but, fundamentally, you must use massage as a learning "experience", rather than as a magic "technique" that saves you. It is the same with the application of diet and all the other general matters of health and of responsibility for the practices of the Reality-Way of Adidam altogether. They are not magical. They are means of intensifying your level of responsibility.

—Avatar Adi Da Samraj
1978

✦ ✦ ✦

Systems of physical manipulation, or massage, serve this above all: They interrupt your physical, emotional, and mental patterns at least temporarily, and show you that you are not relaxed, that you are "uptight", you are armoring yourself, tensing yourself, that you are emotionally obstructed and out of balance. It is the information or "self-knowledge", or the ability to be responsible for yourself, that is the primary effect of any therapy, whether applied by yourself or applied by a therapist.

Seeing your obstruction to the Self-Radiant Current of Divine Life, you can account for that obstruction in terms of how you work and act from day to day. You may have to change your attitude, your activity, your breathing, very likely your physical sensitivity. The change in your action is the cure. More than anything else, that is the healing effect—giving you a degree of sensitivity for which you can (thereafter) be responsible, throughout your life.

—Avatar Adi Da Samraj
"Massage and The Contraction of The Body-Mind-Complex",
The Eating Gorilla Comes In Peace

From the Radiant Life Clinic: Further Guidelines Based on Avatar Adi Da's Instructions

Learn the details of the practice and be accountable. Learn to practice Yogic "conductivity" massage by studying Avatar Adi Da's instructions and receiving formal training from qualified individuals, as possible. And embrace this practice in the context of the cooperative sacred culture of Avatar Adi Da's devotees, in order to support your right orientation and right adaptation to the practice.

Prepare the environment. It is important to consciously prepare the environment in which Yogic "conductivity" massage is given, in order to support bodily relaxation, heart-openness, and (thereby) a depthful feeling-participation in the occasion.

Provide an environment that supports invocation of Avatar Adi Da. His Murti-Form should be in view—and, also, any beautiful objects and elements can be included to help draw participants into depthful feeling-participation in Avatar Adi Da's Living Divine Presence. Avatar Adi Da says Yogic "conductivity" massage should be done in the "Pleasure Dome"—or an environment that invites individuals into the feeling-domain, an environment that satisfies the human need for the sacred domain of life.

In Yogic "conductivity" massage, the heart-disposition is primary. Therefore, the practice of Yogic "conductivity" massage is a devotional matter and, psycho-physically, a feeling matter altogether—a matter of becoming relaxed in the body, creating a pleasurable circumstance for the body. The creation of an environment for Yogic "conductivity" massage is an essential aspect of the practice. The environment is, essentially, like a place of sacramental worship. All the factors to create "Pleasure Dome" should be "considered" in the place itself, and in the manner of approach to the person, and your own appearance, and so forth, so that you do not add anything that can become an obstruction. The total environment and approach should serve the "Pleasure Dome" disposition and the heart-disposition. That is the first thing to establish.

—Avatar Adi Da Samraj
May 5, 1996

Receive and practice massage regularly and in different contexts. In addition to practicing Yogic "conductivity" massage with an appropriate partner, it is advantageous to receive massage in other contexts as well:

- **Professional Massage.** Avatar Adi Da recommends that, whenever possible, His devotees receive massage from individuals who are professionally trained. Optimally, this would be a devotee of Avatar Adi Da, who can therefore apply all of His principles to the massage. However, it can be beneficial to receive massage from others who are formally trained and who can therefore bring specific forms of sensitivity and knowledge to the massage.

271

• **Self-Massage.** Avatar Adi Da gives a simple practice of self-massage to be practiced on a regular basis by all His devotees.

All My devotees should understand that self-massage is a useful form of massage. You need not always go to somebody else to be massaged. You should know how to do this.

—Avatar Adi Da Samraj
May 1, 1995

There are a number of simple ways to practice self-massage. You can perform self-massage sitting, standing, or lying down—whatever affords the greatest ease during the massage:

♦ *Single area of the body.* Select a single area of the body to massage—such as the face, the hands, or the feet.

♦ *Combination of areas.* Massage several (or more) specific areas of the body. When massaging more than one area of the body, be sure to follow the direction of the Circle. For instance, if you were to massage the face, hands, and feet, you would start with the face, then massage the hands, and finish with the feet.

♦ *Down the frontal line.* Massage the whole frontal line of the body—starting with the face, moving down each arm, and then down the body to the feet (similar to how one massages another person down the frontal line). This frontal-line massage can be helpful for countering a too-upward tendency in the frontal line.

♦ *In the full circuit.* For a fuller self-massage, follow the same massage pattern as when giving Yogic "conductivity" massage to another—up the back and down the front. Massage up the back of the body as far as you can, then massage the

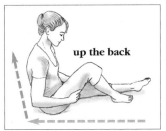

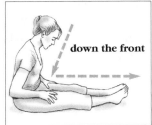

shoulders, the back of the neck, and then the back and sides of the head. Then massage down the front of the body, as described above.

In self-massage, apply the same practice principles as in Yogic "conductivity" massage with another:

• Practice "conductivity"-Communion with Avatar Adi Da during any occasion of self-massage. Relax into the universal field of life-energy, inhale-receiving natural life-energy and exhale-releasing any negative energies that arise during the massage.

• Shake the hands away from your body, both during the massage (occasionally, as needed) and afterward, to release any negative energies that may have collected in the hands.

• Generally avoid massaging the top of your head (although it is, of course, appropriate to touch the top of your own head when necessary, as when washing or brushing your hair).

• You may include the genitals, either as part of massaging down the frontal line, or as a specific area to be massaged.

• Avoid stimulating sexual release when massaging the genitals, in order to maintain bodily relaxation and retain the circuit of "conductivity". Experiment with touch or non-touch approach to one's own genitals during self-massage, if needed.

• If practicing the frontal-line massage or the full-Circle massage, lie down in the dead pose (see p. 343) afterward.

Who should practice Yogic "conductivity" massage. Avatar Adi Da gives the practice of Yogic "conductivity" massage to all of His devotees, at all levels of practice-demonstration, and whether sexually active or celibate.

Contraindications for massage. Consider whether any of the contraindications to massage listed below are the case.

• The one giving the massage is feeling unwell or low in energy or out of balance. If this is the case, the massage should not be given.

• The recipient has one or more of the following conditions:

  ◆ Thrombophlebitis in legs—big blue swollen veins with clots

  ◆ Inflammation, particularly in the joints

  ◆ Recent injury, including conditions like whiplash

  ◆ A cold or fever—although a foot rub might help bring energy down to the feet without stirring up too many toxins for the body to handle

  ◆ Some severe debilitating diseases—check with a qualified medical professional to be sure massage would be beneficial in such cases

If any of the above conditions exist for the recipient, consider using the laying on of hands as an alternative healing modality.

Learn and experiment with different strokes and physical manipulations. As indicated in the practice summary on p. 241, Avatar Adi Da does not prescribe a specific set of physical manipulations, strokes, or techniques for Yogic "conductivity" massage. Therefore, it is recommended that you learn and experiment with a variety of forms of physical touch (while always applying Avatar Adi Da's specific principles of feeling-breathing-massaging, and following the other touch-related guidelines summarized in this section). To learn and incorporate different techniques of touch, you can:

• Experiment with different hand positions and ways to apply pressure. For instance, you can begin the massage with light pressure, using the fingers only, the whole hand, or the heel of the hand—then you can move to a deeper pressure by using the thumbs, or even the elbow for very deep pressure. Always remain sensitive to the recipient's needs, including verbal and non-verbal communications about how much pressure is appropriate and positive in his or her case.

• Study other forms of massage. There are many good resources on massage practice that give detailed descriptions of touch techniques that can be adapted to the practice of Yogic "conductivity" massage. See the list of books under "Healing-Touch Practices—Massage" in appendix E for recommended resources. As you experiment with various styles of physical manipulation, you will discover what is effective and compatible with the specific practice of Yogic "conductivity" massage.

Remain sensitive to the sensations of energy. While feeling-breathing-massaging, notice the feelings and sensations of energy that arise— in your own body-mind, and in relation to the recipient's body-mind. Such sensations might include heat/cold, flow/stagnation, attraction/repulsion, numbness/pain, or "bogginess"/pulsation. Initially, this sensitivity may simply be a tacit awareness of the energy dimension of the body-mind—but it can and should be cultivated over time, through practice of Yogic "conductivity" massage (and through practice of all of the right-life disciplines Avatar Adi Da gives to His devotees).

Intend and move energy in the Circle—through surrender and participation. The more profoundly each participant lets go into the field of natural life-energy and into a depth of turning to Avatar Adi Da (and thereby surrendering into "conductivity"-Communion with Him), the more freely and fully natural life-energy will move in the Circle of the body-mind-complex. Simultaneously, you must be an active participant—exercising the heart-radiant disposition through turning to Avatar Adi Da, intentionally relaxing the frontal line, and actively engaging the "conductivity" breathing associated with Yogic "conductivity" massage (see pp. 261–62). The more proficient you become at participating Yogically in the process, and the deeper the devotional Communion with Avatar Adi Da, the more effective and easeful will be your practice of feeling-breathing-massaging the energy in the Circle.

Stay feelingly connected with the other person. If you are giving the massage, stay feelingly related to the person you are massaging. Do not let your attention drift. Be very aware of the feeling of the recipient's physical body under your fingers and do not go beyond the recipient's pain threshold. Be feelingly related to the recipient's physical body. For example, do not put cold hands or cold oil on his or her body, or bump into the person or into the massage table, or put your hands on the recipient's body too suddenly.

The recipient should also stay feelingly related to the person giving the massage—receiving in a disposition of heart-openness, and invoking Avatar Adi Da and practicing "conductivity"—rather than just passively lying there, "zoning out", or being invulnerable and dissociated.

Use a firm but sensitive touch. Keep your touch strong and focused—that is, firm and deliberate—while staying sensitive to the recipient's body. This is a very direct physical working of the muscles, their surrounding fascia, the lymph system, the circulatory system, and also the nervous system. Although Yogic "conductivity" massage need not take as long as a typical professional massage session, the strokes are not rushed. Depth of massage is very dependent on the individual, the trust between participants, and the purpose of the massage.

Do not strain your body while giving the massage. Use your body-weight instead of muscular strength, by being directly above the part of the body that you are working on (as much as is possible). Do not allow your body to get tense or strained. Be aware of how you are sitting and moving and lifting, particularly when lifting the recipient's leg. Avatar Adi Da also recommends making use of the body's own weight, when possible.

In massage, the principle of allowing the body's weight to do the work, while pulling up on the body from underneath, is a good form. That is one form that should typically be used in massage.
—Avatar Adi Da Samraj
November 13, 1996

Consider what quality to bring to the massage. Observe and notice what characteristics the recipient demonstrates. Feel the quality of the recipient's physical, emotional, and mental state, and base the massage approach on these qualities.

In a given individual, any particular dimension of the body-mind-complex may contract more profoundly than other dimensions. Thus, some people represent more of the sheerly physical level of contraction, others more the emotional-psychic dimension of it, others the mental dimension. Some are more contracted at the level of the nervous system, others at the level of the muscular structure of the body, and still others at the level of the endocrine glands. Therefore, the therapeutic approach should vary from person to person, and may be different at different times in the individual's life.

—Avatar Adi Da Samraj
"Massage and The Contraction of The Body-Mind",
The Eating Gorilla Comes In Peace

Additionally, be sensitive to the various physical conditions that might indicate alterations in the massage techniques, such as:

• Varicose veins: only stroke very lightly over these, and only in the direction of the heart. Optimally each leg is lifted up, and then the calf can be gently massaged in the direction of the heart.

• Pregnancy: modify the massage for pregnant women—be sensitive to the developing fetus and the size of the abdomen (and it may be helpful for her to lie on her side when massaged to avoid unnecessary pressure).

Remember key areas to massage and not to massage. (Avatar Adi Da's instructions on the first two points are given more fully above.)

• Do not massage the top of the head. (See pp. 257–61 for a fuller description.)

• Always include the genitals (and other erogenous zones), either with the non-touch or touch approach. (See pp. 262–64 for a full description.)

• Include the solar plexus when massaging down the frontal line.

In Yogic "conductivity" massage, it is important to massage downward through the solar plexus, pressing it in to relieve tensions and to bring the energy down into the lower body and the legs.

—Avatar Adi Da Samraj
April 27, 2008

• Massage the feet—especially the soles of the feet—regularly. Avatar Adi Da has indicated that the feet are a particularly important part of the body to massage—both during a full occasion of Yogic "conductivity" massage and in general.

It is very important to massage the feet, particularly before retiring. Even self-massage is adequate.

—Avatar Adi Da Samraj
July 1, 1996

In many ancient traditions, the foot is understood to be connected to all of the various organs and systems of the body. Additionally, massaging the feet helps to reverse the tendency for energy to go up and out of the body, by supporting the relaxation of the frontal line and movement of life-energy in the downward direction in the frontal line. Massaging the feet can also help with sleep, as it draws awareness and life-energy away from the head and overactive mental states, down into the body.

Notice where there is an energy block. Signs of such blocks include (but are not limited to): coldness, heat, tightness, dense feeling, pain, sensitivity (including ticklishness), redness, pallor, or a "boggy" (or stagnant) energy sensation or feeling to the touch. Sometimes a physical scar will cause an energy block. Sometimes an emotion will come up while you are massaging in the area of an energy block. For example, the person may feel like crying. Or he or she may have a kriya (a spontaneous, self-purifying movement of body, emotion, mind, and/or breath). Do not be concerned or feel you have to do anything particularly in relation to these signs. Silently allow such signs to arise, and continue to practice devotional turning to Avatar Adi Da Samraj.

Release negative conditions. Maintain the intention not to take on any negative energy or conditions from the recipient. This is primarily accomplished by staying in devotional Communion with Avatar Adi Da and practicing "conductivity" of natural life-energy (in which negative energies are released in association with exhalation). Additionally, in *The Dawn Horse Testament*, Avatar Adi Da indicates particular movements that are useful in this regard:

- During the massage:
  Move [the hands] In Rapid Feeling-exhaling-Releasing Gestures Over and Away From the Immediate bodily zone of the recipient

- At the end of the massage:
  Shake [the] hands In A Feeling-exhaling-Releasing "Throwing-Off" Gesture, Out and Away From his or her own body, and (Generally) Toward the floor or ground

Conclude the session with a period of rest. The recipient should rest for a while at the end of Yogic "conductivity" massage. Avatar Adi Da has emphasized how important this is to the healing process:

Essentially, after any such treatment, there should be a relaxation period, allowing integration with the treatment, for a while, before the person goes back to whatever he or she does from day to day.

—Avatar Adi Da Samraj
May 5, 1996

Release concern about any purifying after-effects. Avatar Adi Da also reminds participants in Yogic "conductivity" massage not to be concerned about any purifying effects that may occur. The practice is always searchless, in Communion with Avatar Adi Da, never about seeking for any particular contents or effects within the body-mind-complex.

Avatar Adi Da Samraj
Adi Da Samrajashram, 2008

The Practice of
Yogic "Conductivity" Massage

Instruction from The Dawn Horse Testament
by His Divine Presence,
Avatar Adi Da Samraj

Avatar Adi Da's final and complete instruction on Yogic "conductivity" massage, as given in His Dawn Horse Testament *(excerpts of which are highlighted in the preceding sections of this chapter) is presented here in full.*

Yogic "Conductivity" Massage Is
An Energy-"Conductivity" Practice

The By-Me-Given Practice Of Yogic "Conductivity" Massage Is An Energy-"Conductivity" Practice Of Whole bodily "Touch". As With All The Forms Of "self"-Discipline In The "Radical" Reality-Way Of The Heart, While Engaged In This Practice (Of Yogic "Conductivity" Massage), My Devotees Participate, Whole bodily, In Devotional "Conductivity"-Communion With Me, and (Thus) My Devotees Demonstrate Right "Conductivity" Of Natural Life-Energy (and, As The Case May Be, Of My Avatarically Self-Transmitted Divine Transcendental Spiritual Energy), In A Cycle Of Energy That Moves Up the back (In The Spinal Line) and Down the front (In The Frontal Line).

The bodily Health and Well-being
Of Both Participants Is Addressed

In The Only-By-Me Revealed and Given "Radical" Reality-Way Of The Heart, Yogic "Conductivity" Massage Is Performed By one person As A Service To another person. Nevertheless, Right Participation (Both By the recipient and By the one Administering The Massage) Is Always and Fundamentally A Matter Of Yogically Exercising The own-body Yogic Responsibility For Managing All The Results or Effects Of The Exercise.

Yogic "Conductivity" Massage Is, Characteristically, Not Engaged As A Mutual Practice Of Massage, Wherein each person Either Simultaneously Or Alternately Massages the other—Although, In Cases Of Appropriately Intimate (and Uniquely "Touch"-Sensitive and Energy-Sensitive) Association Between The Participants, A Mutually Responsive (and Even Limitlessly Free) physical Interplay Between The Participants May (At Least On Some Occasions) Be Both Appropriate and (In Terms Of Yogic "Conductivity" Itself) Useful. Therefore, As A General (but Not Absolute) Rule, Only the person Administering The Massage Is To Be (In A Formal Manner) Active, While the person Receiving The Massage Is To Be Only Passively Receptive (and, Likewise, Participating Formally).

However, In Any Case, It Is Always The bodily Health and The bodily Well-being Of Both Participants—and, As A General Rule, Specifically the (In any moment) recipient Of The Direct Intentional Massage—That Is Being Addressed In Any Specific Occasion Of Right Yogic "Conductivity" Massage. That Is To Say, Even Though It Is the (In any moment) recipient Of Yogic "Conductivity" Massage whose bodily Health and bodily Well-being Is Being Specifically, Directly, Actively, and Intentionally Served, The Entire Context and Occasion Of Right "Conductivity" Massage Practice Must (Itself) Be Entirely bodily-Health-Positive and bodily-Well-being-Positive For Both Participants (Even If and When Only the Administering-individual Is Active, While the recipient Remains Entirely Passive).

The Protocol Of The Massage—
Up the back, Down the front

Throughout The Entire Occasion, The "Conductivity" Purpose Of Yogic "Conductivity" Massage Is To Be Signalled and Served (Primarily, In the body of the recipient, and, Secondarily, In the body of the Administering-individual) By The Protocol Of The Massage Itself—Which Is (As A General Rule) To (First) Intentionally Conduct Energy Up the back of the body, and (Then) Intentionally Conduct Energy Down the front of the body (Thus, and, Altogether, In Accordance With The Total Optimum Pattern-Cycle Of Whole bodily "Conductivity").

Because The Whole bodily Flow Of "Conductivity" Of Natural bodily Life-Energy (and, As The Case May Be, My Divinely Avatarically Self-Transmitted Transcendental Spiritual Energy) Tends To Be Interrupted By ego-Based Obstructive Habit-Patterns Of body and mind, The Energy Must, First, Through "Touch"-Manipulation Of the recipient By Means Of Yogic (and, Therefore, Also Feeling and Breathing) "Conductivity" Massage, Be Intended and Moved Upward (In The Spinal Line) Through Feeling-Breathing-Massaging Of the entire back of the body Upward (Even multiple times), From the feet and legs Upward To the buttocks and hips, lower, middle, and upper back, shoulders, neck, and base of the head— and, Then, The Energy Is To Be Intended and Moved Downward In The Frontal Line Of the body of the recipient Through Feeling-Breathing-Massaging Of the entire front of the body Downward (Even multiple times), From the head and face (Below the brows) Downward To the neck, shoulders and arms, chest, abdomen, hips, thighs, legs, and feet. Altogether, This Is To Be Done In Such A Manner That the entire body of the recipient (and, Simultaneously, and Even Coincidently, the entire body of the Administering-individual) Is A Continuous and Unbroken Circuit (or Circle) Of Right and Optimum Energy-"Conductivity".

Do Not Massage the top of the head

As A General Rule, Yogic "Conductivity" Massage-Practice Should Not Involve Massage Of the recipient Above the brows To the top of the head, Either In Relation To The Spinal Line Or In Relation To The Frontal Line. The top of My Any Devotee's head Should, As A General Rule, Be Reserved For <u>My</u> "Touch"—Either By Direct physical Contact Or (In Any Case) Simply By My Transcendental Spiritual Blessing-Regard—and, Otherwise, As A General Rule (Except In Instances Of Extreme bodily conditions and Extreme physical Emergencies), The Area Of the top of the head Should Not Be "Touched" By anyone Other Than oneself. The Area Of the top of the head, From Above the brows, Is A Principal Locus Of bodily Connectedness To That Which Is Above and Beyond and Prior To the body and the mind, Both In Terms Of Natural Life-Energy and (As The Case May Be) My Divinely Avatarically Self-Transmitted Transcendental Spiritual Energy. The "Conductivity" Of This Area Of the body Can Be Interrupted or Even Reversed By Massage Practice (or By Casual physical Exchanges In General)—and, Therefore, the upper portion of the head (Above the brows) Should, As A General Rule, Not Be "Touched" By others, and (Thus) Not Be "Touched" As Part Of The Specific Practice Of Yogic "Conductivity" Massage.

Practice Yogic "Conductivity" Breathing

During The Entire Occasion, Process, and Event Of Yogic "Conductivity" Massage, <u>Both</u> Participants Should Steadily (and With Deeply Relaxing Feeling) Practice Yogic "Conductivity" Breathing. Thus, In Random (but Relatively Frequent) moments, <u>Both</u> Participants Should Engage inhalation and exhalation <u>Intentionally</u>—and With The Specific Intention To "Move" (or inhale and Draw, and, Alternately, exhale and Release) Both the breath and The Natural Life-Energy (and, As The Case May Be, My Divinely Avatarically Self-Transmitted Transcendental Spiritual Energy)—and, Thus and Thereby, Alternate Between inhalation/ exhalation Upwards Via The Spinal Line (To The Core Of the brain, and, Ultimately, To Infinitely Above the mind and The Total Crown Of the head) and inhalation/exhalation Downwards In The Frontal Line (To the bodily base and, From there, To the feet).

Yogic "Conductivity" Massage Can Be Engaged By any Of My Devotees

Yogic "Conductivity" Massage Can (If It Is Done In A Right and Appropriate Manner) Be Engaged By any Of My Devotees— Whether their Practice Is Otherwise sexually active Or celibate, and Whether they Are Congregationist Practitioners Or Lay Renunciates Or Ruchira Sannyasins,[10] and Even In The Context Of The Seventh Stage Of Life In The Only-By-Me Revealed and Given "Radical" Reality-Way Of The Heart (or "Radical" Reality-Way Of Adidam, or Adidam Ruchiradam).

Polarity Of bodily Life-Energy

Optimally, Yogic "Conductivity" Massage Is To Be Practiced By My Devotees who Naturally Manifest A Polarity Of bodily Life-Energy Opposite To one another. This Is Because A Positive "Conductivity"-Exchange (or Transfer) Of Energy (Between Opposite Poles Of Energy, and, Especially, From the individual who Is Administering The Massage To the individual who Is Receiving The Massage) Is Fundamental To The Yogic Rightness and Effectiveness Of Yogic "Conductivity" Massage. Therefore, The Optimal Circumstance For Yogic "Conductivity" Massage Is One In Which The Yogic "Conductivity" Massage Is Administered By an Appropriately Trained "Touch"-Sensitive and Energy-Sensitive individual of the opposite sex Than the recipient. Nevertheless, Potentially—and, Necessarily, In circumstances wherein There Is No individual of the opposite sex Immediately Available To Properly Administer Yogic "Conductivity" Massage—The Service Of Yogic "Conductivity" Massage May Be Offered By a Competent

10. These are technical terms related to the various practicing orders of the Reality-Way of Adidam, both renunciate and general. The three designations—Congregationist practitioners, Lay Renunciates, and Ruchira Sannyasins—represent three modes of practice that may be engaged by Avatar Adi Da's devotees who have embraced the full life of devotion to Him. (See pp. 394–95.)

individual of the same sex.[11] In Any Case, Yogic "Conductivity" Massage Should Always Be Administered In A Context Of Positive Relatedness and Genuine "Touch"-Sensitivity and Energy-Sensitivity, Wherein Whole bodily "Touch"-Contact Is Both Appropriate and Comfortable To Both Participants. Also, Even In Cases Where Yogic "Conductivity" Massage Is Engaged By individuals of the same sex, The Practice Of Yogic "Conductivity" Massage Should Always Engage The Intrinsic Bi-Polarity Of the recipient's bodily Life-Energy "Conductivity"—First (and In The "Yin", or Negatively Polarized, or "Feminine", or Ingoing Energy-Mode) Up the back of the body and, Then (and In The "Yang", or Positively Polarized, or "Masculine", or Outgoing Energy-Mode), Down the front of the body.

Optimal Environment and clothing

The Practice Of Yogic "Conductivity" Massage Is, Optimally, To Be Done In An Environment That Is Specially Prepared For Such Occasions—a Clean and Even Fragrant place, Quiet and Comfortably Ventilated, Perhaps with Relaxing music, and Non-Glaring soft-lighting. A table or a bed May Be Used, For the recipient To lie down, With the Administering-individual standing (or, Perhaps, kneeling) To the side of the recipient. The recipient May Be Either Un-clothed Or wearing loose clothing. The Administering-individual Should (Generally) Remain clothed, In loose-fitting attire—Although In Any More intimate (or, Otherwise, body-Tolerant) Context, clothing Is (Of Course) Not Necessary.

Including the genitals and other "erogenous" zones

The Practice Of Yogic "Conductivity" Massage Must, Naturally, Include the genitals—Although Not Characteristically (or Necessarily, or Even Usually) In The Form Of Direct "Touch"-Contact With the

11. In this passage, Avatar Adi Da Samraj is making a general statement about the optimal circumstance for practice based on the fact that the majority of human beings are energetically polarized as heterosexuals, and, therefore, to individuals of the opposite sex. For those who are not polarized as heterosexuals, His Instruction in this passage about the optimal form of practice can also be applied in relation to the individual's felt polarity of life-energy. (See p. 250.) And, as previously indicated, if Yogic "conductivity" massage is to be engaged in a mutually responsive manner or in the manner that includes direct touch-contact with the genitals or other erogenous zones, the individuals practicing the massage would necessarily be sexually active intimate partners.

genitals. Unless There Is A Uniquely "Touch"-Sensitive and Energy-Sensitive, and (Also) Appropriately Intimate, and (Even In That Case) Conservatively Disciplined (and, Necessarily, Formally Culturally Approved[12]) Association Between the recipient and the individual Administering The Yogic "Conductivity" Massage, the genitals of the recipient Should Always Be Addressed In The Mode Of The Non-"Touch" Alternative I Will Describe (and Not In The Mode Of Direct "Touch"-Contact).

Right Yogic "Conductivity" Massage Of the genitals—Whether In The Manner Of Direct "Touch"-Contact Or In The Non-"Touch" Manner—Is Simply A Matter Of Non-puritanically Including the genitals In Seamless Energy-Continuity With The Total "Conductivity"-Circuit Of The Intrinsic Unity Of The Whole bodily Pattern. And, Even If Direct "Touch"-Contact Is Appropriate, The Yogic "Conductivity" Massage Of the genitals Should, Characteristically (and As A General Rule), Be Limited To A Positively Energizing Right Address, Which Is Consistently Whole-body-Based (Rather Than genitally-Compartmented), and Which Is Energy-Conserving (and, Thus, As A General Rule, Not Purposed Toward degenerative orgasm), and Which Is Actively and Positively Both Energy-Effective genital "Touch"-Contact and (Altogether) Right True Yogic "Conductivity"-Practice.

In All Cases, the genitals (and other "erogenous" zones of the body of the recipient) May—and, Indeed, Unless The Necessary Unique Qualifications Have Been Demonstrated,[13] Should—Be "Included" In The Process Of The Yogic "Conductivity" Massage Simply By Means Of The Non-"Touch" Alternative. In The Non-"Touch" Alternative, the individual who Is Administering The Massage Passes his or her hands Over and Above (Rather Than

12. This is a reference to the process that Avatar Adi Da's devotees go through when choosing to enter into a committed intimate relationship. Because of the profound effect that emotional-sexual intimacies have on the integrity of practice of the Reality-Way of Adidam, Avatar Adi Da gives a formal process of cultural consideration, approval, and accountability to His devotees who choose to enter into intimate relationship, whether sexually active or celibate. This process is based on intimacy, discriminative intelligence, and mutual agreement—and is intended to support each individual's ego-transcending practice.

13. Measure of a devotee's qualifications would generally occur in the context of a formal cultural consideration (with others with whom the devotee otherwise meets regularly to discuss practice of the Reality-Way of Adidam), in which the devotee reports on his or her signs of practice.

physically "Touching") the genitals (and other "erogenous" areas of the body of the recipient), With An Effortless Feeling-Breathing-Intention (and A Tacit Feeling-Breathing-Observation) Of Energy Flowing Through those bodily areas (and, Altogether, Within and From the Whole bodily person of the individual who Is Administering The Yogic "Conductivity" Massage and To and Within the Whole bodily person who Is Receiving The Massage).

Yogic "Conductivity" Massage Is Not sex-Purposed

Right Yogic "Conductivity" Massage Is Not A Specifically and conventionally sex-Purposed (and, Thus, degenerative-orgasm-Intending) Practice. Rather, The By-Me-Given Practice Of Yogic "Conductivity" Massage Is, Specifically, A Whole bodily Energy-Conserving Yogic "Conductivity" Massage Practice, In Which the genitals of the recipient (whose Fullest Right Whole bodily "Conductivity" and General Good Health Are Always To Be Specifically and Intentionally Served In and By Means Of The Occasion Of Yogic "Conductivity" Massage) Are Simply Part Of The Whole bodily Continuum Of Natural Life-Energy (and, As The Case May Be, My Divinely Avatarically Self-Transmitted Transcendental Spiritual Energy) That Is Being Served By The Process Of The Massage.

In The Practice Of Yogic "Conductivity" Massage, Any "Touch"-Address To another With An Overt Intention To erotically Stimulate the genitals Would Also Tend (In Most Cases) To Become Associated With erotic Stimulations Of the mind. Whenever the mind Is erotically Stimulated, the Total body-mind—Apart From Fullest Whole bodily Devotional Turning Of All The psycho-physical Faculties To Me—Tends To Become Subject To Being Controlled By Previously Established egoic sexual memories and Habit-Patterns. Thus (and As In Every Other Context and Circumstance Of life), and Regardless Of Whether (In The Particular Instance) The Yogic "Conductivity" Massage-Practice Is Of The "Touch" Variety Or The Non-"Touch" Variety (Relative To the genitals and other "erogenous" zones of the body of the recipient), In Order That The Practice Of Yogic "Conductivity" Massage Be Truly

and Consistently ego-Transcending and Right, Both The Partici-
pants In An Occasion Of Yogic "Conductivity" Massage Should Be
Constantly Devotionally (and, Thus, Recognition-Responsively)
Turned To <u>Me</u>, In Such A Manner That The psycho-physical
Faculties (Of Both Participants) Are Not Contracting Upon the
Habit-Patterned ego-"self", and (Instead) My Own and Very (and
Intrinsically egoless and Self-Evidently Divine) State Is Directly
"Located", In Constant Real Devotional (and, As The Case May Be,
Transcendental Spiritual) "Conductivity"-Communion With Me.

The Discipline Of Right Yogic "Conductivity" Massage Is Not
Intended To Strategically Arouse and Activate sexual-Release-
Motivation In the body and the mind Of Either Of The Participants
(Such That Either Participant Is, Thus and Thereby, Intentionally
"caused" To Achieve Pleasurable Release Through degenerative
orgasm). In Any Case, Right Yogic "Conductivity" Massage (As
With All Other Matters Of Right-Life Practice In The Only-By-Me
Revealed and Given "Radical" Reality-Way Of The Heart, or
"Radical" Reality-Way Of Adidam, or Adidam Ruchiradam) Is—In
Principle, and Necessarily—<u>Always</u> A Matter Of The Constant
Yogic Discipline and Exercise Of Fundamental <u>own-body
Responsibility</u> Relative To the bodily (and Total psycho-physical)
domain As A Whole, and (Therefore) Relative To the genitals In
Particular, and All The Possibilities Associated With Exercises Of
the sex-function, and Any and All Stimulations Of Energy
Associated With the genitals and The Possibilities Associated With
Exercises Of the sex-function.

The Intention and Purpose Of Right Yogic "Conductivity"
Massage Is To Stimulate and Serve The "Conductivity" Process In
the body of the recipient (and, Coincidently, but Secondarily, In
the body of the Administering-individual) As A Unified Totality.
Therefore, Right Practice Of Yogic "Conductivity" Massage Is Not
A Matter Of puritanically Avoiding the genitals of the recipient, but
Of Positive (and Appropriate)—"Touch" or Non-"Touch"—Energy-
Stimulation Of the genitals of the recipient, By Means Of Feeling-
Breathing Yogic "Conductivity"-Address To and Via the genitals of
the recipient, In The Context Of his or her bodily Totality.

If bodily Signs Of Sexual Arousal Occur

If, During The Process Of Yogic "Conductivity" Massage, genital Energy-Stimulation (Whether In The Course Of A genital "Touch" Or A genital Non-"Touch" Approach) Becomes Observable In the recipient To A Significant Degree (Demonstrated, In the male recipient, By Responsive bodily movements, or By One or Another Degree Of penis erection, or, In the female recipient, By Responsive bodily movements, or By vaginal secretions, and so on), It Should Always Be Immediately Understood and Used (By the recipient and By the Administering-individual) As A Positive (or Non-Problematic) Energy-Indicator Of The Process Of Right and Regenerative Yogic "Conductivity". Thus, When, In The Circumstance Of Yogic "Conductivity" Massage, Significant genital Energy-Stimulation Is Indicated In The bodily Signs Of the recipient (Just As Should Also Be The Case When Energy-Stimulation Is Indicated anywhere else In the body of the recipient During Yogic "Conductivity" Massage), The Evident Energy Should Simply (As A Matter Of The Yogic Exercise Of own-body Responsibility, Especially By the recipient) Be Intentionally (but Effortlessly, or Searchlessly) Felt and Breathed (By the recipient, and By the Administering-individual) To Be Flowing Into the recipient's bodily Circle Of "Conductivity"—Downward (Via inhalation) In The Frontal Line, Turning About (As the inhaled breath Is Retained) In the bodily base (which Should Be Lightly or Rhythmically Tensed Toward In and Up), and, Then (With exhalation), Passing Upwards Via and Within The Total Spinal Line (and, Thus and Thereby, Including the entire head).

More Specifically (and Altogether), In The Case Of Signs Of Specific genital Energy-Stimulation Of the recipient (or, Otherwise, Of the Administering-individual) In The Circumstance Of (Either genital "Touch" Or genital Non-"Touch") Yogic "Conductivity" Massage, The genital-Specific Energy Indicated In the body of the recipient (or In the body of the Administering-individual) May Be Effortlessly and Searchlessly Felt and Breathed (By Both Participants) To Flow (Even Via a single Continuous inhalation) From the genitals, Down Into the bodily base, Then Upwards, Via The Spinal Line, To A Point Just Below The Level Of the navel, Then Forward and Slightly Down, In A Spiral-Like Curve, Into The bodily (or abdominal) "Battery" (Just Above the genitals)—With The Energy Thus Flowed To The bodily "Battery" Constantly Drawn Into Place, and (At Last) Retained In Place, By A Light or Rhythmic Inward-Upward Tensing Of the bodily base. Right Practice Of This Yogic "bodily-Battery Conductivity-Process" Will, Inevitably and Spontaneously, Regenerate and Strengthen The Vitality Of the recipient (and The Vitality Of the Administering-individual), As Well As Serve his or her General bodily Balance and Well-being.

Yogic "Conductivity" Massage Is Not Merely A physical Exercise

In The Only-By-Me Revealed and Given "Radical" Reality-Way Of The Heart, Yogic "Conductivity" Massage Is A <u>Yogic</u> <u>Energy-</u> <u>"Conductivity"</u> Practice, and Not Merely (or Exclusively) A gross physical Exercise In muscle-Massage or "body-Work". By Right Practice Of Yogic "Conductivity" Massage, The Yogic (or Altogether Right) Energy-"Conductivity" Of the Whole and Total body of the recipient (and, Coincidently, but Secondarily, the Whole and Total body of the Administering-individual) Is—By A Natural Means That Simply Uses, Supports, and Is Supported By The Energy-Pattern That Is Always Already An Inherent Characteristic Of the Natural physical body—Systematically Re-Asserted, Regenerated, and Kept Right. Therefore, By Means Of The Right Practice Of Yogic "Conductivity" Massage, the physical body of (Always Especially and Specifically) the recipient Is Helped To self-Regulate and self-Maintain its Natural Integrity and Equanimity—Such That, Characteristically, There Are No Knots (or Obstructions) In The bodily Flow Of Energy, No bodily Stresses Of Energy (Frontal or Spinal), and No Trapping Of Energy, Whether In the genitals Or In any other bodily part, place, or function.

Persist In Searchless Right Practice, Regardless Of "experience"

In This Process (Both During and After The Specific Occasions Of Yogic "Conductivity" Massage), the recipient (and, Perhaps, Also the Administering-individual) May "Experience" Spontaneous Deep Reveries (or the arising Of mental, emotional, and physical Memory-Patterns), Even Progressively Passing Backwards In time, "Regressing" Toward and Into An Even embryonic Stage (or, Perhaps, Even Into What Appear To Be past-lifetime Indications). All Such Occurrences—and, Indeed, All Otherwise or Coincidently "experienced" Energy-phenomena—Should Be Tacitly Accepted, and Freely Allowed To arise and pass As They Will, and Neither Sought Nor Held On To. All Such Happenings Are Merely Modes Of The self-Adjustment (or Spontaneous and Automatic Purification, and Transformation, and Energy-Regeneration) Of The psycho-physical Patterns Associated With human embodiment. Therefore, Let all such "experiences" (and Even all the phenomena of human "experience" Altogether) arise and (As They Inevitably Will) pass away. And Always Persist In The Searchless Right Practice I Have Revealed and Given To You (Including This Searchless Right Practice Of Yogic "Conductivity" Massage) Until The present-time Event Becomes (and, Indeed, Is) Only A Resonant Equanimity— Calm and Stress-Free, and Free Of all contents Otherwise.

"Shake Away" Negative energies and Obstructions

As A Means To Relax, Relieve, and Even (Potentially) Remove The Accumulated Patterns Of Knots (or Obstructions) In the recipient's bodily (and, Perhaps, Also mentally and emotionally perceived) Flow Of Energy, and The Frontal or Spinal Stresses Of Energy In the body of the recipient, and The Trapping Of Energy In the genitals of the recipient, The Administering Of Yogic "Conductivity" Massage Should Not Only Include muscle-Massage, but, As The Process Proceeds, the hands of the Administering-individual Should, Periodically, Move In Rapid Feeling-exhaling-Releasing Gestures Over and Away From the Immediate bodily zone of the recipient, In Order (Thus and Thereby) To "Pull Off" and "Shake Away" all Negative energies and Pattern-states, All Knots and Obstructions In The Pattern and Flow Of Energy In and Through the Immediate bodily zone Being Addressed, and All Trapping (or "Location-Fixating") Of Energy (Whether In the genitals Or elsewhere) In the body of the recipient. Also, After Every Occasion (or Even, Periodically, Within The Occasion) Of Administering Yogic "Conductivity" Massage, the Administering-individual Should Shake his or her hands In A Feeling-exhaling-Releasing "Throwing-Off" Gesture, Out and Away From his or her own body, and (Generally) Toward the floor or ground, In Order To "Clear Away" any and all Negative energies and Pattern-states that May Have Been Contacted or "Drawn From" the recipient (or Even Otherwise Stimulated or Remembered In the Administering-individual) In The Course Of The Occasion Of Administering Yogic "Conductivity" Massage.

Energy-Visualization May Occur, but It Is Not Necessary

Altogether, It Is Sufficient For The Practice Of Yogic "Conductivity" Massage To Simply Be Associated With Energy As A Tacit Feeling-Breathing "Exercise" Of Energy (Both By the recipient and the Administering-individual). However, In The Case Of some individuals, Energy-Sensitivity May Become Spontaneously Accompanied By Energy-Visualization. The Energy-Field Closest To the physical body Corresponds To The Outermost Field-Colors Of The Cosmic Mandala. Thus, The Energy-Field Most Directly Specific To Yogic "Conductivity" Massage Is Of A Radiant Yellow-Red Hue (or A Flame-Like Color-Pattern, Suffused With The Colors Of Yellow, Orange, and Red). If any individual (recipient or Administering-server) Spontaneously (Without Seeking) Sees The Energy-Field Of the body In Such Colors (or, Indeed, Any Color At All, and Especially Either Blue or White), or (Either Simultaneously Or Otherwise) Sees or Feels The Energy-Field Of the body As A body-Surrounding Sphere or Great Oval, he or she Should, Of Course, Freely Participate In Yogic "Conductivity" Massage By "Exercising" The Feeling-Breathing Process In Conjunction With Such Spontaneous Visualizations and Feeling-Signs. However, If No Such Visualizations or Feeling-Signs arise, The Feeling-Breathing Process Of Yogic "Conductivity" Can Function Equally As Well If It Is Engaged Simply On The Basis Of Feeling-Breathing Sensitivity To The "Sensation" Of Energy Itself.

In and Of Themselves, All Manipulations and Exercises Of A psycho-physical Kind Are "cause-and-effect" Devices For Stimulating (or Otherwise Achieving) Some Kind Of conditional Result. However, The By-Me-Given Right-Life Disciplines Of The "Radical" Reality-Way Of The Heart Are Not, In Fundamental Principle, Search-Purposed (or Effort-Bound) To "cause" Any Result. Rather, The Right-Life Disciplines Of The "Radical" Reality-Way Of The Heart Are, Fundamentally, Simply The Intrinsically Searchless Right-Life Demonstration Of <u>Always</u> <u>Prior</u> (or Always Already Existing) Devotional Communion With Me and <u>Always</u> <u>Prior</u> (or Always Already Existing) "Conductivity"-Communion With Me, In Always Whole bodily (or Total psycho-physical) Devotional Recognition-Response To Me. The Only-By-Me Revealed and Given "Radical" Reality-Way Of The Heart Is Not A Seeker's "cause-and-effect" Discipline or A Seeker's "cause-and-effect" Way Of Life. Rather, The "Radical" Reality-Way Of The Heart Is Always An Intrinsically Searchless Matter Of The Always Prior, and Tacit, and In-present-time "Root"-Transcending Of egoity (or "point of view", or Separate "subjectivity") In The Always Perfectly Prior, and Self-Evident, and Intrinsically egoless, and Non-Separate, and Indivisible, and Perfectly Acausal Self-Nature, Self-Condition, and Self-State That <u>Is</u> Reality Itself.

Right Education, Right Training, and Full Accountability

In The Only-By-Me Revealed and Given "Radical" Reality-Way Of The Heart (or "Radical" Reality-Way Of Adidam, or Adidam Ruchiradam), The Practice Of Yogic "Conductivity" Massage Is To Be Always Rightly Purposed, Rightly Engaged, and Altogether

Right In All Of Its psycho-physical Signs—and, Therefore, Yogic "Conductivity" Massage Must (Necessarily, and As A Culturally Formally Accountable Obligation) Be Engaged (By My Any Devotees) In The Context Of Right Education, Right Training, and Full Cultural Accountability, Such That The (However Frequent or Infrequent) Practice Of Yogic "Conductivity" Massage Simply Becomes A Constituent Part Of The Total Right-Practice-Process Of The Always Prior and Tacit Transcending Of The (Otherwise) psycho-physically "self"-Contracted (or egoically Patterned) Totality Of body-mind. ■

PART FOUR

SUPPLEMENTAL PRACTICES

CHAPTER 8

Additional Practical Recommendations for Balancing the Yellow-Red Conjunction

*T*he body is a paradox of pairs—not a dilemma (or opposition of two), and not a simple line from Light to Darkness. Its two potentials are not separable, and neither one of its coils[1] is (itself, and independently) identical to the Ultimate and Perfect Source that is Truth. At best, one may say that a balance, a dynamic harmony of the two tendencies of the bodily being, is appropriate and most conducive to a normal (or pleasurable) fulfillment of the life-cycle.

—Avatar Adi Da Samraj
"The Seahorse: The Hidden Structure of All Experience"
The Paradox of Instruction

Avatar Adi Da recommends a number of supplemental practices that serve the integration and balance of the yellow-red conjunction.[2] Many of these additional recommendations address not only the "conductivity" of natural life-energy in the Circle of the body-mind-complex but also the energetic polarities of the physical body— specifically between the left and right sides of the body and

1. With the word "coil", Avatar Adi Da is referring to the Indian Yogic understanding of the left (*ida*) and right (*pingala*) energy channels (nadis), which spiral (or coil) around the central channel (*sushumna*) in the body. See also note 4 on pp. 300–301 below.

2. Also see appendix D for brief descriptions of a number of general right-life disciplines Avatar Adi Da gives to His devotees that, although not typically thought of as energy-healing practices, are important means of serving the body's relationship with energy.

between the two branches of the autonomic nervous system (the sympathetic and parasympathetic). Thus, this chapter begins with a summary of Avatar Adi Da's instruction on the energetic principles related to these dynamic pairs in the human structure.

Balancing Dynamic Opposites in the Human System

The physical dimension of the human system is characterized by various dynamically paired functions and energies, which, when brought into balance, assist the conscious integration of the etheric and physical dimensions of the being. Because the human being is a single integrated system, the magnification of the flow of natural life-energy in the principal energy-circuit of "conductivity" (down the frontal line and up the spinal line) inherently serves the balancing of all the energetic systems in the human being. However, Avatar Adi Da also recommends a number of supplemental practices that balance specific energetic "pairs" within the system of the body-mind-complex.[3]

The Two Sides of the Body

In numerous healing traditions, each side of the physical body is understood to be related to distinct functions and types of energy. These functions and energies are generally associated with a right/left energy polarization of the body (just as the Circle of "conductivity" in the body-mind-complex is associated with a kind of "vertical" energy polarization of the body between the crown of the head and the bodily base). They are also related to the right and left hemispheres of the brain.[4]

3. Note these practices are particularly useful in the re-balancing phase of the healing process, whereby the nervous system is brought into balance—after the purification phase has completed, and thus allowing the regenerative phase of healing to occur. See appendix C for a summary description of the three phases of healing as described by Avatar Adi Da.

4. In *Yoga and Ayurveda: Self-Healing and Self-Realization* (Twin Lakes, WI: Lotus Press, 1999), David Frawley illustrates a traditional understanding of the qualities of the right and left sides of the body (nadis are energy channels, tamasic is the quality of inertia, rajasic is the quality of action):

> *The ida is the left nadi. It has a lunar, feminine, cooling or kapha energy and is tamasic in quality. Ida provides inspiration of vision, speech and imagination and elevates our devotional*

[There are] two parallel nerve currents that operate the two sides of the body and represent the two sides and aspects of the brain. In most people, the right side and the right hand are positive and dominant. The left hemisphere of the brain operates the right side of the body, and the right hemisphere of the brain operates the left side of the body. The right side of the body is generally associated with expansive emotional and physical conditions, and the right hemisphere of the brain is generally associated with the psychic, intuitive, or preverbal realms of the mind. The left side of the body is generally associated with passive or internalizing tendencies, and the left hemisphere of the brain is generally associated with verbal-mental activities. The nerve currents extend from the brain to the entire body via the spinal cord, apparently alternating with one another, or crossing and balancing one another, at the various primary centers of the body.[5] And the two halves of brain and body must be understood to be in a cooperative relationship, sharing rather than dividing the various physical, emotional, and mental functions.

—Avatar Adi Da Samraj
"The Key to Enlightenment Is at the Center of the Body",
The Enlightenment of the Whole Body

This right/left energetic polarization of the body is commonly understood (and can even be measured) in terms of electromagnetic energy—which is, as Avatar Adi Da describes, the most basic energy of the physical body. Relative to the physical-etheric energy-spectrum, electromagnetic energy can be thought of as more closely associated with the gross dimension than the subtle dimension—although the currents of electromagnetic energy do, of course, influence the flow of etheric energy.

---

inclinations, making us more caring and loving. The pingala is the right nadi. It has a solar, masculine, heating or pitta energy and is rajasic in quality. Pingala provides motivation, drive, and determination and allows us to pursue deeper knowledge and perception. . . . [T]he two nadis relate to right and left brain functioning. Left brain functioning relates to the opposite or right nadi and makes us rational, independent and aggressive. Right brain functioning relates to the opposite or left nadi and makes us emotional, sensitive and receptive.

5. Avatar Adi Da is referring to the subtle energy centers associated with the physical body, also known as chakras.

When the right- and left-sided patterns and energies are in balance and integrated, there is equanimity and well-being in the human system. As Avatar Adi Da describes, "The integration of the two tendencies yields a harmony, a pleasurable equalization, which is effectively at rest."[6] Such harmonization supports the free flow of natural life-energy in the Circle of the body-mind-complex, and also frees attention and energy to participate in the Divine Reality Prior to all the patterns of the human structure.

The Truth of the whole bodily being is not to be found by appeal to the separate dispositions of either the right hemisphere of the brain or the left hemisphere of the brain, the right half of the body or the left half of the body, the extroverting or the introverting tendencies. Truth, or Reality, is not Itself contained in either the vital or the mental realms of the bodily being. Rather, the Truth of the whole bodily being, or body-mind-complex, is intuited in the unified, or balanced, consciousness, in which all the parts are in an harmonious equalization and relaxed beyond their "objects" into the "radical" (rather than extended or reductive) intuition of the True Condition, or Prior Intensity, of all "experience".

—Avatar Adi Da Samraj
"The Truth of the Whole Bodily Being",
The Enlightenment of the Whole Body

The Two Halves of the (Autonomic) Nervous System

Another dynamic pair that is served by the supplemental practices recommended by Avatar Adi Da is what He describes as the "two halves of the nervous system". This is a reference to the two systems of the autonomic nervous system: sympathetic and parasympathetic. The autonomic nervous system, as generally understood, is the part of the nervous system that is not controlled by conscious thought or intention. In other words, these are involuntary functions that occur without us having to think about them.

- **Sympathetic nervous system**: Sometimes referred to as the "fight or flight" mechanism; responsible for priming the body for action.

6. From *Twirling and Jet Lag.*

• **Parasympathetic nervous system:** Sometimes referred to as the "rest and digest" mechanism; conserves energy as it slows the heart rate, increases intestinal and gland activity, and relaxes muscles in the gastrointestinal tract.

The practices recommended by Avatar Adi Da that re-balance the two halves of the autonomic nervous system (see appendix C for a list of such practices) support these involuntary functions, allowing them to come into their natural state of equilibrium. The etheric body functions through and corresponds to the nervous system—therefore, keeping the "halves" of the autonomic nervous system in synergistic balance is key to health and well-being. And, a balanced, resonant nervous system is essential to free participation in the Radiance of the Divine Reality.

The nervous system is the connection, or "mediator", for human beings to the Ocean of Self-Radiant Consciousness, or the Divine and Absolute Personality of Reality Itself.

The epitome of the nervous system is the heart, or the "root" of life-feeling.

The heart is the monitor of present relationship to the All-Pervading Identity.

You must enter whole bodily, or as a disposition of the total nervous system, into unobstructed (or intuitive) feeling-sacrifice, or Divine Communion. This is made possible by Listening to My Revelation-Teaching of "Perfect Knowledge", on the basis of devotional recognition-response to Me, the Divine Avataric Master, Who Is the Incarnation of Conscious Light.

At first, enter into sacrificial relationship to the Self-Radiant Divine, through devotional recognition-response to Me and ego-transcending love, releasing all contractions of the nervous system and all contracted "programs" of personal, relational, and subtler psycho-physical "experience".

Ultimately, you must be a Perfect Sacrifice, when you transcend the personal limits of the contracted or "self"-monitoring nervous system, and Realize Perfect Identification with the Absolute Personality of Reality Itself. Then only the Paradox of Infinite Existence and Ecstatic Divine "Play" is Obvious. Then there is Only Real God.

—Avatar Adi Da Samraj
"The Method of the Nervous System",
The Enlightenment of the Whole Body

Dynamic Opposites in the Human System

System	Side (or Halves)	Functions/Qualities
whole body	right side of the body	expansive, active; with a positive energetic charge
	left side of the body	inward, passive; with a negative energetic charge
brain (central nervous system)	right hemisphere (and its extensions)	intuitive, perceptual
	left hemisphere (and its extensions)	logical, conceptual
autonomic nervous system	sympathetic	"fight or flight"
	parasympathetic	"rest and digest"

Addressing Imbalance

During the day, physical and mental action is generally required, meaning right side and left brain are predominant. If there is not the conscious intention to balance this energy in the other "direction", the usual habits and patterns of daily life will throw the energies of the body-mind-complex out of balance. In fact, the overuse of the right side of the body and the left side of the brain—which is common in the present-day culture dominated by outward, active, and mental activities—establishes a specific pattern of bodily energies that causes stress, which in turn throws the autonomic nervous system out of balance.

Stress in daily life tends to stimulate the automaticity of the "fight-or-flight" reaction, the technical term for what I call the "stress reaction". Under stress, you want to become aggressive and angry. You also want to fall back and flee and disappear. The conflict between these two motives creates stress, a "problem" of opposing motives in the living personality.

—Avatar Adi Da Samraj
The First Three Stages of Life

Thus, stress is a characteristic sign that the right-sided, left-brained bodily energies and the sympathetic nervous system are over-functioning and creating imbalance. Conversely, the tendency to depression and apathy are signs that the left-sided, right-brained bodily energies are dominant and creating imbalance.

Avatar Adi Da points out that oftentimes something that is considered to be a difficult emotional, mental, or psychological problem might simply be a sign of an imbalance of the nervous system or even of the two sides of the body. A simple, straightforward address to balancing the energy systems of the body can often immediately and effectively relieve symptoms of imbalance—and also free attention and energy for devotional Communion with Avatar Adi Da.

When you are out of balance, you need not engage in psychological introspection. Just change the functioning of the nervous system and relax a little bit. . . .

These "techniques" are very simple, very practical, and physically based. They provide a balanced physical disposition. They do not Divinely Enlighten you. They are not sufficient for anything like Divine Enlightenment. Nevertheless, they are simple, practical aids for achieving a balanced physical state and relieving yourself of stress. You need not engage all kinds of introspective activities to do this, because your emotional and mental symptoms of stress are built upon a physical base. It is better and more direct to deal with physical stress at the physical level. . . .

I have Given you all kinds of other practices that serve the purpose of bodily equanimity—right dietary and sexual practices, gentle physical exercises such as Da Namaskar, right living, and right discipline altogether.[7] All of these practices simply serve to

7. See appendix D for a brief summary of these other supportive practices.

balance you, to provide a basic physical disposition wherein you may embrace the devotional Yoga of whole bodily turning to Me, in devotional recognition-response to Me. Merely by making these adjustments in the physical, or achieving a balanced physical state, you will not achieve Divine Enlightenment or even any advanced Spiritual state at all. Nevertheless, you will at least achieve psychophysical balance.

—Avatar Adi Da Samraj
January 24, 1983

Although not Divinely Enlightening, the balancing of the dynamic polarities of the body-mind-complex (as with serving the yellow-red conjunction altogether) does serve and support the great process of transcending the ego-"self" utterly in the whole bodily devotional recognition-response to Avatar Adi Da.

[I] . . . forever Call humankind to the only Way That Is Single, Whole, and not based on egoity. The only-by-Me Revealed and Given Reality-Way of Adidam is not developed from the exclusive (or dominant) "point of view" of either the frontal line or the spinal line, or from the exclusive (or dominant) "point of view" of either the left or the right hemisphere of the brain. Rather, the only-by-Me Revealed and Given Reality-Way of Adidam involves (and requires) the whole of the human structure, the full Circle, the resonant nervous system, the total brain, all aligned and surrendered, in tacit recognition-response, to Me—and this, Most Ultimately, to the degree of Inherently Most Perfect Dissolution in My Avatarically Self-Revealed Non-conditional, Transcendental, Perfectly Subjective, Inherently Spiritual, Intrinsically egoless, Inherently Perfect, Perfectly Acausal, and Self-Evidently Divine Self-Nature, Self-Condition, and Self-State.

—Avatar Adi Da Samraj
"Alpha / Omega",
The Aletheon

Therefore, as with all the practices given in this book, engage the practices recommended below as forms of turning whole bodily to His Divine Presence Avatar Adi Da Samraj, and (by this turning) participating fully in the universal field of natural life-energy. And apply these supportive practices judiciously, and, as with all secondary (supportive) practices in the Reality-Way of Adidam, "In A Truly Simple (or Uncomplicated, and Non-Seeking) Manner".[8]

Supplemental Practices[9]

1. Polarity Screens

Polarity screens (also known as Eeman screens or Eeman biocircuits) were developed from various devices created by the healer L. E. Eeman, based on experiments he performed in the early 1900s. Polarity screens are simple tools that work with the energetic polarity of the body. By influencing the positive and negative charges associated with the physical body—right/left and head/base—polarity screens affect the body's electromagnetic field, and, thus, the other energetic patterns associated with the body-mind-complex, including the flow of etheric energy in the Circle.

Polarity screens are a set of simple rectangles of copper mesh[10] (generally measuring 4–8 inches per side), each of which is attached to a length of coated copper wire with a copper metal handle at the end. One mesh screen is placed under the body at the base of the spine and the other is placed under the head at the top of the spine.

8. From *The Dawn Horse Testament*.

9. Sources for more detailed instruction from Avatar Adi Da on a particular practice are indicated within the practice description. Additionally, see "Literature on Energy Healing from Avatar Adi Da's *Basket of Tolerance*" (appendix E), under the relevant heading section.

10. Polarity screens can also be made out of silk (or other energy-conducting material), but copper is generally considered to be the most effective material for this device.

Then the connected handles are held in the hands. This connects the top and base of the spine to the right and left sides of the body with a material that conducts electromagnetic energy.

The right side of the body and the top of the spine are positive in charge, while the left side and lower spine are negative. (Note: In rare cases, an individual may have reverse polarity in the body, so these circuits would be reversed.) Thus, if you connect the base of the spine to the right side of the body (via the right hand), you are connecting opposite charges (base = negative, right = positive). If you connect the base of the spine to the left side of the body (via the left hand), then you are connecting like charges (base = negative, left = negative). And vice versa for the top of the spine.

Connecting oppositely charged poles creates a different influence on the body-mind-complex than connecting like-charged poles. Thus, there are two distinct circuits that can be created with the polarity screens:

• **Relaxation circuit**: created by connecting oppositely charged poles, positive to negative

• **Energizing circuit**: created by connecting similarly charged poles, positive to positive and negative to negative

Avatar Adi Da makes the point that polarity screens do not add, or transmit, energy to the bodily system—they simply support the natural polarity and movement of electromagnetic energy already associated with the bodily system. In other words, polarity screens support the self-correcting system of the body-mind-complex.

Via polarity screens, you are enhancing the body's own capability. The influence must be rather gross (or physical), because it must deal with the basic energy of the physical body, which is, according to current description, electromagnetic. Therefore, you simply connect up the natural circuit of the body by adding some wiring to it, to counteract the body's own present state in which it has lost equanimity due to stress, and so forth. By applying the polarity screens, you enforce the body's natural circuit—which is what does the work, not the materials out of which the appliance is made.

When the natural circuit is established, then the body feels well. When sympathetically associated with that natural circuit, you find that, paradoxically, after ten, fifteen, or twenty minutes, you feel a relaxation of the solar plexus, the body relaxes, you feel the polarization base to crown, you feel some energy in the head, and a certain sense of well-being occurs.

—Avatar Adi Da Samraj
January 31, 1988[11]

I have had chronic fatigue syndrome (CFS) for the past twelve years. The symptoms are cyclic and at times become debilitating—my energy gets very low, even though I feel "hyper". I can't concentrate, and my sleep is disturbed by frequent awakening. At these times, I use the polarity screens every afternoon around 4:00 p.m., when my energy is at its lowest.

What I feel first is that my exhausted but "hyper" energy calms down in about 5 to 10 minutes. Then, at a certain point after 10 to 15 minutes, I feel myself drop into a deeply relaxed state. After 30 minutes or so, I either fall asleep or feel it is time to get up.

I find my bodily energy is restored, my mood is lifted, and my concentration improves to the point where I can once again think clearly. I have been able to avoid taking any prescription medication for my CFS by using polarity screens.

—Devotee of Avatar Adi Da Samraj

11. For the full version of this essay, as well as additional instruction on polarity screens from Avatar Adi Da, see *Polarity Screens: A Safe, Simple, Naturally Effective Method of Restoring and Balancing the Energies of the Body.*

When to Use Polarity Screens

Polarity screens can be used any time, for the sake of general well-being and equanimity and free attention. They may also be used in specific circumstances or to address specific conditions:

To support "conductivity" in the Circle. Any time energy in the frontal line is tending to move upward rather than downward, you can use polarity screens to help reestablish the downward polarization.

Polarity screens enhance the natural circuit of "conductivity" by polarizing the descending energy down the frontal line of the body and the ascending energy up the spinal line of the body. Whenever the body is under stress, enervated, or out of balance, this natural "conductivity" is obstructed, so that a counter-circuit of energy ascends up the frontal line and descends down the spinal line. Polarity screens work to reestablish the natural descending-ascending circuit of bodily energy.

—Avatar Adi Da Samraj
September 7, 1991

To correct general energy imbalances. For example, at the end of a day in which the dominant activity has been outward (or right-sided) and there is overstimulation of the thinking/conceptual mind, use the polarity screens in the relaxation circuit to re-balance these energies directly and simply. You can also experiment with using polarity screens in either the relaxation circuit or the energizing circuit to address enervation, depression, or apathy.

To directly counter patterns (and symptoms) of stress. Polarity screens help counteract the specific right-left energy patterns created by chronic overuse of the right side of the body (and the left side of the brain).

The reason the relaxation circuit is relaxing is because it establishes a different rotation from the one that makes stress. In the stress pattern, energy comes from the head down the right side, up the left side, back to the head. You are reversing that when using this relaxation circuit. You are establishing the right side with the base rather than the head, and you are establishing the left side with the head rather than the base. In other words, you are establishing a counter-rotation.

If you lie on the polarity screens, you might even perceive this feeling of rotation, coming up from the base, up the right side down the left side. This counter-rotation is relaxing—it un-wheels the stress that has been made by the opposite rotation, which has tightened up the knot over the solar plexus.

There is a kind of knot over the navel that is both yin and yang, centrifugal versus centripetal. A certain rotation tightens the knot and another rotation loosens the knot. This is how polarity screens influence the body.

—Avatar Adi Da Samraj
January 31, 1988

To remedy symptoms of jet lag. Polarity screens help to realign the etheric-energy field to the physical body—and such realignment is very helpful in relieving symptoms of jet lag. (See more details on jet lag on pp. 338–40.)

Prior to meditation.

It May Be Useful (At times when the body is either in an agitated state or in an enervated state) To Lie Down On Polarity Screens (In The Relaxation Circuit, or Mode, When There Is a bodily feeling of over-stimulation, and Either In The Relaxation Circuit, or Mode, Or In The Energizing Circuit, or Mode, When There Is a bodily feeling of enervation), and This For Perhaps ten or fifteen minutes, At The Very Beginning Of (or, Otherwise, Immediately Previous To) The Occasion Of Formal Meditation. . . . This Will Tend To Balance and Relax the body-mind-complex By Directly Affecting the etheric Energy-Field Of the body.

—Avatar Adi Da Samraj
The Dawn Horse Testament

To be reminded that you are energy, and even to transcend negative circuitry. Polarity screens are a particularly effective means to experientially recall that you are only energy.

If you become doubtful and want to prove that you are energy, use polarity screens for a few minutes. Remarkably, they will communicate to you that whatever else you are, you are a field of energy. Energy is running through your hands, your fingers, your back, your head. You will discover that you can change your sensations and emotional moods simply by causing those currents to run differently. If you do this even once, you will gain a sense of yourself that you perhaps did not have before. In the natural state, however, everyone has this sense of themselves as energy.

On the basis of discoveries such as this, you must awaken to a great presumption. You must enter into the Radiant Condition of the being, instead of fastening yourself through tension into the "meat" mode of conventional perception and presumption, in which you are obsessively oriented toward a petty sense of release through physical exploitation.

—Avatar Adi Da Samraj
August 11, 1979

General Guidelines for Polarity Screens

Use the polarity screens in a quiet, private setting, whenever possible. The setting should support maximum relaxation. Feel free to create a sacred, contemplative space in which to lie on the polarity screens. This will support your ongoing invocation of Avatar Adi Da and the free flow of energy through the body-mind-complex.

Use screens, handles, and cords made of a material that maximally conducts natural energy. Avatar Adi Da recommends copper as the most effective metal for the screens and handles of the polarity screens.

Handles should fit your hands. They should be of comfortable size for holding loosely while you relax.

Your body should be in contact with natural materials, not synthetics. For optimal "conductivity" of energy while using the polarity screens, lie on a surface of natural material (such as wool, wood, or cotton) and also wear clothing of natural fibers (wool, cotton, silk, and so forth). Synthetic surfaces and clothing do not conduct energy as effectively as natural materials. *Note:* Polarity screens do not need to be in direct contact with the skin to be effective. You may even place a towel over them for comfort without diminishing the flow of energy through the circuits. Just make sure the towel or cloth is made of natural fibers.

Experiment and observe. Because there are some individuals who have a reverse polarity, it is crucial that you observe which configuration induces relaxation and calm, and which induces invigoration of energy. L. E. Eeman found that a very few people are polarized so that the left hand and head and the right hand and lower body have the same charge. For such people it is necessary to reverse the circuits to achieve the desired effect. Otherwise, the relaxation circuit can cause a "tension circuit" that causes nervousness, irritability, and other negative mental-emotional conditions, which only aggravate disease symptoms. Experiment to discover your own polarization.

Using Polarity Screens

Relaxation Circuit

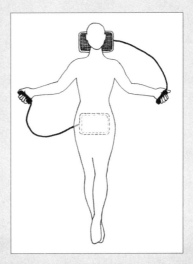

- Lie on your back, on your bed or on a non-synthetic and soft mat or rug on the floor.

- Place one polarity screen under your <u>head</u> and hold the attached handle in your <u>left</u> hand.

- Place the second polarity screen under the <u>base of your spine</u> and hold that handle in your <u>right</u> hand.

- Cross your legs at the ankles, left over right. This prevents energy from flowing out the legs and feet. If crossing the ankles with the legs outstretched causes any discomfort in the lower back or ankles, you can pull the legs up, bending the knees and crossing the ankles as in a simple cross-legged sitting pose (or otherwise placing the bottoms of the feet together).

- Relax completely for 20–30 minutes. After a few minutes, you should observe a natural relaxation throughout the body. Any number of effects could also be experienced, such as emotional release, intense movements of energy, repolarization (from head to bodily base or left to right), or deep sleep—or there may be only very subtle effects. The more you use the polarity screens, the more sensitized you will become to the effects on the body-mind-complex.

Energizing Circuit

In Eeman's experiments, he found that this arrangement often caused hyperstimulation or irritability. However, this configuration can be effective for some as a "recharging circuit" for restoring vitality when the body is enervated or fatigued. In general, the "relaxing circuit" is more dramatic and more effective than the influence of the "energizing circuit".

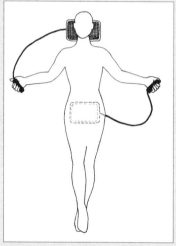

Perform the same steps as above but switch the hands:

• Hold the handle of the screen placed at your <u>head</u> in your <u>right</u> hand.

• Cross your legs at the ankles, <u>right</u> over <u>left</u>.

• Hold the handle of the screen placed at the <u>base</u> <u>of</u> <u>your</u> <u>spine</u> in your <u>left</u> hand.

• Relax completely for 20–30 minutes.

(continued on next page)

Note: The same principles of these circuits can be applied without the polarity screens themselves—simply using one's own left and right hands as if they were the screens.

Eeman also experimented with the screens in a procedure that he called "cooperative healing". By using several screens with long lead wires, you can place two or more people in the same circuit of energy. Some may find it beneficial to likewise experiment with such a "multiple circuit".

2. Pranayama

Pranayama literally means control, restraint, or regulation (yama) of life-energy (prana). It is an ancient practice of controlling the breath and, via the breath, the life-energy in the body-mind-complex. When practiced with great feeling and concentration, pranayama brings balance and energy to the entire body, including the nervous system and the Circle, thus supporting the yellow-red conjunction.

Working with the cycle of the breath and its passage through the nostrils is an effective means to directly influence various qualities and functions of the body-mind-complex:

• Inhalation is associated with inward motion, coming "in" toward the "self", with the passive quality (like the left side of the body)

• Exhalation is associated with expansive and outward motion, radiating throughout and moving out from the body, with the active quality (like the right side of the body)

• The right nostril is connected to the left side of the brain, which is associated with the conceptual/logical function

• The left nostril is connected to the right side of the brain, which is associated with the perceptual/intuitive function

In traditional forms of pranayama, inhalation and exhalation are controlled in precise ratios (such as 1:2), by counting the length of each phase. This technique is applied in order to achieve specific experiential intentions or goals—for instance, to purify the nerve channels (or nadis) associated with the left and right sides of the body in order to awaken and concentrate all available life-force in the central nerve current, at the base of the spine. When this central channel opens and the life-force begins to rise in it in concentrated form, powerful experiences of energy, inner vision, and subtle sound often ensue.

In contrast, Avatar Adi Da's recommendation to His devotees is "to breathe each phase of the cycle fully, equally, and with feeling".[12] Engaging the breath with full feeling-attention is what brings about balance in the inhalation-exhalation cycle, rather than any relatively mechanical effort to control the duration of each phase of the breath cycle. Furthermore, the practice of pranayama recommended by Avatar Adi Da is not intended to produce any particular experience of the body-mind-complex. Certainly there may be purifying effects in the body-mind-complex, and possibly blisses and elevated states may be experienced in some cases—but the practice of pranayama for His devotees is simply an expression of whole bodily participation in the universal field of natural life-energy and the Radiance of Avatar Adi Da's Divine Reality-State.

The most significant factor in the "conscious exercise" of prana-yama is, as in all forms of "conscious exercise", the stabilization of feeling-attention of the entire body-mind-complex in devotional Communion with Me, so that the living being is radiating rather than contracting. The exercise itself is to be performed on the basis of a prior sense that life-energy is full, constant, and all-pervading, regardless of the present state of relative fullness or emptiness sensed "experientially" (and, secondarily, in the phasing of the breath). . . . Inhalation, in general, represents the tendency of contraction (or centering) because inhalation is a motion toward the body (or an in-filling). Exhalation, in general, represents the expansive, relational tendency. In the usual person—adapted (as people are) to "experience" itself, rather than to the Divine Condition and the

12. From "Establishing Whole Bodily Balance Through The Exercise of Feeling-Attention", in *Conscious Exercise and The Transcendental Sun.*

Principles That are Prior to all "experiences" (just as Energy is Prior to the phasing of the breath)—the tendency toward contraction becomes more or less exclusive and overwhelming. Thus, one's adaptation leads to ego-possession, or possession by the illusions of "subjectivity". The pattern of the breath reflects this, in that one tends to inhale with emphasis—at least fitfully or occasionally—but one tends also to exhale weakly. Therefore, even inhalation tends, in general, to be shallow, since the lungs are not properly emptied. Likewise, one generally manifests a low-grade level of feeling, such that feeling becomes dramatic only when one is reacting negatively. And one thinks obsessively, so that there is little free attention available for one's relations or for devotional Communion with Me, and (thus and thereby) with the Reality in Which one is appearing.

Through "conscious exercise" of pranayama, sensitivity to this dilemma may increase, and some control or responsibility relative to the whole affair may begin to appear. Thus, it may be observed, as one consciously requires the feeling-breathing cycle to become more full and complete during both inhalation and exhalation, that there are tendencies toward shallow breathing, scattering of attention, withdrawal of feeling—and a hunger to be filled with life, but a lack of interest or intention relative to the responsibility to communicate life. But, as feeling-attention stabilizes, these tendencies also are diminished. Likewise, the tendency toward weak exhalation, common to most people under most circumstances, will diminish as heart-feeling moves attention into the relational pattern of life.

—Avatar Adi Da Samraj
"Establishing Whole Body Balance Through The Exercise of Feeling-Attention",
Conscious Exercise and The Transcendental Sun

When to Practice Pranayama

Daily, as part of the formal disciplines given by Avatar Adi Da to His devotees. An optimal time to practice pranayama is in the late afternoon or early evening, after Hatha Yoga poses (after completing the dead pose, at the end of the Hatha Yoga series).

Optimally, when the body is already relaxed and full of energy (although not limited to such times). The beneficial effects of pranayama are maximized when the breath cycle is at ease, and attention and energy are free to notice and participate fully in the flow of natural life-energy.

When there are signs of imbalance such as agitation, dullness, or reactive emotion.

At random, informally, from time to time throughout the day.

General Guidelines for Pranayama

Practice pranayama in a quiet, private setting. Pranayama can be done outdoors, if there is privacy, or else indoors, preferably near an open window or other source of fresh air (unless you live in a highly polluted area, in which case it would be better to practice pranayama in purified air indoors, with the windows closed). If possible, practice pranayama while beholding a Murti-Image of Avatar Adi Da Samraj, to focus your invocation of His Divine Blessing-Presence throughout the exercise.

Use an upright, stable, and relaxed sitting posture. Sit as you would for meditation, in a manner that allows maximum bodily ease and "conductivity".

Close the energy-circuits with conscious positions of the tongue and hands. The tongue should rest on the hard palate just behind the upper front teeth. (The tongue is the principal conduit of life-force between the region of the midbrain and nose and the regions of the throat and lower portions of the body.) In the simple form of pranayama, the hands should rest folded in the lap, or else on each respective knee, palms up and receptive, with thumbs and index fingers touching, to close the circuits of energy.

Practice pranayama on an empty stomach. Generally, you should not practice pranayama less than an hour after a meal (so that circulation is general to the body and not concentrated in digestion at the stomach).

Use natural, non-synthetic materials for your cushion or chair, and for clothing. These are preferable because they best conduct the living energy that pervades the body, the environment, and the atmosphere.

Complete each session of pranayama with a period of rest and reintegration.

Practicing Pranayama

Instructions included here cover the simple form of pranayama practice in association with natural life-energy. (Avatar Adi Da also recommends several forms of technically more detailed pranayama practice, including alternate-nostril breathing.[13]) For those who are Transcendentally Spiritually Awakened by Avatar Adi Da Samraj, the practice would be engaged in relation to His Transcendental Spiritual Current as well.

Simple Form of Pranayama

Repeat the breath-cycle described below in a single sitting of 10–15 minutes.

• Inhale fully, with whole bodily feeling, consciously receiving life-energy.

♦ Feel that you are gazing into and resting in the field of all-pervading life-force, or natural life-energy.

♦ Initiate the breath, with feeling, from the heart—breathing via the nose, to the bodily battery.

♦ Slowly fill the lungs with air and the body with life-energy—as much as you comfortably can. Do not strain or force the breath beyond your capacity.

♦ The chin should be slightly lowered, so that the windpipe is opened and the flow of air and life-force is directed against the back of the throat, which should be relaxed and fully opened.

♦ The slow intake of breath should make a slight "rasping" sound against the back of the throat. This practice stimulates the chakra (or energy-plexus) at the throat.

13. See *The Dawn Horse Testament* and *Conscious Exercise and The Transcendental Sun* (new edition forthcoming) for descriptions of those technical practices. *Conscious Exercise* also includes more instruction from Avatar Adi Da on pranayama in general.

• You should notice that, as the breath naturally moves downward to the vital center, it presses first upon the region of the solar plexus, then swells out the whole lower abdomen, and then fills the entire body, above and below, from the throat to the perineum, finally permeating even the head and legs and feet with vibrant force.

• Breathe from the heart to the vital center below, with full emotional and physical feeling of the whole body.

• Completely relax, opening the entire body to the intensity of unlimited energy. Do not be concerned about upward or downward energy currents in the body, but simply allow the faculties to be attracted to Avatar Adi Da and allow your total body-mind to be filled and sustained by the universal life-force.

• As you come to the end of the inhalation, you may wish to close your eyes briefly.

• Hold the inhalation for just a few seconds before you begin to exhale.

• Do not attempt to prolong this retention. Do not strain yourself in any way. You will simply find it natural and enjoyable to pause between the two phases of the cycle of breathing.

• Exhale fully, consciously releasing all physical, emotional, and mental toxicity.

• As you start to exhale, open your eyes again. Continue to feel that you are gazing into and resting in the field of all-pervading life-force, or etheric energy. Through both nostrils, release all the air that you have brought into the body.

(continued on next page)

♦ Exhale for a period about as long as you inhaled, and exhale about as much breath content as you inhaled.

♦ Like the inhalation, the exhalation should be slow and deliberate—not ragged, nervous, or forced. (Exhaling too quickly may tend to throw off life-force, limiting the positive effects of the exercise.)

♦ Feel that you are eliminating not only biochemical waste (by physically emptying the lungs), but also psycho-physical waste: negative thoughts, unhappy emotions, bodily tension, and disease.

♦ As you are completing the exhalation, allow the stomach cavity to be drawn in and up slightly, to help expel all the air that you inhaled.

• Pause for an instant before beginning the next cycle of the breath.

• Relax and reintegrate.

♦ After you have completed 10–15 minutes of prana-yama practice, remain seated for a while. Relax and reintegrate yourself slowly and smoothly into action and speech and contact with others.

3. Hamsadanda (or Short Crutch)

The hamsadanda,[14] also called the "short crutch", is a T-frame typically made of wood or some other natural, energy-conducting material. Used by Indian Yogis for thousands of years, the hamsadanda works directly with the nostrils and the breath to balance the two halves of the brain (and, thereby, to balance emotions and mind).

If you observe your breathing throughout the day, you will notice that one nostril is usually more "open" than the other (or breathing more freely). You will also notice that this tends to change at different times during the day. (The natural pattern of such change of openness in the nasal passageways that occurs through the course of a day is known as the "nasal cycle".) As described above, the right nostril is associated with the left side of the brain (logical, conceptual) and the right side of the body (active, expansive). The left nostril is associated with the right side of the brain (intuitive, perceptual) and the left side of the body (passive, inward). Therefore, the balance and openness of the nostrils influences (and otherwise reflects) the quality of attention and the energies of the body-mind-complex.[15]

Not only the pattern of breath, but the pattern of attention changes with that pattern of breath. There is a relationship between

14. The name literally means "swan [hamsa] staff [danda]" in Sanskrit.

15. Numerous studies provide evidence that working with the connection between the nostrils and the brain is an effective means to support mental and emotional equanimity. For example, see A. Price, R. Eccles, "Nasal airflow and brain activity: Is there a link?", *The Journal of Laryngology & Otology* 130 no. 9 (2016): 794–99, https://doi.org/10.1017/S0022215116008537; and B.B. Schiff, S. A. Rump, "Asymmetrical Hemispheric Activation and Emotion—The Effects of Unilateral Forced Nostril Breathing", Brain and Cognition 29 no. 3 (December 1995) 217–31, https://doi.org/10.1006/brcg.1995.1279.

the side in which you are breathing most openly and the quality of your energy and attention. Right-sidedness, or people's more fiery (or energetic) aspect, corresponds to the analytical thinking mind and the left hemisphere of the brain. The cooling, more passive energy, or left-sidedness, corresponds to the opening of the right hemisphere of the brain and the opening of that entire domain of imagination and intuitive inspection of phenomena, and so forth.

There is a kind of paradox involved in this fact that the left brain is associated with the right side of the body and the right brain with the left side of the body. You would think that, if you are fiery and energetic, you would be expansive. But it is the left brain (or thinking mind) that is associated with that right-sided quality. Therefore, the more right-sided you become, the more (in fact) you may feel limited or contracted. Whereas, if you relax, cool the energy, and (thereby) become associated with the right brain and its processes (which transcend thinking, and so forth), you are likely to feel calmer and more open, and (in that sense) more expanded in conscious awareness.

What you must realize is a condition that is neither left-sided nor right-sided, but a condition in which both nostrils are flowing freely, both hemispheres of the brain are simply awake and awake to one another.

—Avatar Adi Da Samraj
February 21, 1980

The hamsadanda is a very simple way to balance the breath evenly through both nostrils. When placed under the armpit, the hamsadanda puts pressure on key points in the nervous system that are associated with breath control and, thereby, the energetic qualities of the body-mind-complex. By supporting the free passage of breath through the nostrils, the associated brain hemispheres are affected. For example, if you place the hamsadanda under your right armpit:

- the energies of the right side of the body will be economized, thereby calming the activities and effects of the left side of the brain, and

- the left nostril will naturally open, thereby energizing or stimulating the activities and effects of the right side of the brain.

When you press or simply rest the hamsadanda in the armpit on the side of the body where you are breathing most freely, the pressure thus created economizes the life-force on that side of the body and in the opposite hemisphere of the brain. It also introduces an opening into the opposite nostril, or the other half of the mechanism for breathing, and stimulates and awakens the effects and activities of the opposite hemisphere in the brain. The Yogic "trick" is not to breathe forcefully in the clogged nostril—that is not what you should do. You should easefully control the side that is freely breathing by using the hamsadanda.

The same results can be achieved without a hamsadanda by simply lying on your side—the side that is open—and placing your fist (of the opposite arm) in the armpit on that side. Even simply lying on that side (without using the fist) may achieve the same effect, though it might take a bit longer.

The underlying principle in all these "methods" is that you control the side that is active rather than forcefully trying to open the side that is inactive. This is the rule that has been learned in the traditional Yogic setting.

—Avatar Adi Da Samraj
January 24, 1983

When to Use the Hamsadanda

The hamsadanda may be used at any time, for the sake of general well-being and equanimity and free attention. It may also be used in specific circumstances or to address specific conditions, including the following:

To correct specific signs of energy imbalance. When there are signs of imbalance, the hamsadanda is a very practical means to correct this and bring balance to the body. In particular, when the thinking mind is hyperactive, use the hamsadanda in the right armpit to calm the left side of the brain and its associated functions.

To address acute or chronic imbalances. It can be beneficial to make frequent use of the hamsadanda when you experience an acute imbalance (such as the onset of a cold or flu, or if you have nasal allergies). If you notice that one or the other nostril is chronically dominant, forcing a chronic imbalance of emotional disposition, frequent use of the hamsadanda also is recommended. It is possible to use it at any time during the day, even while at work or when simply relaxing. Keep the crutch with you as long as there is some chronic imbalance that you are addressing, such that you can correct it at will, throughout the day. Freely use it at any time. Once you have achieved a general condition of balance, you may find that intensive use of the hamsadanda is no longer necessary.

Before and/or during meditation. Adi Da Samraj recommends the use of the hamsadanda previous to meditation, or at the beginning of a period of meditation, or even (if necessary) throughout an occasion of meditation. Avatar Adi Da gave the following instruction about this simple and effective means of supporting depthful meditation:

> *Throughout the cycle of twenty-four hours, the body naturally alternates the life-current through the nervous system, frontally and spinally, through the mechanism of the spine or the total nervous system. It is quite natural, then, as the phases of the day change— from light to dark in all the stages of the day and night—for the breathing to change, such that, at some hours, one nostril is open and the other closed, and, at other times, this circumstance is reversed. And so it goes, in cycles, throughout the twenty-four hours of the day. Therefore, whenever you sit to meditate—and, because you sit for meditation several times a day, you could be sitting at just about any time, perhaps—one or the other of the nostrils may seem to be not breathing freely.*
>
> *In and of itself, this circumstance in itself is not unhealthy. In fact, it is quite a natural part of the cycling of the body. But the natural cyclings of the body may not be altogether auspicious for the ultimate purposes of meditation. Therefore, you must go beyond this simple natural orientation of the body and prepare the body specifically for meditation by balancing the current.*
>
> *The breath in the nostrils indicates how the current is functioning in the body. Thus, the tendency that is registered in how the nostrils are working suggests whether the body is being more right-sided or more left-sided, more yang or more yin, more open in the right-sided nerve or the left-sided nerve.*

Meditation should be done with the body balanced and the current functioning centrally, rather than too right-sided or too left-sided. Many things that take time could accomplish this balance, but balance can be reached very simply and directly with the hamsadanda. For example, you could do various kinds of pranayama exercises, perform alternate-nostril breathing, and (perhaps) eventually accomplish what you may accomplish with the hamsadanda in a very short period.

If your meditation does not simply move toward deep meditation but (perhaps) moves in and out of it—in other words, if there are intervals in your meditation, or if it takes some time to enter into deep meditation—the hamsadanda can continue to be used during the time of sitting. Therefore, it is always good to carry the hamsadanda to the Communion Hall. Use it while sitting in meditation— and, if convenient, perhaps use it at other times of the day. But certainly use it in meditation, or at least as a preliminary to meditation, such that you enter into meditation in a balanced state, with the life-current functioning centrally. When you sit for meditation, you may be basically balanced. Just test the nostrils. If they are balanced, there is no need to use the hamsadanda.

—Avatar Adi Da Samraj
March 24, 1986

General Guidelines for Use of the Hamsadanda

Be sure the hamsadanda is fitted to your body. The hamsadanda should be tall enough to stand upright in your armpit and apply basic pressure. It is not necessary to apply much pressure to the armpit with the hamsadanda, so it should not be so tall that it creates stress on the shoulder or other parts of the arm. But neither should you need to lean into it to create that pressure.

Use the hamsadanda in a quiet, private setting, whenever possible. If you are making use of the hamsadanda in a public setting where you do not have privacy, such as at work, find a place where you can release "self"-consciousness as much as possible, thereby supporting the principal process of devotional Communion with Avatar Adi Da Samraj, as well as general "conductivity" practice.

Using the Hamsadanda

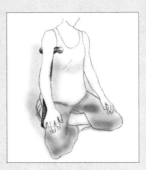

General Use of the Hamsadanda

• Be sure you are in a stable, comfortable sitting position. Maintain a normal, upright position, with the body supported on the axis of the spine. Such an asana will maximize the effectiveness of the hamsadanda and allow easeful observation of the changes in bodily energies and breathing patterns.

• Notice which nostril is breathing more freely, and place the hamsadanda into the armpit on that same side of the body. The hamsadanda should press lightly in the armpit, but do not lean on it to support the weight of your body.

• Notice the effects on the breath and the bodily energies. You will feel the opening of the closed nostril, and a balancing of the breath. In time, you will also feel a balancing of bodily, emotional, and mental energies.

• Alternate the hamsadanda from side to side, as needed. When the open nostril is closed, and vice versa, switch the hamsadanda to the opposite arm. Alternate between arms until both nostrils are breathing freely and equally, and the body and the breath are relaxed.

If You Do Not Have a Hamsadanda

• **Fist pressure.** If you do not have a hamsadanda, you can place your fist firmly into the armpit on the same side of the body as the nostril that is breathing more freely. The knuckles should press into the area toward the front of the body but behind the curve of the pectoral muscle that stretches across the chest.

• **Lying down.** It is also possible to simply lie down on one side of the body and have a similar effect, although the change in breath-pattern will take longer. Simply lie down on the same side as the more "open" nostril. To increase the effectiveness of this exercise, you may also place your fist in the armpit on the same side.

---

4. Water Immersion

Immersing oneself in water is an important energy-healing practice that Avatar Adi Da describes as essential to whole bodily well-being. He categorizes it as a form of healing touch, with benefits similar to massage (as described in chapter 4 and chapter 7):

Rightly Administered Massage Breaks The Apparent Isolation Of the body-sensation—"Reminding" the one Being Massaged That the body Is Not a Separate "something", but (Rather) Part Of An Indivisible Energy-Field.

"Touch"-Association and (Also) Association With water—Both Of Which Should Be Engaged By My Any Devotee With Significant Frequency (For Relatively Extended periods of time, and, Also, For brief periods of time)—Break Down The Tendency For people To Become physically Isolated and Shut Down, and Serve To Magnify Whole bodily Energy-"Conductivity". Indeed, Traditions Of water-Baptism Are, In General, Related To bodily Health, As Well As Being A Spiritual Matter—Because Immersion Of the body In

water (or "Touch" By water itself) Is A Means For Unifying the body's Life-Energy and For Establishing "Touch"-Continuity With The Indivisible Energy-Totality Of The Natural Domain.

Immersion Of the body In Natural Healing waters (such as hot springs, clean lakes, or moving streams and rivers, or at ocean beaches, or Even In Such A Simple Form As a bath or a shower), and Even Any Kind Of bodily "Touch" By water (either hot or cold or Alternately hot and cold), Unifies the body's Life-Energy, and (Thereby) Serves The General Energy-"Conductivity" and Well-being Of the body and The Wholeness Of body-Integrity, Restoring The Connectedness Of the body To The Universal Energy-Environment (As Well As The Universal physical Environment) Of Which it Is Inherently A Part.

Both "Touch"-By-Massage and "Touch"-By-water Restore the body To Its Natural Condition Of Non-"Difference" From The Universal Energy Of Which it Is Inherently A Part. Therefore, Practices Involving "Touch"-By-Massage and Practices Involving "Touch"-By-water Are Both Basic (and Even Necessary) To The Maintenance Of bodily Health and Well-being.

—Avatar Adi Da Samraj
The Dawn Horse Testament

Immersion in water is an effective energy-balancing practice in part because of the energetic properties of water. Those who intensively study the qualities of water have discovered that water is a highly conductive and responsive medium.[16] Thus, etheric energy is easily conducted in water, supporting the equalization of the etheric field in relationship to the physical, the release of toxins (physical as well as emotional), and the balancing of bodily energies altogether.

As Avatar Adi Da indicates, there are a variety of ways and settings in which to practice water-immersion (detailed below, p. 331). Water immersion can be practiced in private, but it can also be engaged in a larger social context, such as in public hot springs or resorts or spas. Optimally, these circumstances are what Avatar Adi Da describes as "body positive" settings, wherein there is an enjoyable and straightforward culture of acceptance of the human body. Avatar Adi Da described such a circumstance as

16. For example, see *The Hidden Messages in Water* by Masaru Emoto (Hillsboro, OR: Beyond Words Publishing, 2004) and *The Water Wizard: The Extraordinary Properties of Natural Water* by Viktor Schauberger, translated by Callum Coates (Dublin: Gill & MacMillan, 1999).

healing in and of itself, saying "there is something regenerative and life-positive about it".[17]

When to Practice Water Immersion

Regularly, and even daily, as part of the formal disciplines given by Avatar Adi Da to His devotees. At times when you do not have access to a bath or to an appropriate body of water, a shower can serve as a means of water immersion.

When there are signs of imbalance in attention and energy.

When you are feeling isolated or disconnected from the environment and others.

To prevent illness. Hot and cold showers and hot foot baths are particularly useful for this purpose (see below for specific instructions).

General Guidelines for Water Immersion

Practice water immersion in a safe, body-positive environment. If in a larger social circumstance, select a location and setting that is conducive to contemplative participation in the healing process of water immersion. If immersing yourself in rivers, lakes, or oceans, be sure the location is safe, and (optimally) enter the water in the company of others.

It is important to consider the source and quality of the water. Natural spring waters are ideal, as are waters from unpolluted lakes, rivers, and oceans. This is not to say that one should not make use of showers and baths from municipal water sources—such water still carries the capability to conduct energy and to balance the body's energies. But it is very beneficial to make use of pure, natural sources of water whenever possible. Ocean water and mineral waters bring additional benefits to detoxification and healing of the physical body.

Make use of hot and/or cold water. Hot and cold water have different and complementary effects on bodily energies, and both are important to make use of, depending on the body's needs. See descriptions below for details.

17. From spoken instructions given on October 23, 2008.

Specific Water Immersion Practices

In addition to the simple practice of immersing yourself in a body of water, there are also several specific practices recommended by Avatar Adi Da.

Immersion in Hot Water

Immersing oneself in hot water has many proven benefits—but chief among them is that it mimics the purifying effects of fever. Fever is a powerful form of self-purification through intense elimination. During a fever, the metabolism of every cell increases dramatically, quickly consuming excess accumulations of toxic waste (thus causing the heat or fever) and speeding up the processes of elimination, especially through the skin via perspiration.

Immersion in hot water increases the heat of the body, creating an eliminative episode similar to a natural fever. This should only be engaged to the point of revitalizing and strengthening the body, never to the point of enervation.

- Immerse yourself in hot water (whether in a tub or hot spring, and so forth).

- Remain immersed until the body is quite hot and the face perspiring.

- End the hot bath by cooling off over an extended period of time or by using a cold bath or cold shower.

Hot Footbaths

Hot footbaths are particularly effective when there are signs of reversal of the current in the frontal line of the body. One sign of this reversal is that instead of the head being cool and the feet being warm, the head will be hot and the feet cold.* This often occurs in someone who is coming down with a cold or a flu.

- Wrap yourself in blankets. You can also have a cup of warm herbal tea to warm the core of the body.

- Place feet in a tub of hot water. Make the water as hot as you can tolerate.

- Keep the feet immersed until you break into a sweat. This usually occurs in about 10–20 minutes. Add hot water if the water in the tub cools.

Taking a hot footbath to the point where you break out into a sweat is best. That is the crisis that makes the difference. It usually takes about twenty minutes or so. It is good to wrap yourself in a blanket or towel, maybe even have hot herbal tea or something to heat the navel also. After some time, up to twenty minutes, there is perspiration and a feeling of the energies normalizing, and so forth. If you have some sickness, like a flu or whatever, it, of course, may not be able to be reversed immediately.

—Avatar Adi Da Samraj
April 2, 1998

Hot and Cold Showers

It is important to make use of both warmer water and cooler water. Using the opposites—hot and cold alternately— is a part of engaging what water can do to stimulate and calm the physical and make it whole, unify it with the universal environment of which it is inherently a part.

—Avatar Adi Da Samraj
August 11, 2007

Avatar Adi Da recommends using hot and cold water in the shower as a simple way to make use of the benefits

(continued on next page)

* Another way to heat (and retain the heat in) the body is to wrap the vital region or "hara" (Japanese for "abdomen")—either with a cloth made specifically for this purpose (known as a "hara warmer", or "haramaki"), or with a shawl or blanket.

He describes above. If practiced on a regular basis, alternating hot and cold waters can strengthen the body and make it more adaptable to sudden environmental and weather changes.

- Take a hot shower for several minutes, until the body becomes hot. The optimal temperature of the water will vary from person to person and season to season, but it should be noticeably hot, not warm.

- Quickly make the water completely cold. Stay under the cold water for up to a minute or more, exposing every part of the body to it.

- Repeat twice or more, if you like, ending with cold.

5. Tensing-and-Relaxing

This simple exercise involves first tensing and then relaxing the whole body, or a particular area of the body, in coordination with the breath-cycle. The tensing (in conjunction with focused inhalation-reception) serves to intensify and direct life-energy, and the relaxation (in conjunction with focused exhalation-release) allows the intensified life-energy to flow.

Therefore, tensing-and-relaxing is a means to bring life-energy to the whole body or to a particular place in the body where energy is stuck, or where an influx of healing life-energy is needed (such as in the case of a specific injury or illness). In some basic sense, this is a way to perform the laying on of hands on yourself. (The laying on of hands is described in detail in chapter 6.) Instead of using your hands to direct energy to another person, you are using your muscles and other bodily parts (as well as the breath and attention) to direct healing life-energy in your own body.

This exercise benefits the physical body in many ways:

- Invigorates and refreshes the body

- Expands blood vessels and arteries

- Brings freshly oxygenated blood to obstructed or toxified tissues and organs

- Can, in some circumstances, help to lower high blood pressure

When to Practice Tensing-and-Relaxing

Daily. Several times a day, and at random, to serve and maintain full "conductivity", and (thus) a state of overall bodily well-being and balance.

As a means of first aid. The tensing-and-relaxing exercise may be used as a kind of first aid to bring oxygenated blood to and to intensify the life-force in an area of the body that is beginning to manifest illness or that has experienced injury. If, for example, you get a sore throat, you can practice tensing-and-relaxing in the area of the throat. Or, if you are recovering from a sprained or painful joint, you can focus tensing-and-relaxing there to aid the healing process. See below for specific instruction on tensing-and-relaxing as first aid.

To energize and clear the mind. Focusing tensing-and-relaxing on the lower brain (at the locus where the back of the neck meets the base of the head) frees obstructions and intensifies "conductivity" in the spinal line between the body and the head. It also energizes the brain, clears the mind and sharpens it, permits the free flow of cerebrospinal fluid, and coordinates the motor responses of the brain with the general bodily activities below the head.

General Guidelines for Tensing-and-Relaxing

Maintain equanimity in breath and bodily posture. The exercise should be performed without jerking the muscles or the breath.

Spend equal time on the inhalation and exhalation phases. If you inhale-tense for about five seconds, then exhale-release for about five seconds.

Repeat. When practicing this exercise, always repeat it several times in succession.

Practicing Tensing-and-Relaxing

Whole Bodily Tensing-and-Relaxing

• Stand in a relaxed position. Keep the spine straight and the hands open.

• Inhale to the vital with the feeling of a whole bodily "yawn" (contracting the bodily base—or the urethra, sex organs, perineum, and anus—at the end of the inhalation).

• Hold the breath and tense every part of the body with the feeling that life-energy is "locked" into every part. Tense every area of the body—including the fingertips, scalp, face, toes, and back.

• Exhale and relax-release life-energy to every part of the body and, via every part, to Infinity.

• Pause while holding out the exhaled breath. Allow the body-mind-complex to relax profoundly in total feeling-participation with the universal field of natural life-energy, and allowing that life-energy to continue to radiate via every function of the body-mind-complex into all relations, to Infinity.

• The lengths of inhalation and exhalation should be balanced, or essentially equal in measure. The length of time for each phase could be 2–5 seconds or more—but does not need to be specifically measured, and will vary from individual to individual. The important point is to keep the inhalation and exhalation phases balanced.

Tensing as First Aid

• Inhale, tensing the specific location of the body (such as the throat, an ankle, and so forth) as you breathe. Place your attention on the bodily area.

• With the inhalation, feel healing energy and attention collect in that area of the body.

• Exhale, and relax the specific bodily location you are focusing on. Relax your attention there.

• On exhalation, release the disease or symptom of illness, feeling negative energies flow out of the body to Infinity, through the bloodstream and the lungs and even the entire surface of the skin. Feel that all toxic waste has been returned to its lawful place in the realm of the natural elements.

• The length of inhalation and exhalation will vary from individual to individual, but should always be balanced, or approximately equal in length.

Tensing the Region at the Base of the Skull

The ascending flow of natural life-energy in the spinal line is often obstructed at the base of the skull, where the back of the head and neck meet. This region is associated with the lower part of the brain, which is the area of connection between the brain and body. That area is the part of the brain that controls the body's involuntary life-processes, such as respiration and heartbeat. Tensing and relaxing the muscles in that region, at the base of the skull, helps free obstructions in the energy flow in the spinal line, thereby magnifying "conductivity" in the Circle.

• Relax the whole body. Bring feeling-awareness to the lower rear of the head where it meets the back of the neck. Concentrate attention and feeling in that specific location.

• Inhale and physically tense the muscles in that region of the head and neck, maintaining the concentration of feeling-attention in the area. Initially, practice broad contraction of the muscles in the region. With practice, you will be able to isolate the muscles at the upper part of the neck and the base of the skull, performing the tensing there

(continued on next page)

without moving the head or engaging the jaw or other neck muscles. Increase tension as you inhale, and then hold the tension for 2–5 seconds, or more.

• Exhale and completely release all the contraction in the area. Do not focus on the area of obstruction—but feel the renewed flow of enlivening natural life-energy radiating from the lower rear of the head to the entire brain and even throughout the entire body.

• Allow the magnified natural life-energy to flow in its natural circuit in the frontal and spinal lines.

• Do this at random times during the day.

---

*I*n 1977, I was at the Mountain Of Attention Sanctuary, serving as Avatar Adi Da's personal physician. One day I received a message that Avatar Adi Da's throat was sore and so I should come to His house. The message also said that Avatar Adi Da wanted to speak to His devotees, and so He wanted me to come to His house to heal His throat—not to just diagnose it, but to heal it. I went directly to Avatar Adi Da's house, not knowing exactly what I was going to do—but when I arrived Avatar Adi Da was already outside, and His throat problem was gone. He said, "I did it Myself." And Avatar Adi Da then described the practice of first-aid tensing-and-relaxing that He had used to heal His throat, and which He then gave to all of His devotees to practice.

—Daniel Bouwmeester, MD

6. Twirling

Twirling is a simple exercise that realigns and reintegrates (or "reharmonizes") the physical body and the etheric body, thereby serving the yellow-red conjunction. It is used specifically as a means to re-balance right/left energy imbalances, and Avatar Adi Da also recommends it as an effective way to help prevent and remedy jet lag.

Twirling is a natural exercise in which the physical (elemental) body and its etheric energy-field are realigned and reintegrated, thereby equalizing (or refreshing) the living being. This is done in two ways: (1) Through the concentration of feeling-attention in the exercise, the etheric is made to fully pervade the elemental, and (2) through the action (or movement) of twirling, the elemental and the etheric are made into a single vortex, whereby they become equalized (or integrated) in a mutual harmony, a common "speed".

—Avatar Adi Da Samraj
Twirling and Jet Lag

For the fullest instruction on the practice of twirling, including Avatar Adi Da's full essay about the practice, please see the Dawn Horse Press booklet *Twirling and Jet Lag*.

When to Practice Twirling

Daily. Because the Earth's rotation is a constant influence on the body and its etheric-energy field, it may be useful for some people to practice twirling on a daily basis. Twirling is generally recommended as part of the daily practice of right-life disciplines. It can be done at the end of the calisthenics routine, before performing the dead pose. It can also be done randomly, at any time of day, as needed.

To correct specific signs of energy imbalance. When there are signs of imbalance, twirling is an effective means to bring balance to the body's energies.

Particularly when you feel "uptight" (or contracted), twirl left to right, with a fully expansive and radiant feeling, as in conscious exhalation. When you feel more enervated or "washed out", twirl right to left, with a feeling of being in-filled, collected, centered, and intensified, as in conscious inhalation.

—Avatar Adi Da Samraj
Twirling and Jet Lag

Before and after fast travel—particularly to remedy symptoms of jet lag. Traveling at a rapid speed—whether by car or train or plane, and so forth—dissipates etheric energy, thereby weakening the conjunction of the physical body and the etheric field. Avatar Adi Da explains that this is the cause of jet lag. Therefore, it is useful to make use of twirling to re-harmonize the physical body and its etheric-energy field, thereby strengthening their conjunction. Of course, travel by plane causes the most extreme disharmony, because of the speed and distance covered in such a short period of time. Specific instructions about applying twirling when traveling are included below.

General Guidelines for Twirling

Breathe fully, to and from the vital center, and specifically to the crown of the abdomen (three to four finger breadths below the navel) as you twirl. Practice the three parts of general "conductivity" practice throughout any session of twirling: Radiate from the heart, relax the frontal line, and inhale-receive/exhale-release.

As Avatar Adi Da says, "Twirl with great feeling and abandon." In twirling, the body becomes a vortex, or conduit, that pulls the etheric energy down into the body, to the bodily base. When twirling is done with "great feeling", it increases the intake of etheric energy into the body from above and facilitates the flow of etheric energy in the physical body, thereby maximizing the effectiveness of the physical twirling.

Maintain an erect posture throughout the exercise. Keep the eyes open and softly focused straight ahead as much as possible. (You can experiment with twirling with the eyes closed if nausea or extreme dizziness are tending to occur—however, eyes open is preferable.) You should not "skate" around the room, but maintain your feet in essentially the same spot as you twirl.

Note that twirling is not for everyone. Some find that they cannot maintain upright stability when twirling, and others find the side effects of dizziness and nausea to be too strong. In such cases, do not continue twirling, or engage the practice only minimally.

Practicing Twirling

General Form of Twirling

• Stand erect, facing straight ahead, with arms extended straight out to the sides at shoulder level. The head, arms, and upper body should be held erect in this original position throughout this exercise.

♦ **Twirl toward your right (clockwise) when you feel agitated** and "uptight", in order to relax and expand your energy. When twirling in the clockwise (or left-to-right) direction, hold the right palm up and the left palm down.

♦ **Twirl toward your left (counterclockwise) when you are feeling enervated** and "washed out", in order to increase and concentrate energy. When twirling in the counterclockwise (or right-to-left) direction, hold the left palm up and the right palm down.

Note: In rare cases, an individual may find that the normal polarity described here is reversed, such that twirling clockwise increases energy and twirling counterclockwise relaxes

(continued on next page)

and expands energy. Every individual should experiment and find what works in his or her case (or even discontinue the practice if needed).

• Twirl with great feeling and abandon—speeding up gradually and going as fast as is comfortable for you. Remember to keep your eyes looking straight ahead, without really focusing, and your feet in one spot as you twirl.

• Twirl 10–12 times, or as many times as you like—until you are spontaneously moved to finish.

• When you stop twirling, stand still and breathe deeply and intentionally into the bodily "battery". This allows the steadiness of the eyes and the composure of the body to return. Look straight ahead in one direction. Avoid collapsing and falling down, if possible. You will likely feel very dizzy and the impulse to lie down might be strong, especially when you are first learning to twirl. But, if at all possible, remain standing, practicing intentional breathing to the core of the abdomen. Standing and intentional breathing will help the dizziness and other effects of the twirling quickly subside. After practicing for a short period of time, all of these effects will be resolved quickly and twirling will cause little or no dizziness, the eyes will quickly revert to normal, and the body will come to balance.

• Begin another cycle of twirling, if desired. Do this only after bodily composure has returned. Perform as many twirling cycles as you feel are useful.

• Lie down and begin the dead pose. Once you have completed your final cycle of twirling, allow the visual and other bodily effects of twirling to subside before lying down. Maintain the dead pose for 5–10 minutes.

The Dead Pose

• Lie on your back with the legs extended and with the arms extended to either side of the body at a comfortable distance.

• Close the circuits of the hands by touching the thumb and forefinger of each hand.

• With deep feeling, intentionally and completely relax each part of the body in descending order, beginning with the crown of the head and moving downward, including all the muscles, the ligaments, each internal organ, and the entire surface of the skin. Relax the brain, hair, forehead, eyes, sinuses, ears, teeth, jaw, tongue, throat, and neck. Relax the arms, in downward sequence from the shoulders to the fingertips. Relax the sternum, the heart, the lungs, the solar plexus, the stomach, the navel, the genitals, and the perineum. Relax the legs, in downward sequence, from the hips to the toes. (This intentional and systematic relaxation, from the crown of the head to the toes, can also be applied to relaxation of the frontal line in "conductivity" practice.)

• Maintain normal breathing (receiving natural life-energy on inhalation, and radiating life-energy in all directions on exhalation), remaining in the pose for up to 3–4 minutes or longer, or until the breath is even and you feel relaxed and energized.

• A variation on the dead pose is to cross the left ankle over the right to create the relaxation circuit (as described on pp. 314–15). Note that in some individuals the polarity is reversed, and in such a case the right ankle should be crossed over the left. Experiment to determine which is more relaxing in your case.

(continued on next page)

Twirling to Prevent or Remedy Jet Lag

Fast travel sets up a motion in the energy-feeling system that takes a little time to return to human speed. Therefore, rest at least briefly in the "dead pose" after travel, and twirl several times every hour or so after traveling in a conveyance.
—Avatar Adi Da Samraj
Twirling and Jet Lag

When twirling to prevent or remedy the symptoms of jet lag, follow these additional guidelines:

• As soon as possible after your flight, rest in the dead pose and then begin an intensified program of twirling, following the instructions given above.

♦ If you traveled in a westward direction, twirl toward your left (counterclockwise).

♦ If you traveled in an eastward direction, twirl toward your right (clockwise).

♦ If you traveled northward or southward (not crossing any time zones), symptoms of jet lag do not tend to arise. However, if signs of imbalance occur after north/south travel, follow the instructions under "General Form of Twirling" given at the beginning of this section (twirling toward your right if you feel agitated, and turning toward your left if you feel enervated).

• Perform several sessions of twirling, or whatever number of cycles you are moved to do, every hour or so.

• Complete your twirling session (as well as each twirling cycle) with the dead pose, as described above.

• Magnify the effectiveness of the dead pose by using polarity screens, especially when you have traveled in an eastward direction. Use the relaxation circuit in this case (see pp. 314–15).

Avatar Adi Da Samraj
Adi Da Samrajashram, 2008

Transcend One-Sidedness
In Every Moment

by His Divine Presence,
Avatar Adi Da Samraj

By controlling the nervous system—or, in other words, becoming responsible for the nervous system over time and fitting it to intelligent practice—the body-mind-complex will tend to maintain a condition of harmony. Naturally, throughout the day, the body is responding to changes in the energies of the natural environment and to the various kinds of patterns associated with the natural cycles—such as waking and sleeping, for instance. The breath is constantly moving side to side, sympathetic and coincident with these other changes that appear and are noticeable in the environment. The body-mind-complex is always involved in the dynamics of the life-principle, expressed as two "playful" opponents.

However, that which appears as "two" in the body and in the "world", that which appears as "play", is simply a "play" upon One Fundamental Reality. By tendency, human beings have a rather primitive "cartoon" sense of mind and body. This "cartoon" is a reflection of the dualistic "point of view" of ordinary "experience". In Reality, there is no such thing as mind apart from body. They are the same thing. What you see as body is only modifications of the One Prior Condition. You can become profoundly frustrated if you try to find some inner "mind" part of you that you can separate from the physical part of you. . . .

There are not two things, except in the sense that there is a "play". Everything that is in your "experience" is a form of dynamics—a dynamo, a game of apparent opposites. But both halves are the life-principle, the single Divine Reality. Therefore, you must understand this, and enjoy a greater realization (or disposition) than that which is simply tending to be played out hour after hour. Yes, the breathing changes from side to side throughout the day and night, and your habits change during the course of a day, and you wake and move about, and you rest and you go to sleep, and you do all kinds of things in cycles, and you have moods and changes of state of all kinds. But every aspect of that is a modification of the One Essential Condition in Which you priorly inhere. You must always remember and fundamentally realize That Condition. If you forget to do that, and merely become involved in the dynamics of "experiencing" itself, you become ultimately frustrated by changes, by one-sidedness. All one-sidedness is always threatened by its opposite. Everything passes. Everything changes in the "play of experience".

You must Realize your Identity with That Single Field in Which the body-mind-complex is arising. Therefore, you must enjoy the advantage of being able to transcend the dynamic "play of experience". You must transcend the thinking mind—because it is only one half. You are afraid to die when you are thinking, and you are afraid to stop thinking. But it is just half of the brain. There is another half of the mind that is silent and receptive and does not contain any words. You must not only know the other side, the quietness of the mind, but you must also realize that Single Reality, Single Principle in which the quietness of the mind and the chattering of the mind both arise.

You must enjoy the capability to transcend one-sidedness in every moment. Be released from the opposites of psycho-physical life, and become capable of naturally intuiting and resting in the Prior Current in Which all aspects of the "experiential" body and mind and brain are arising. ∎

From a discourse given by Avatar Adi Da Samraj on March 5, 1980.

PERFECTLY FREE ENERGY

Perfectly Free Energy

by His Divine Presence,
Avatar Adi Da Samraj

In the form of any apparent human individual, There <u>Is</u> <u>Only</u> The Intrinsically egoless Self-Presence of Perfectly Free Energy (or Self-Existing Self-Radiance) <u>Itself</u>.

The <u>Only</u> Self-Identity of any apparent human individual <u>Is</u> The Intrinsic Self-Awareness of and <u>As</u> The egoless Self-Presence of Perfectly Free Energy (or Self-Existing Self-Radiance) <u>Itself</u>.

Reality Itself <u>Is</u> <u>Only</u> Perfectly Free Energy (or Self-Existing Self-Radiance) <u>Itself</u>.

There <u>Is</u> <u>Only</u> The Self-Existing Self-Radiance of Reality <u>Itself</u>.

There <u>Is</u> <u>Only</u> The Intrinsic Self-Evidence of Self-Existing and Self-Radiant Self-Presence <u>Itself</u>.

There <u>Is</u> <u>Only</u> The Self-Radiant Self-Presence of Perfectly Free Energy—Self-Conscious <u>As</u> "It" <u>Is</u>.

<u>That</u> Self-Evident Self-Presence <u>Is</u> The "It" of <u>Is</u>.

"It" <u>Is</u> Conscious Light.

"It" <u>Is</u> One and Indivisible.

"It" <u>Is</u> Self-Existing Bliss.

"It" <u>Is</u> Intrinsically Without "location" (or "point of view").

"It" <u>Is</u> Intrinsically Without "separateness" (or "<u>a</u> self").

"It" <u>Is</u> Intrinsically Without "difference".

"It" <u>Is</u> Intrinsically Without modification, modulation, or mediation.

"It" is not an "object".

"It" <u>Is</u> Perfectly Subjective-<u>Only</u>.

"It" <u>Is</u> egoless Love.

"It" <u>Is</u> all-and-All.

"It" <u>Is</u>—<u>As</u> "It" <u>Is</u>—Perfectly Sufficient.

The epilogue is drawn from the essay "The Way To <u>Be</u> 'It'", in *The Aletheon*.

APPENDICES

The Colors of the Cosmic Mandala

Avatar Adi Da's description of the colors of the Cosmic Mandala is given in the following essay excerpt, and then summarized in the table on the next page. (See also color plate after p. 36.)

The Cosmic Mandala of abstract inner lights is a display that is (otherwise) associated with planes of possible inner (or subtle) "experience". Thus, the red light inwardly represents (and, literally, illuminates) the gross body and the gross "world". . . . However, all of the other lights (golden yellow, soft-white, black, and bright blue) represent (and, literally, illuminate) the several hierarchical divisions within the subtle body and the subtle "worlds"—and the causal body (which is associated with attention itself, or the "root" of egoity itself, and which is, itself, only felt, and not seen, and which is expressed as the fundamental feeling of separateness, relatedness, otherness, and "difference", and which is "located" as a knot of "self"-contraction in the right side of the bodily apparent heart) is not visually represented (nor is it, otherwise, literally illuminated) by the lights and "worlds" of the Cosmic Mandala.

The wide golden yellow circle of the Cosmic Mandala represents (in conjunction with the outermost red circle) the outermost (or lowest) dimension of the subtle body—which is the etheric (or pranic, or life-energy) body (or dimension) of conditional "experience". The narrower soft-white circle of the Cosmic Mandala represents the ordinary (or sense-based) mind. The narrow black circle (or band) is a transitional space, where mental activity is suspended. The blue circle of the Cosmic Mandala is the domain of the mental observer, the faculty of discriminative intelligence and the will, and the very form of the subtly concretized ego-"I" (or the inner-concretized subtle "self"). And the Brilliant White Five-Pointed Star is the Epitome and Very Center of the Cosmic Mandala—Such That It Provides the Uppermost Doorway to What Is (altogether) Infinitely Above (and, Ultimately, Beyond) the Cosmic Mandala (or Above and Beyond the body itself, the brain itself, and the mind itself).

—Avatar Adi Da Samraj
"I (Alone) Am The Adidam Revelation",
Eleutherios

357

The Colors of the Cosmic Mandala

Color Field	Dimension of Existence	Associated Conditional Appearance and/or Function
red	gross	physical
golden yellow	subtle (outermost)	etheric (natural life-energy)
soft-white	subtle (mid-range)	lower mental (sense-based mind)
black	(transitional space— apparently lightless)	mental activity suspended
blue	subtle (highest)	upper mental (discriminative intelligence and will)
Brilliant White (Star Form)	Uppermost Doorway to What Is Infinitely Above and Beyond the Cosmic Mandala	the perceived Source-Light, Beyond all energy dimensions and planes of mind

Sources: *Easy Death* and *Eleutherios.*

What is Above and Beyond is Conscious Light, Avatar Adi Da's Radiant "Bright" Form. Here Avatar Adi Da further clarifies the relationship between His Star-Form and His "Bright" Divine Form Above and Beyond.

I may . . . be perceived above the body, As the Pentagrammic Star—but even that Form is intermediate (or merely "objectively perceived") within the conditional (or psycho-physical) realm (and the body-mind-complex). I (Myself) Am "Bright" Above the Star— Found, primarily (or most directly), by touch, rather than by some other sense (such as sight).[1] In Truth, My "Bright" Sun-Form . . . cannot be perceived by the faculties. I am not an "Object"—whether Above or Deep. When all contraction is felt beyond, when all limits are transcended in devotional Communion with Me—then My "Bright" Sun is Realized, My "Bright" Form is Realized, My "Bright" Person is Realized.

—Avatar Adi Da Samraj
"Be Washed, From Head To Tail, By Heart-Devotion To Me",
Hridaya Rosary

---

1. See pp. 152–55 for more on finding Avatar Adi Da via the sense of touch.

The Five Sheaths of the Human Structure

Avatar Adi Da Samraj, in agreement with traditions of eso-teric understanding, describes five functional levels, or sheaths, of the human being. Each sheath belongs to one of the three (broader) categories of existence: gross, subtle, or causal.

The gross dimension is a single sheath, the subtle dimension is composed of three sheaths, and the causal dimension is a single sheath. Avatar Adi Da sometimes uses the traditional Sanskrit names for these functional bodies (or "koshas"). Avatar Adi Da's descrip-tion of the five sheaths of the body-mind-complex is given by Him in the following quotation, and then summarized in the table below.

According to the Hindu Yogic tradition (the propositions of which can, and should, be duplicated by real present-time obser-vation), the human being is composed of five parts (or sheaths):

(1) the physical body, or the physical sheath (called "anna-mayakosha", or the "food-sheath", which is the gross body),

(2) the sheath of systematic life-energy (called "prana-mayakosha", which is the first of the three parts of the subtle body), consisting of natural, bodily-structured, and body-activating energy plus the operations and "experiencings" and emotional associations of the physical senses,

(3) the sheath of sense-based mind (called "manomayakosha", which is the second of the three parts of the subtle body), con-sisting of the mental and psychic operations associated with the impressions of the physical senses,

(4) the sheath of intelligence (called "vijnanamayakosha", which is the third, or last, of the three parts of the subtle body), consisting of functional awareness in the form of discrimina-tive thought, mentally presumed egoity, and will, and

(5) the sheath of Inherent Being, Consciousness, and Bliss (apparently individualized, and, thus, limited, and, as such, called "anandamayakosha", which is the causal body).

These five sheaths are arranged in an hierarchical order—with the gross body as the outermost (or most descended) dimension, and with all parts (apparently) arising as apparent relations of the fifth sheath (and, Really, with each and every part arising in, or as an apparent modification of, the Self-Existing, or Transcendental, and Self-Radiant, or Inherently Spiritual, and Self-Evidently Divine Self-Nature, Self-Condition, Source-Condition, and Self-State Itself).

—Avatar Adi Da Samraj
"The Hidden and Ultimate (Though Chronically Frustrated)
Purpose of J. Krishnamurti's Effort", *The Basket of Tolerance*

The Five Sheaths			
Sheath	Associated Dimension	Sanskrit Terminology	Associated Cosmic Mandala Color
physical body	gross	annamayakosha ("the food body")	red
etheric body	subtle (first)	pranamayakosha (the "pranic body", or the "body of personal life-energy")	golden yellow
brain-mind	subtle (second)	manomayakosha (the "sheath of the lower mind")	soft-white
will and discriminative intelligence	subtle (third)	vijnanamayakosha (the "sheath of higher mind, or intellect")	blue
root-presumption of "self"	causal	anandamayakosha (the "causal body" or "sheath of conditional bliss")	(does not appear in Cosmic Mandala vision)

Sources: *The Basket of Tolerance* and *Eleutherios*.

APPENDIX C

The Three Phases of Healing

Avatar Adi Da describes the practice of healing (and health maintenance) as unfolding in three phases:

1. Purification
2. Re-balancing
3. Regeneration

Each of these phases is associated with a functional system of the body that is utilized to bring about that phase of the healing process:

1. The **circulatory system** principally serves the **purification** phase.

2. The **nervous system** principally serves the **re-balancing** phase.

3. The **endocrine system** principally serves the **regeneration** phase.

Understanding the three phases—through personal study of Avatar Adi Da's instructions, as well as through the educational means offered by the Radiant Life Clinic—can help guide what actions need to be taken to re-establish (or maintain) well-being, and will naturally orient the healing process to a systems-based approach. (See chapter 3 for a full discussion on the systems-based approach to healing.)

Following is a summary list of right-life disciplines that can be engaged to support each phase of the healing process (and the general practice of maintaining health and well-being). The practices listed below that are also described in this book are followed by the chapter number (or specific appendix) where they are discussed. For Avatar Adi Da's *Dawn Horse Testament* instruction on the three phases of healing, see *Right Life Is Free Participation In Unlimited Radiance*.

First Phase of Healing = Purification

Participate in this phase via:

- Intensified turning of the faculties to Avatar Adi Da (chapter 4) and study of His instruction (on health and healing, and in general)

- Inspecting life-patterns leading to illness or imbalance

  Note: Such inspection occurs in the cultural context of consideration with other devotees of Avatar Adi Da with whom you are intimate, for the sake of in-depth observation and understanding of the unconscious physical, emotional, and mental patterns behind any imbalance. Make note of habit-patterns related to diet and health in your diary, and write a "life and meditation confession" to assist the consideration process.

- Engaging the Devotional Prayer of Changes (chapter 5) and the laying on of hands (chapter 6)

  Note: Both the Devotional Prayer of Changes and the laying on of hands are effective in all three of the phases, and therefore can be used throughout the healing process (and in the health maintenance process).

- Abandoning contracted (or reactive) emotion, engaging free feeling-attention

  Note: This practice is directly related to the etheric body. Avatar Adi Da states in *The Dawn Horse Testament*: "The emotional condition of the body-mind-complex Directly Affects The Energy Of the etheric body, Including The Energy Of the bodily-Based being In General. . . . In its usual condition, the body-mind-complex Contracts emotionally—and The Resulting emotional Obstructions Have Their physical Counterparts In the organs of the body. The Processes Of Assimilation and Elimination Are Interrupted—and, Instead Of Simply Being Nourished Through The Process Of breathing and eating, the body Is Made toxic (Primarily, By the Obstructed <u>emotional</u> condition of the body-mind-complex)." Therefore, abandoning emotional reactivity is key to the purification phase of health and healing.

- Eating a purifying raw fructo-vegetarian diet (appendix D)

- Fasting

- Getting adequate rest

- Avoiding aggressive, manipulative, and reactive behavior (in your own life, and as depicted in forms of entertainment)

- "Conscious exercise" (appendix D), modifying the forms as needed to account for physical limits experienced during a health crisis

Second Phase of Healing = Re-balancing

Participate in this phase via:

- Meditation

- Sacred activity (such as devotional chanting and sacramental worship)

- "Conscious exercise" (appendix D), again modifying your routine if experiencing physical limits due to a health crisis

- Pranayama (chapter 8)

- General "conductivity" practice (including the formal three-part exercise of general "conductivity") (chapter 5)

- Yogic "conductivity" massage (chapter 7)

- Use of hamsadanda and/or polarity screens, as well as other therapeutic modalities and/or devices that have a re-balancing effect on the body (chapter 8)

- Twirling, water immersion, tensing-and-relaxing (chapter 8)

- All forms of functional, practical, relational, and cultural "self"-discipline

Third Phase of Healing = Rejuvenation

Regenerated endocrine chemistry should be naturally produced by the body itself once purification and re-balancing are established. Support this regenerated chemistry via:

- Persisting in a non-toxic and stress-reduced life and dietary habit

- Conserving and re-circulating sexual energy altogether, including by means of "own-body Yogic sexual practice" (if there are signs that this practice is called for), or (for those who are sexually active) in "emotional-sexual conscious exercise", or "emotional-sexual devotional Communion" (appendix D)

• Meditative retreats

> Note: Going on retreat supports all three phases of healing and health maintenance, but especially the regeneration phase.

A Note on Right Use of the "Objective" Approach to Health and Healing

Avatar Adi Da instructs His devotees to apply the systems-based approach when accounting for the three phases of healing. However, He also indicates that the conventional analytical approach to health and healing should be used as a secondary approach when appropriate.

The "objective" Approach—Including The Assessment Of signs and symptoms, Analysis Of Test Results, Diagnosis, and The Suggesting Of A Regime Of Remedy (All Based On Conducting An "objective" Analysis Of the body From Without)—Should Be Applied Intelligently By My Devotees, Whenever Appropriate and Necessary, In The Context Of Consultation With Rightly Qualified medical Practitioners. Although The "objective" Approach To Health-Related Matters Is A Secondary Approach For My Devotees, That Approach Has Its Right Use In the hands of those Skilled and Qualified To Engage It, and In circumstances in which It Is Necessary and Required (Including Cases In Which the body Does Not Currently Have The Strength To Effectively Engage The systems-Based Approach). My Devotees Must Never Disregard The Potential Necessity Of The "objective" Approach (Depending On The Particular Health Issue In Question). Furthermore, My Devotees Should Never Indulge In Any Kind Of Illusions That Disease Will Somehow Be "Magically" Cured. Rather, My Devotees Must Understand That Disease Is An Opportunity To Be Responsible For one's Health, For Right Participation In Life, and For All The Factors That Govern The Health and The Equanimity Of the body-mind-complex.

—Avatar Adi Da Samraj
The Dawn Horse Testament

General "Conductivity" Practice:
Right-Life Disciplines Relating to
Diet, Exercise, and Emotional-Sexual Practice

All of the right-life disciplines given by Avatar Adi Da relate to the energy dimension of existence, and, thus, support the yellow-red conjunction.

All the practices that have to do with health and well-being in the Reality-Way of Adidam are energy-based. They are "conductivity" practice with a "conscious process" dimension of responsibility. And that is everything, including diet and exercise, emotional-sexual practice, Yogic "conductivity" massage practice, and so on. All of it is energy-based and associated with "conductivity" in the Circle of the body-mind-complex.

A very basic dimension of the right-life practice of the Reality-Way of Adidam has to do with these yellow-red health responsibilities.

—Avatar Adi Da Samraj
August 3 and July 30, 2008

There are three categories of right-life discipline in the Reality-Way of Adidam that very directly serve and support the balance and integration of the yellow-red conjunction:

- Right Diet
- "Conscious Exercise"
- Emotional-Sexual Practice

Right Diet

The specific diet Avatar Adi Da recommends to His devotees, and to all of humankind, is a 100-percent raw fructo-vegetarian diet.[1] Because there is readily available life-energy in raw food (whereas life-energy is compromised, or "dumbed down", when food is cooked), it is particularly effective at supporting the relationship between the physical and the etheric.

1. Avatar Adi Da notes that right medical advice should be followed if other foods are needed in the individual case. See *Green Gorilla* for details on adapting to and applying the raw diet in an intelligent and self-responsible manner.

The raw diet is a diet that allows for the physical to be optimally associated with its energy-field, whereas the grosser forms of diet are constantly making the bodily form gross, and disconnecting (or dissociating) it from the etheric, and creating imbalances and obstructions in the etheric and the relationship between the etheric and the physical.

—Avatar Adi Da Samraj
July 30, 2008

For Avatar Adi Da's summary instructions on the raw diet as an ego-transcending practice that establishes bodily well-being, frees attention and energy for the Spiritual process, and restores balance to the Earth-system as a whole, see *Green Gorilla: The Searchless Raw Diet.*[2]

"Conscious Exercise"

"Conscious exercise" is both a series of formal exercise routines and a fundamental disposition brought to all ordinary activities of life.

The By-Me-Given Discipline Of "Conscious Exercise" Is Simply The Conscious (or Natural and Intentional) Coordination Of body and Life-Energy, Through Feeling, In The Midst Of activity. The Disciplines Of Right Posture, Right Bodily Movement, and Right breathing—Associated With Full and Constant Feeling-attention, and Full and Constant Whole bodily Devotional Turning To Me, During the Natural activities of everyday life—Are The Fundamental Regimen (or Practice) Of "Conscious Exercise". . . .

. . . "Conscious Exercise" Naturally Re-Aligns and Integrates the physical body With the etheric body (or Energy-body), With The Natural Life-Energy, and (As The Case May Be) With The Divine Transcendental Spiritual Energy That I Avatarically Self-Reveal and Self-Transmit.

—Avatar Adi Da Samraj
The Dawn Horse Testament

---

2. The forthcoming edition of *The Eating Gorilla Comes In Peace: The ego-Transcending Principle Applied To Diet and The Regenerative Discipline of True Health* will present Avatar Adi Da's comprehensive instruction on diet and health.

The formal exercise routines of "conscious exercise" are engaged in devotional response to Avatar Adi Da and include: Da Namaskar (a form of the traditional Surya Namaskar), Da Fours (a simple physical exercise created by Avatar Adi Da, with feet and hands placed on the ground), Da Chi Gong (a form of Chi Gong created by Avatar Adi Da), a recommended sequence of Hatha Yoga poses, and a recommended sequence of calisthenics.

For Avatar Adi Da's *Dawn Horse Testament* instruction on "conscious exercise", see pp. 190–225 of *Right Life Is Free Participation In Unlimited Radiance*. Avatar Adi Da's full instruction on the formal "conscious exercise" routines, and on "conscious exercise" in general, is given in *Conscious Exercise and The Transcendental Sun* (new edition forthcoming).

Emotional-Sexual Practice

Avatar Adi Da gives His devotees a range of disciplines for the right "conductivity" of sexual energy. These disciplines involve taking responsibility for one's emotional-sexual patterning and for conducting sexual energy in the Circle of the body-mind-complex—which He calls "own-body sexual responsibility".

For those who are in a sexually active intimacy, the beginning form of emotional-sexual practice is called "emotional-sexual conscious exercise", and, for those who are initiated into the Transcendental Spiritual process, this becomes "emotional-sexual devotional Communion". In *The Dawn Horse Testament*, Avatar Adi Da describes these practices as a process of "Obliging sexual activity itself To Become A Rightly intimate (but Not ego-Binding), and Positively Life-Energy-Conserving, and Truly Rejuvenative Form Of 'Conscious Exercise' (and, Potentially, In Due Course, Of Transcendentally Spiritually Active 'Emotional-Sexual Devotional Communion')".

The disciplines Avatar Adi Da gives for right "conductivity" of sexual energy are devotional and ego-transcending in nature, and help to keep the Circle rightly polarized and the body-mind-complex as a whole in balance.

*In The Only-By-Me Revealed and Given "Radical" Reality-Way
Of The Heart (or "Radical" Reality-Way Of Adidam), The Primary
Characteristic Of Right Practice Relative To emotional-sexual
Discipline (Whether sexually active Or celibate) Is <u>ego-Transcending
Equanimity</u>.*

—Avatar Adi Da Samraj
The Dawn Horse Testament

Avatar Adi Da's detailed instructions on emotional-sexual practice are given in *Always Enact Fidelity To Me*. Additional instruction is given in *The Complete Yoga of Emotional-Sexual Life* and *Love of The Two-Armed Form* (new edition forthcoming).

Literature on Energy Healing from Avatar Adi Da's *Basket of Tolerance*

The publications listed in this appendix are drawn from Avatar Adi Da's *Basket of Tolerance*. *The Basket of Tolerance* is a library collection and associated bibliography (with accompanying commentarial essays by Avatar Adi Da Samraj) of many thousands of books, articles, and audio-visual materials on all significant aspects of the collective wisdom and understanding of humankind.

Avatar Adi Da has revealed that all cultural traditions are actually part of the "common inheritance" (or collective treasure) of humankind, which He has named "the Great Tradition". To truly understand the human condition, and the history of the various human cultural endeavors (both ordinary and extraordinary), all the traditions within this Great Tradition must be seen as a single totality. To serve this understanding, Avatar Adi Da has comprehensively organized works exemplary of these traditions into *The Basket of Tolerance*. *The Basket of Tolerance* is also a tool for comprehending the completing nature of the Reality-Way of Adidam. The full purpose of *The Basket of Tolerance* is encapsulated in its subtitle: *The Perfect Guide To Perfectly <u>Unified</u> Understanding of The One and Great Tradition of Humankind, and of The Divine Reality-Way of Adidam As The Perfect <u>Completing</u> of The One and Great Tradition of Humankind.*

Avatar Adi Da writes:

> *If it is embraced in its totality,* The Basket of Tolerance *should prove itself to be a useful and valuable resource for right study and right understanding of the historical traditions of truly human culture, practical "self"-discipline, perennial "religion", universal*

"religious" mysticism, esoteric (but now openly communicated) Spirituality, Transcendental Wisdom, and would-be Most Perfect (or Divine) Enlightenment.

—"The Collective (Exoteric <u>and</u> Esoteric) Gathering of The Great Tradition", *The Basket of Tolerance*

This appendix offers a selection of publications from *The Basket of Tolerance* on energy healing, in the particular subject areas covered in *Conductivity Healing*. This list is not intended to account for all energy-healing practices and traditions, but rather was created to demonstrate the universal principles and ancient origins of energy healing (as they appear in both ancient traditions and modern practices), and to offer a practical resource for learning and experimenting with different forms of healing touch that can be applied in the context of Avatar Adi Da's instructions and principles. The selection of publications was made by the staff of the Adidam Library, guided by Avatar Adi Da's indications (given over many years) of publications that are particularly useful to study or particularly representative of certain areas of study. In each of the subject areas delineated below, there are more titles included in the full *Basket of Tolerance* bibliography. Thus, this appendix is a selected bibliography intended to be representative, rather than exhaustive. As with *The Basket of Tolerance* itself, the publications within each subject category are listed in a sequence that is intended to form a kind of "argument"—rather than being organized alphabetically (by author name or book title) or chronologically (by publication date).

Note that Avatar Adi Da calls His devotees to experiment with all healing modalities with intelligence, discrimination, and personal responsibility—and with the intention to discover what supports free attention and energy for living the Reality-Way of Adidam. He does not recommend that His devotees pursue any healing practice as a form of seeking, or as a replacement for practice of the full life of right-life discipline He gives.

For more information on Avatar Adi Da's *Basket of Tolerance*, visit **www.adidamlibrary.com**.

Beyond Materialism

Space-Time Is Love-Bliss, by the Divine World-Teacher, Ruchira Avatar Adi Da Samraj. Truth For Real, no. 2. Middletown, CA: The Dawn Horse Press, 1999.

The Bridge to God, by Avatar Adi Da Samraj. Middletown, CA: The Dawn Horse Press, 2013. CD, recorded in 1980.

The Western Prohibition Against Higher Knowledge and Realization, by the Divine World-Teacher, Ruchira Avatar Adi Da Samraj. The *Basket of Tolerance* Booklet Series, no. 1. Middletown, CA: The Dawn Horse Press, 1999.

Direct Examination of the Structure and Roots of One's Own Body-Mind Provides Immediate Evidence of the Hierarchical Structure of Reality and Immediate Proof of the Divine Nature and Purpose of Existence, by the Divine World-Teacher, Ruchira Avatar Adi Da Samraj. The *Basket of Tolerance* Booklet Series, no. 2. Middletown, CA: The Dawn Horse Press, 2001.

The Transmission of Doubt: Talks and Essays on the Transcendence of Scientific Materialism through Radical Understanding, by Da Free John [Adi Da Samraj]. Clearlake, CA: The Dawn Horse Press, 1984.

The Living Energy Universe: A Fundamental Discovery that Transforms Science and Medicine, by Gary E. Schwartz and Linda G. Russek. Newburyport, MA: Hampton Roads Publishing, 2006.

Quantum Shift in the Global Brain: How the New Scientific Reality Can Change Us and Our World, by Ervin Laszlo. Rochester, VT: Inner Traditions, 2010.

The Realm of Supraphysics: Mind, Energy and Matter in the Light of the Vedas, by Rishi Kumar Mishra. New Delhi: Rupa and Company, 2003.

Science Consciousness Freedom, by Manoranjan Basu. Varanasi: Indica Books, 2005.

Transcendence of the Western Mind: Physics, Metaphysics, and Life on Earth, by Samuel Avery. Lexington, KY: Compari, 2003.

Conscious Acts of Creation: The Emergence of a New Physics, by William A. Tiller, Walter E. Dibble, Jr., and Michael J. Kohana. Walnut Creek, CA: Pavior Publishing, 2001.

Psychoenergetic Science: A Second Copernican-Scale Revolution, by William A. Tiller. Walnut Creek, CA: Pavior Publishing, 2007.

Energy Healing—General

Overviews—

Energy Medicine East and West: A Natural History of Qi, by David F. Mayor and Marc S. Micozzi. Edinburgh: Elsevier, 2011.

The Healing Arts: A Journey Through the Faces of Medicine, by Ted J. Kaptchuk and Michael Croucher. London: British Broadcasting Corporation, 1986.

World Medicine: The East West Guide to Healing Your Body, by Tom Monte. New York: Putnam Publishing Group, 1993.

Healing and Restoring: Health and Medicine in the World's Traditions, edited by Lawrence E. Sullivan. New York: Macmillan Publishing Company, 1989.

Planet Medicine: Origins, by Richard Grossinger. 7th ed. Berkeley, CA: North Atlantic Books, 2003.

Planet Medicine: Modalities, by Richard Grossinger. 7th ed. Berkeley, CA: North Atlantic Books, 2003.

The Tao of Bioenergetics: East-West, by George A. Katchmer, Jr. Jamaica Plain, MA: Yang's Martial Arts Association, 1993.

Ancient Traditions of Energy Healing—

Shamanic Traditions of Energy Healing

Aboriginal Men of High Degree: Initiation and Sorcery in the World's Oldest Tradition, by A. P. Elkin. Rochester, VT: Inner Traditions, 1994.

The Straight Path: A Story of Healing and Transformation in Fiji, by Richard Katz. Cambridge, MA: Addison-Wesley, 1993.

The Secret Science Behind Miracles, by Max Freedom Long. Santa Monica, CA: DeVorss & Company, 1997.

Boiling Energy: Community Healing among the Kalahari Kung, by Richard Katz. Cambridge, MA: Harvard University Press, 1982.

Shamanic Healing and Ritual Drama: Health and Medicine in Native American Religious Traditions, by Ake Hultkrantz. New York: Crossroad Publishing, 1992.

Shamans, Healers, and Medicine Men, by Kalweit Holger. Boston: Shambhala, 1992.

The World We Used to Live In: Remembering the Powers of the Medicine Men, by Vine Deloria, Jr. 2nd ed. Golden, CO: Fulcrum Publishing, 2006.

Western Traditions of Energy Healing

The Nature of the Whole: Holism in Ancient Greek and Indian Medicine, by Vicky Pitman. Delhi: Motilal Banarsidass, 2006.

The Expressiveness of the Body and the Divergence of Greek and Chinese Medicine, by Shigehisa Kuriyama. New York: Zone Books, 2002.

Healing in the History of Christianity, by Amanda Porterfield. New York: Oxford University Press, 2010.

Hildegard von Bingen's Physica: The Complete English Translation of Her Classic Work on Health and Healing, translated by Priscilla Throop. Rochester, VT: Healing Arts Press, 1998.

The Healing Secrets of the Ages, by Catherine Ponder. Rev. ed. Marina Del Rey, CA: DeVorss Publications, 2000.

The Abkhazian Book of Longevity and Well-Being, by Murat Yagan, edited by Ya'qub ibn Yusuf. Vernon, BC: Kebzeh Publications, 1999.

Alternative Healing the Sufi Way, by Shaykh Taner Ansari and Shaykh Kevin Germain. 2nd ed. Nassau, NY: Ansari Publications, 2012.

The Book of Sufi Healing, by Shaykh Hakim Abu Abdullah Ghulam Moinuddin. Rev. ed. Rochester, VT: Inner Traditions, 1991.

Indian Traditions of Energy Healing (Including Ayurveda)
(See also relevant titles under "Healing-Touch Practices")

Ayurveda: The Science of Self-Healing, by Dr. Vasant Lad. Twin Lakes, WI: Lotus Press, 2009.

Eternal Health: The Essence of Ayurveda, by Partap Chauhan. Faridabad, India: Jiva Institute, 2000.

Ayurveda: The Ancient Indian Art of Natural Medicine and Life Extension, by Birgit Heyn. Rochester, VT: Healing Arts Press, 1990.

The Ayurveda Encyclopedia: Natural Secrets to Healing, Prevention, & Longevity, by Swami Sadashiva Tirtha. 2nd ed. Unadilla, NY: Ayurveda Holistic Center Press, 2012.

Recipes for Immortality: Medicine, Religion, and Community in South India, by Richard S. Weiss. Oxford: Oxford University Press, 2009.

Daoist Traditions of Energy Healing (Including Qi Gong)

Tao of Health and Longevity, by Da Liu. Rev. ed. New York: Paragon House Publishers, 1991.

Health and Long Life: The Chinese Way, by Livia Kohn. Cambridge, MA: Three Pines Press, 2005.

Chi Gong: The Ancient Chinese Way to Health, by Paul Dong and Aristide H. Esser. Berkeley, CA: Blue Snake Books, 2008.

Ki: A Practical Guide for Westerners, by William Reed. Tokyo: Japan Publications, 1986.

Healing Light of the Tao: Foundational Practices to Awaken Chi Energy, by Mantak Chia. Rochester, VT: Destiny Books, 2008.

Wisdom Chi Kung: Practices for Enlivening the Brain with Chi Energy, by Mantak Chia. Rochester, VT: Destiny Books, 2008.

Traditional Chinese Medicine

Yinyang: The Way of Heaven and Earth in Chinese Thought and Culture, by Robin R. Wang. New York: Cambridge University Press, 2012.

The Web That Has No Weaver: Understanding Chinese Medicine, by Ted J. Kaptchuk. Rev. ed. New York: Macgraw-Hill, 2008.

Between Heaven and Earth: A Guide to Chinese Medicine, by Harriet Beinfeld and Efrem Korngold. New York: Ballantine Books, 1991.

The Complete Book of Chinese Health and Healing: Guarding the Three Treasures, by Daniel Reid. Boston: Shambhala, 1995.

Health and Long Life: The Chinese Way, by Livia Kohn. Cambridge, MA: Three Pines Press, 2005.

Tibetan Traditions of Energy Healing

Tibetan Healing: The Modern Legacy of Medicine Buddha, by Peter Fenton. Varanasi: Pilgrims Publishing, 1999.

Healing from the Source: The Science and Lore of Tibetan Medicine, by Yeshi Dhonden, translated and edited by B. Alan Wallace. Ithaca, NY: Snow Lion Publications, 2000.

Tibetan Medicine: A Unique and Comprehensive Amalgamation of Science, Art, and Philosophy, by Dr. (Amji) Tsering Dhondup. Sidphur, India: Tsering Lhamo Dolmaling Institute, 2003.

Modern Traditions of Energy Healing—

Energy Medicine, by Laurence E. Badgley, MD. San Bruno, CA: Human Energy Press, 1985.

The Energy Healing Experiments: Science Reveals Our Natural Power to Heal, by Gary E. Schwartz, with William L. Simon. New York: Atria Books, 2008.

Matrix Energetics: The Science and Art of Transformation, by Richard Bartlett. New York: Atria Books, 2007.

Vibrational Medicine for the Twenty-First Century: The Complete Guide to Energy Healing and Spiritual Transformation, by Richard Gerber. New York: HarperCollins, 2000.

Vibrational Medicine: The #1 Handbook of Subtle-Energy Therapies, by Richard Gerber. Rochester, VT: Bear & Company, 2001.

The Energy Within: The Science Behind Eastern Healing Techniques, by Richard M. Chin. New York: Paragon House, 1995.

Inner Bridges: A Guide to Energy Movement and Body Structure, by Fritz Frederick Smith. Atlanta: Humanics New Age, 1986.

Medicine for the Twenty-First Century: The Key to Healing with Vibrational Medicine, by Keith Mason. Rockport, MA: Element, 1992.

The Subtle Body Practice Manual: A Comprehensive Guide to Energy Healing, by Cyndi Dale. Boulder, CO: Sounds True, 2013.

The Quantum Doctor: A Quantum Physicist Explains the Healing Power of Integral Medicine, by Amit Goswami. Rev. ed. Charlottesville, VA: Hampton Roads, 2011.

The Other Medicine that Really Works!: How Energy Medicine Can Help You Heal in Body, Mind and Spirit, by Heidi DuPree. CreateSpace, 2013.

Energy Healing: The Essentials of Self-Care, by Ann Marie Chiasson. Boulder, CO: Sounds True, 2013.

Energy Medicine: The Scientific Basis, by James L. Oschman. 2nd ed. Oxford: Elsevier, 2016.

Energy Medicine: Balancing Your Body's Energies for Optimal Health, Joy, and Vitality, by Donna Eden, with David Feinstein. London: Penguin Books, 2008.

Brief Selections Related to Specific Elements of the Human Psycho-Physical Structure—

The Vital Center and Energy Healing

The Solar Plexus or Abdominal Brain, by Theron Q. Dumont. Des Plaines, IA: Yoga Publication Society, 1974.

Hara: The Vital Centre of Man, by Karlfried Graf Durckheim. New York: Samuel Weiser, 1975.

The Mind and Energy Healing

The Seven Day Mental Diet: How to Change Your Life in a Week, by Emmet Fox. Originally published New York: Harper and Brothers, 1935. Numerous editions of this brief pamphlet are available in a variety of formats.

The Intention Experiment: Using Your Thoughts to Change Your Life and the World, by Lynne McTaggart. New York: Atria Books, 2013.

Cultivating Stillness: A Taoist Manual for Transforming Body and Mind, by Lao-Tzu, with commentary by Shui-ch'ing Tzu, translated by Eva Wong. Boston: Shambhala, 1992.

Meditation Saved My Life: A Tibetan Lama and the Healing Power of Mind, by Phakyab Rinpoche. Novato, CA: New World Library, 2017.

Healing-Touch Practices

The Laying On of Hands—

The Rainbow in Your Hands, by Albert Roy Davis and Walter C. Rawls, Jr. Hicksville, NY: Exposition Press, 1976.

Hands of Light: A Guide to Healing through the Human Energy Field, by Barbara Ann Brennan. Toronto: Bantam Books, 1988.

Therapeutic Touch: A Practical Guide, by Janet Macrae. New York: Knopf, 1988.

Massage—

The Book of Massage: The Complete Step-by-Step Guide to Eastern and Western Techniques, by Lucinda Lidell. 2nd ed. New York: Simon and Schuster, 2001.

The History of Massage: An Illustrated Survey from Around the World, by Robert Noah Calvert. Rochester, VT: Healing Arts Press, 2002.

The Complete Book of Massage, by Clare Maxwell-Hudson. New York: Random House, 1988.

Massage Therapy: Principles and Practice, by Susan G. Salvo. St. Louis, MO: Elsevier, 2016.

Ancient Indian Massage: Traditional Massage Techniques Based on the Ayurveda, by Harish Johari. Delhi: Munshiram Manoharlal, 1984.

Ayurvedic Massage: Traditional Indian Techniques for Balancing Body and Mind, by Harish Johari. Rochester, VT: Healing Arts Press, 1996.

Ayurvedic Massage for Health and Healing: Ayurvedic and Spiritual Energy Approach, by S. V. Govindan. 2nd ed. New Delhi: Abhinov Publications, 2000.

Amma Therapy: A Complete Textbook of Oriental Bodywork and Medical Principles, by Tina Sohn and Robert Sohn. Rochester, VT: Healing Arts Press, 1997.

Thai Yoga Massage: A Dynamic Therapy for Physical Well-Being and Spiritual Energy, by Kam Thye Chow. Rochester, VT: Healing Arts Press, 2004.

Chinese Qigong Massage: General Massage, by Dr. Jwing-Ming Yang. Jamaica Plain, MA: Yang's Martial Arts Association, 1992.

Chi Nei Ching: Muscle, Tendon, and Meridian Massage, by Mantak Chia and William U. Wei. Rochester, VT: Destiny Books, 2013.

Other Healing-Touch Modalities—

Polarity Therapy

Your Healing Hands: The Polarity Experience, by Richard Gordon. Oakland, CA: Wingbow Press, 1978.

Polarity Therapy: The Complete Collected Works, vol. 1, by Dr. Randolph Stone. Sebastopol, CA: CRCS Publications, 1986.

Polarity Therapy: The Complete Collected Works, vol. 2, by Dr. Randolph Stone. Sebastopol, CA: CRCS Publications, 1987.

Polarity Therapy: Healing with Life Energy, by Alan Siegel. London: Masterworks International, 2006.

Reflexology

The Original Works of Eunice D. Ingham: Stories the Feet Can Tell Thru Reflexology, by Eunice D. Ingham. St. Petersburg, FL: Ingham Publishing, 1938.

The Reflexology Manual: An Easy-to-Use Illustrated Guide to the Healing Zones of the Hands and Feet, by Pauline Wills. Rochester, VT: Healing Arts Press, 1995

The Reflexology Atlas, by Bernard C. Kolster, MD, and Astrid Waskowiak, MD. Rochester, VT: Healing Arts Press, 2005.

Total Reflexology: The Reflex Points for Physical, Emotional, and Psychological Healing, by Martine Faure-Alderson. Rochester, VT: Healing Arts Press, 2008.

Acupressure

Press Point Therapy, by G. Bendix. New York: Avon Books, 1978.

Trigger Point Self-Care Manual for Pain-Free Movement, by Donna Finando. Rochester, VT: Healing Arts Press, 2005.

Ortho-Bionomy: A Path to Self-Care—Simple Techniques to Release Pain and Enhance Well-Being, by Luann Overmyer. Berkeley, CA: North Atlantic Books, 2009.

The Natural Healer's Acupressure Handbook: G-Jo Fingertip Technique, by Michael Blate. New York: Henry Holt, 1976.

The Acupressure Atlas, by Bernard C. Kolster, MD, and Astrid Waskowiak, MD. Rochester, VT: Healing Arts Press, 2007.

Shiatsu: Japanese Massage for Health and Fitness, by Elaine Liechti. 2nd ed. Shaftesbury, England: Element, 1998.

Meridian Qigong Exercises: Combining Qigong, Yoga, and Acupressure, by Dr. Jwing-Ming Yang. Wolfeboro, NH: YMAA Publication Centre, 2016.

Buddhist Healing Touch: A Self-Care Program for Pain Relief and Wellness, by Ming-Sun Yen, MD, Joseph Chiang, MD, and Myrna Louison Chen. Rochester, VT: Healing Arts Press, 2001.

Marma Points of Ayurveda: The Energy Pathways for Healing Body, Mind, and Consciousness with a Comparison to Traditional Chinese Medicine, by Vasant Lad and Anisha Durve. Albuquerque, NM: The Ayurvedic Press, 2015.

Supplemental Practices
Polarity Screens—

Polarity Screens: A Safe, Simple, and Naturally Effective Method for Restoring and Balancing the Energies of the Body Based on the Practical Instruction of the Divine World-Teacher and True Heart-Master, Da Avabhasa (The "Bright") [Adi Da Samraj]. Middletown, CA: The Dawn Horse Press, 1991.

The L. E. Eeman Report: The Pioneering Years of Biocircuitry, compiled by Tom Brown from the writings and lectures of Leon Ernest Eeman. Garberville, CA: Borderland Sciences, 1989.

Co-operative Healing: The Curative Properties of Human Radiations, by L. E. Eeman, with J. Cecil Maby. Mokelumne Hill, CA: Health Research, 1987.

Biocircuits: Amazing New Tools for Energy Health, by Leslie Patten, with Terry Patten. Tiburon, CA: H.J. Kramer, 1988.

Pranayama—

The Secrets of Prana, Pranayama, and Yoga-Asanas, by Swami Narayanananda. 5th ed. Gylling, Denmark: Narayanananda Universal Yoga Trust & Ashrama, 1979.

Breath, Mind, and Consciousness, by Harish Johari. Rochester, VT: Destiny Books, 1989.

Swara Yoga: The Tantric Science of Brain Breathing, by Swami Satyananda. Munger, India: Bihar School of Yoga, 1984.

Prana and Pranayama, by Swami Niranjanananda Saraswati. Munger, India: Yoga Publications Trust, 2016.

Pranayama: A Path to Healing and Freedom, by Allison Gemmel Laframboise, with Yoganand Michael Carroll. CreateSpace, 2015.

The Tao of Natural Breathing: For Health, Well-Being, and Inner Growth, by Dennis Lewis. Berkeley, CA: Rodmell Press, 2006.

Water Immersion—

Healing Springs: The Ultimate Guide to Taking the Waters, by Nathaniel Altman. Rochester, VT: Healing Arts Press, 2000.

The Indian Spa: Ayurveda, Yoga, Wellness, Beauty, by Kim Inglis. Singapore: Talisman Publishing, 2008.

Deep Immersion: The Experience of Water, by Robert Lawrence France. Sheffield, VT: Green Frigate Books, 2003.

The Healing Energies of Water, by Charlie Ryrie. Boston: Journey Editions, 1999.

The Complete Book of Water Healing, by Dian Dincin Buchman. Chicago: Contemporary Books, 2002.

WATSU: Freeing the Body in Water, by Harold Dull. Middletown, CA: Harbin Springs Publishing, 1997.

Twirling—

Twirling and Jet Lag: A Simple and Effective Method for Overcoming Jet Lag, Tension, and Fatigue. Based on the practical Instructions of the Divine World-Teacher and True Heart-Master, Da Avabhasa (The "Bright") [Adi Da Samraj], by Bill Gottlieb. Clearlake, CA: The Dawn Horse Press, 1992.

GLOSSARY

This glossary contains technical terms and phrases not otherwise defined in the text. (See the index to find where in the text other technical terms and phrases are defined and discussed.) Unless otherwise indicated, all books mentioned in the glossary are published by the Dawn Horse Press (www.dawnhorsepress.com).

A

Adi Da Samrajashram—See **Hermitages and Sanctuaries**.

Adidam Ruchiradam—See **"Radical" Reality-Way of Adidam Ruchiradam**.

Avatar/Avataric—See **Divine Avataric**.

B

The Basket of Tolerance—Avatar Adi Da's master bibliography and commentary on the one "Great Tradition" of humankind. For more detail and a selection of *Basket of Tolerance* publications related to energy healing, see appendix E.

Beloved—A Title of intimate respect and devotional acknowledgement for Avatar Adi Da Samraj.

Bhagavan—The Title "Bhagavan" is an ancient one used over the centuries for many Spiritual Realizers of India. It means "blessed" or "holy" in Sanskrit. When applied to a great Spiritual Being, "Bhagavan" is understood to mean "bountiful Lord", or "Great Lord", or "Divine Lord".

body-mind-complex—This term is used by Avatar Adi Da specifically to indicate the "aggregate" of the four principal faculties (of mind, emotion, body, and breath) that are the complete functioning structure of the human being.

"Bright"—By the word "Bright" (and its variations, such as "Brightness"), Avatar Adi Da refers to Conscious Light, the Self-Existing and Self-Radiant Divine Reality. Avatar Adi Da named His own Self-Evidently Divine Self-Condition "the 'Bright'" in His infancy, as soon as He acquired the capability of language. This term is placed in quotation marks to indicate that Avatar Adi Da uses it with the specific meaning described here.

C

Company (Avatar Adi Da's)—While Avatar Adi Da Samraj sometimes uses the word "Company" to indicate being directly in proximity to His physical Body during His physical human Lifetime, more commonly the word describes being directly turned to Avatar Adi Da's Divine Avataric Form, Presence, and State, and thus and thereby coming into His Divine Avataric Company. Therefore, Avatar Adi Da's Company is Eternal, and not limited to His physical human Lifetime.

Consciousness Itself—The Real (Prior) Self-Nature, Self-Condition, and Self-State of every being and thing, rather than the awareness associated with a conditional (and apparently separate) "point of view".

"consider"/"consideration"—Avatar Adi Da uses the word "consider" (and its variants) to refer to "a process of one-pointed (but, ultimately, thoughtless) concentration on and exhaustive observation of a particular 'object', function, person, process, or condition, until the essence or ultimate obviousness of that 'object' is clear" [*Love of The Two-Armed Form*].

D

Darshan—A Hindi word literally meaning "seeing", "sight", or "vision". Devotees of Avatar Adi Da commonly use this to refer specifically to a formal occasion of sacred sighting of His bodily (human) Form. Darshan of Avatar Adi Da also occurs (both during and after Avatar Adi Da's physical Lifetime) via beholding photographs or video recordings of His bodily (human) Form, and through the remembered recollection of His bodily (human) Form.

degenerative/regenerative—Degenerative activity is characterized by a depletion of energy and a breaking of the circuit of "conductivity". Regenerative activity is characterized by equanimity and magnification of energy in the Circle. In terms of sexual activity in particular, a degenerative orgasm is one in which energy is depleted from the circuit via the sudden release of life-energy and/or ejaculation of bodily fluids. Regenerative orgasm (and regenerative sexual activity in general) is characterized by continuous and magnified "conductivity" of energy in the Circle.

Divine Avataric—This phrase encapsulates the Nature of Avatar Adi Da's Appearance and Work. "Avatar" (from the Sanskrit "avatara"), is a traditional term for a Divine Incarnation, and literally means "One who is descended, or 'crossed down' (from, and as, the Divine)". A unique Intervention is indicated—not merely a man or woman who has attained Enlightenment by Spiritual effort, or even a reincarnating Master, but a direct appearance, in physical form, of the One Supreme Reality and Infinite Consciousness.

Divine Self-Realization—The Most Perfect Awakening to Avatar Adi Da's "Bright" (and Infinitely Love-Bliss-Full) Divine Reality-State, in which Awakening all traces of egoic limitation are perfectly transcended. Synonymous with "Divine Enlightenment". See also **stages of life**.

E

Enlightenment/En-Light-ened—Divine Enlightenment is a matter of the actual conversion of the body-mind-complex to the State of Divine Conscious Light Itself. Avatar Adi Da sometimes writes the noun "Enlightenment" (and also the verb "Enlighten") with "Light" set apart by hyphens, in order to emphasize this point.

F

faculties (four principal)—The four principal faculties of the human body-mind are body, emotion (or feeling), mind (or attention), and breath. These four principal faculties account for the entirety of the human being.

frontal line / spinal line—The principal subtle energy-pathways in the human structure. Natural life-energy, Spiritual Energy, and Transcendental Spiritual Energy flow downward (or in a descending direction) through the frontal line, which extends from the crown of the head to the bodily base. Likewise, natural life-energy, Spiritual Energy, and Transcendental Spiritual Energy flow upward (or in an ascending direction) through the spinal line, which extends from the bodily base to the crown of the head. (Many traditional Yogas espouse mystical ascent via the spinal line and the brain core.)

functional, practical, and relational disciplines (of the Reality-Way of Adidam)—The most basic functional, practical, and relational disciplines are forms of appropriate action and responsibility in relation to diet, health, exercise, sexuality, work, service to and support of Avatar Adi Da's Work, and cooperative association with other practitioners of the Reality-Way of Adidam.

G

Great Tradition—Avatar Adi Da's term for the total inheritance of human, cultural, religious, magical, mystical, Spiritual, and Transcendental paths, philosophies, and testimonies, from all the eras and cultures of global humankind—which inheritance has (in the present era of worldwide communication) become the common legacy of humankind.

H

Hermitages and Sanctuaries—Traditionally, Realizers have been provided with set-apart places where they were free to do their Spiritual work in an appropriately secluded circumstance. And these places became Spiritually Empowered through their Presence and work.

In this same traditional manner, devotees of Avatar Adi Da provided places where He lived during His physical human Lifetime—set-apart places in which He could Do His Blessing-Work for the sake of humankind as a whole, as well as Doing His specific Transcendental Spiritual Work with His devotees. Avatar Adi Da's Transcendental Spiritual Presence and Blessing-Force are constantly Active in His Hermitages and Sanctuaries, and (as such) they are set apart and preserved and glorified for the sake of His Eternal Divine Work with all beings.

During His Lifetime, Avatar Adi Da Established and Transcendentally Spiritually Empowered three Hermitages and two Sanctuaries:

• Adi Da Samrajashram, the Island of Naitauba in Fiji, Avatar Adi Da's principal Hermitage and the primary Seat from which His Divine Transcendental Spiritual Blessing Flows to the entire world

  • Tat Sundaram Hermitage, in Northern California

  • Ruchira Dham Hermitage, on Lopez Island in Washington State

  • The Mountain Of Attention Sanctuary, in Northern California

  • Da Love-Ananda Mahal, in Hawaii

K

"know"—Avatar Adi Da Samraj places this word (and its variants, such as "knowing" and "knowledge") in quotation marks to indicate that the ego's characteristic presumption of separation between the "knower" and that which is "known" is, in Reality, an illusion. For a definition of "Know" (capitalized, and in quotation marks), see **"Locating" (and "Knowing") Avatar Adi Da Samraj**.

L

Listening to Me, and Hearing Me, and Seeing Me—A summary description of the course of unfolding practice of the Reality-Way of Adidam:

"Listening" to Avatar Adi Da entails literally listening to His Divine Word and Leela (Revelation-stories of His Lifetime and Work), as well as embrace of the life of devotion and discipline in His Company.

"Hearing" Avatar Adi Da is the Gracefully Awakened capability to most fundamentally understand and (thereby) consistently transcend the presumption of separateness (or the activity of the ego).

"Seeing" Avatar Adi Da is the practice of His devotee who is fully Awakened to His Transcendental Spiritual Blessing-Transmission and (thus) fully capable of responsibly and consistently participating in that Transmission.

The process of Seeing culminates in the most mature demonstration of practice in the Reality-Way of Adidam, which is called the "Perfect Practice". The "Perfect Practice" is practice in the Domain of Consciousness Itself (as opposed to practice from the "point of view" of the body or the mind).

"Locating" (and "Knowing") Avatar Adi Da—To "Locate" Avatar Adi Da is to truly (whole bodily) Find Him. Avatar Adi Da places "Locate" (and its variants) in quotation marks to indicate the sense of "so to speak"—because He is, in Reality, Omni-Present, without any specific location. To "Know" Avatar Adi Da Samraj is a wordless, tacit Apprehension of Him, rather than any form of "subject-object"-based "knowledge"—and is, therefore, also placed in quotation marks.

M

Man of "Radical" Understanding—See **"self"-understanding / "radical" understanding / the Man of "Radical" Self-Understanding**.

Mountain Of Attention Sanctuary—See **Hermitages and Sanctuaries**.

Murti / Murti-Form—"Murti" is Sanskrit for "form", and, by extension, a "representational image" of the Divine or of a Guru. In the Reality-Way of Adidam, Murtis of Avatar Adi Da are most commonly photographs of Avatar Adi Da's bodily (human) Divine Form, but they may also be painted (or other artistically or technically rendered) images.

O

Outshine/Outshining—When the Radiance of Consciousness Itself is infinitely magnified, all objects and conditions are no longer noticed. This is Avatar Adi Da's description of the final phase of Divine Enlightenment, which He also calls "Divine Translation". See also **stages of life**.

P

"Perfect Contemplation"—Avatar Adi Da uses "meditation" and "Perfect Contemplation" as a pair of related, but distinct, terms. "Meditation" is the form of meditative practice engaged by the practitioner of Adidam who is still (to some degree) patterned by egoic "self"-identification with the body-mind-complex. Once the devotee makes the transition to the most mature demonstration of practice (called the "Perfect Practice"), egoic "self"-identification with the body-mind-complex has been fully transcended, and meditation is replaced by "Perfect Contemplation"—or effortless "Contemplation" of Avatar Adi Da as Consciousness Itself, Prior to body and mind.

"Perfect Knowledge"—See **"radical" devotion, right life, and "Perfect Knowledge"**.

prior unity—Avatar Adi Da's term "prior unity" points to the unity that is inherently the case—at the "root"-level that is deeper than all the apparent differences and conflicts in the world. That unity, in other words, is senior to all apparent signs of dis-unity. Avatar Adi Da also calls this the "unifying life-principle" and the "cosmically extended pattern of Oneness". (In the phrase "prior unity", Avatar Adi Da uses the word "prior" in the sense of "always already being the case", not in the sense of "earlier in time or sequence".)

psycho-physical—A phrase that Avatar Adi Da Samraj uses to indicate that the human being is not a purely physical phenomenon, but a phenomenon with both physical and psychological/psychic dimensions. He also uses this description to characterize not only the human being but the world altogether.

R

"radical" devotion, right life, and "Perfect Knowledge"—The three fundamentals of the Reality-Way of Adidam. Even from the earliest moment of the embrace of the Reality-Way of Adidam, these three characteristics of practice are both the <u>means</u> and the <u>demonstration</u> of abiding in devotional Communion with Avatar Adi Da Samraj (and, thereby, transcending the ego, or identification with the separate body-mind-"self").

The foundation of the Reality-Way of Adidam is *"radical" devotion* to His Divine Presence Avatar Adi Da Samraj, Who is recognized at heart to be the Revelation of Reality Itself in bodily (human) Form. Such devotion is "radical" because it is a response to Avatar Adi Da's Divine Avataric Self-Revelation at the very "root" of the being, Prior to the presumption of a separate "self". Once practice of devotional turning to Him is rightly established, it becomes a moment to moment devotional Communion that Avatar Adi Da calls "searchless Beholding" of Him.

In the context of devotional response to Avatar Adi Da Samraj, the devotee is moved to embrace the comprehensive discipline of *right life* Given by Him—based on the non-seeking disposition Revealed in devotional Communion with Him. This includes specific practices relative to all aspects of practical and relational life—including "money, food, and sex" and social relations—as well as a sacred life of meditation, worship, and service in cooperative association with other devotees of Avatar Adi Da Samraj. This life purifies, balances, and rejuvenates the body-mind-complex in the equanimity of devotional Communion with Him.

On the foundation of devotional response to Him and the living of right life, Avatar Adi Da Samraj calls His devotee to "consider" and be established in the *"Perfect Knowledge"* of Reality Itself. This is engaged first via a preliminary Listening-practice—which entails listening to Avatar Adi Da's "Perfect Knowledge" Teachings in "The Teaching Manual of Perfect Summaries" (as published in *The Aletheon, The Gnosticon,* and other texts). Ultimately, for mature practitioners, it is engaged via a "Perfect Practice" of "Perfect Knowledge". When the devotee is in Communion with Him, Avatar Adi Da Reveals that no "object" or "knowledge" or "subject" or "point of view" is True or Real—but, rather, Reality Itself is shown as the Prior and egoless Condition That Is Always <u>Already</u> The Case. See also discussion on pp. 138–40.

"Radical" Reality-Way of Adidam Ruchiradam—The full formal name of the Reality-Way that Avatar Adi Da offers to all.

"radical" understanding—See **"self"-understanding / "radical" understanding / the Man of "Radical" Self-Understanding**.

Real God / Real (Acausal) God—Avatar Adi Da uses the term "Real God" to refer to the God which is Reality (or Truth) Itself, not a conventional theistic deity. Avatar Adi Da also often qualifies this phrase with the word "Acausal"—"Real (Acausal) God"—to emphasize that Real God Exists Beyond and Prior to the realm of duality in which the law of "cause-and-effect" is operative.

Reality-Way of the Heart—An alternative reference to the Reality-Way of Adidam.

regenerative—See **degenerative/regenerative**.

right life—See **"radical" devotion, right life, and "Perfect Knowledge"**.

S

Sanctuaries—See **Hermitages and Sanctuaries**.

Self-Nature, Self-Condition, Self-State—A phrase used by Avatar Adi Da to indicate His own True "Self" (or Identity), which Is the True Identity of Reality Itself—and, thus, the True Identity of everything and everyone. Avatar Adi Da's use of this phrase implies that the *Nature* of Reality is Transcendental, the *Condition* of Reality is Spiritual, and (thus) the *State* of Reality is Conscious Light (or the Indivisibility of the Transcendental Principle of Consciousness and the Spiritual Principle of Energy).

"self"-understanding / "radical" understanding / the Man of "Radical" Self-Understanding—Avatar Adi Da uses the word "understanding" to indicate the process of observing and transcending egoity (or the root-contraction of "self"). "The Man of 'Radical' Understanding" is Avatar Adi Da's reference to Himself as the True Guru, who Reveals and Transmits this process of "radical" understanding.

Self-Existing and Self-Radiant—Terms describing the two fundamental aspects of the One Indivisible Reality: Existence (or Being, or Consciousness) Itself, and Radiance (or Energy, or Light) Itself. "Self-Existing" is correlated to "Transcendental", while "Self-Radiant" is correlated to "Spiritual".

seventh stage of life—See **stages of life**.

"Source-Texts"—The books of Avatar Adi Da's writings and discourses which He designated as comprising His Eternal Message to humankind. These Texts present, in complete and conclusive detail, His Divine Revelations, Confessions, and Instructions. See pp. 416–26.

spinal line—See **frontal line / spinal line**.

stages of life—Avatar Adi Da Samraj has "mapped" the potential developmental course of human experience as it unfolds through the gross, subtle, and causal dimensions of the being. He describes this course in terms of six stages of life. These six stages of life, He explains, account for and correspond with all possible orientations to religion and culture that have arisen in human history. Avatar Adi Da describes Realization of His Divine "Bright" State—Prior to all experience and all dimensions of the being—as the seventh stage of life.

The first three (or foundation) stages of life constitute the ordinary course of human adaptation—bodily, emotional, and mental growth. Each of the first three stages of life takes approximately seven years to be established. Every individual who lives to an adult age inevitably adapts (although, generally speaking, only partially) to the first three stages of life. In the general case, this is where the developmental process stops—at the gross level of adaptation. Traditions based fundamentally on beliefs and moral codes (without direct experience of the dimensions beyond the material world) belong to this foundation level of human development.

The fourth stage of life is characterized, in its beginnings, by a deep impulse to Communion with the Divine, felt to be a great "Other" in Whom the being aspires to become absorbed through devotional love and service. In the fifth stage of life, attention naturally moves into the domain of subtle experience and seeks the Samadhi states associated with ascending energy in the spinal line. The esoteric Spiritual traditions associated with mystical experience correspond with this higher level of human potential.

The Realizer of the sixth stage of life is focused in the causal depth of the being. He or she identifies with Consciousness (in profound states of meditation) by excluding all awareness of phenomena, both gross and subtle. And, when phenomena do arise, the Realizer stands as the "Witness" of phenomena, unimplicated by body, mind, or world. Such is genuine Realization of the sixth stage of life—but Avatar Adi Da has also pointed out the tendency in some traditional circles to attempt to identify with Consciousness (or "the Self") based on a "talking"-school approach that is founded in mind, rather than on genuine Realization.

The seventh stage of life, or the Realization of "the Bright" uniquely Revealed through the Incarnation of the Divine Avatar, Adi Da, transcends this entire course of human potential. In that Awakening, it is suddenly, tacitly Realized that there is no "difference" between Consciousness Itself and the objects of Consciousness. Thus, the seventh stage Realization (or Divine Enlightenment) wipes away every trace of dissociation from the body-mind and the world. In the seventh stage of life, the world is Divinely Self-Recognized to be simply a modification of Consciousness Itself. Consciousness Itself, or Being Itself, Is all there is, and Consciousness Itself is found to be Radiant, or Love-Bliss-Full. Thus, every "thing" and every "one" that appears is a mere modification of the One Divine "Brightness" (or the Divine Conscious Light).

For Avatar Adi Da's detailed description of the seven stages of life, see "God Talk, Real-God-Realization, Most Perfect Divine Self-Awakening, and The Seven Possible Stages of Life" in *The Aletheon* (or *The Gnosticon* or *The Pneumaton*).

T

Transcendentally-Spiritually-Initiated devotees—Those (rightly prepared) devotees who have been Initiated by Avatar Adi Da's Blessing-Grace into the process of "Locating" and "Knowing" Him in Transcendental Spiritual terms. For a discussion of the meaning and import of "Transcendental Spiritual", see pp. 82–86.

U

understanding—See **"self"-understanding / "radical" understanding / the Man of "Radical" Self-Understanding**.

W

whole bodily / whole body—Terms Avatar Adi Da specifically used to indicate the "aggregate" of the four principal faculties (of mind, emotion, body, and breath) that are the complete functioning structure of the human being.

Avatar Adi Da Samraj
Adi Da Samrajashram, 2008

The Universal Offering of
Avatar Adi Da Samraj

by Ruchiradama Quandra Sukhapur Rani Naitauba
(on behalf of the Ruchira Sannyasin Order
of Adidam Ruchiradam)

In response to all the human voices calling out to the Divine, Avatar Adi Da Samraj took Birth on Earth, in bodily (human) Form, in November 1939. In His sixtieth year, His Divine Avataric Incarnation culminated in the most consequential Event ever to occur in the cosmic domain: In April 2000, His Holy Body was Divinely Translated, becoming the utterly transparent Doorway to the Divine Domain of Reality Itself. After that supremely consequential Event, His Divine Body and Life became as if ash from a sacred fire, and His Body Stood as the Universal Channel of connection to the Divine, Perfectly.

In His Divine Avataric Lifetime, Avatar Adi Da Samraj had a Single Purpose, which was to re-connect all cosmic worlds to That Which Is Reality Itself, or Truth at the "root", prior to any separate identity in time or space. The vast undifferentiated field of Divine Conscious Light was His only Awareness. In His Awareness, there were no separate beings. Only all beings were there, in prior unity—to be Awakened and re-connected to the Infinite Truth of existence. In His Divine Avataric Lifetime, Avatar Adi Da Established the Eternal Means for the Perfect Awakening of all beings— and then, on November 27, 2008, Outshined even His own Bodily Incarnation, in the Perfect "Brightness" of His Divine Mahasamadhi. Now Avatar Adi Da Exists in His Eternal Form for all time. Avatar Adi Da Appeared in human Form for a time, in order to Reveal His Divine Form—thus tangibly Manifesting His Divine Transcendental Spiritual Presence, so that His Blessing-Transmission could be Perpetually Alive and Always Blessing all. This was His Divine Purpose.

Throughout His human Lifetime, Avatar Adi Da Samraj established "Channels", or "Agents", through which His Communication and Transmission of Reality-Truth would forever flow. Avatar Adi Da wrote an extraordinary number of books of the most pristine Transcendental Spiritual Revelation and esoteric Instruction ever revealed—books that infuse the heart and mind with overwhelming "Perfect Knowledge" and profoundest "Brightening" Force. Avatar Adi Da created a vast body of groundbreaking artwork—including paintings, drawings, photographic work, video work, and digitally-created work (in both two and three dimensions)—which artwork conveys His Liberating Message in a non-verbal form that He called "Transcendental Realism". Avatar Adi Da also created "Transcendental Realist" theatre, as a means of enabling a "performance-assisted subjective process" that actually leads to a transformation of the being for anyone who engages the performance in a fully participatory manner. Avatar Adi Da also Spiritually Empowered Hermitages and Sanctuaries in different parts of the world—places from which His Blessing Radiates with unique potency, now and forever. Avatar Adi Da bequeathed to humankind the entire legacy of His Divine Life-History—all of the Divine Yogic stories of everything He did and of His constant Liberating Work with those who came to Him. And Avatar Adi Da also undertook a comprehensive inspection of the Great Tradition of humankind, creating *The Basket of Tolerance*, His Supreme Clarifying Revelation relative to all human endeavor—religious, Spiritual, philosophical, artistic, and practical. All of these Divine Gifts of Transcendental Spiritual Revelation are "Doorways" created by the Divine Avatar, Adi Da Samraj, through which human beings can enter into "egoless participation in Reality Itself".

In the last years of His Life, Avatar Adi Da Gave a unique Gift to the human family—His description of how the human sphere of strife and conflict can be transformed into a world of cooperation, tolerance, and peace. In His book *Not-Two Is Peace*, Avatar Adi Da calls for the creation of a "Global Cooperative Forum", in which all of the people on Earth—or, in His words, "everybody-all-at-once"—are enabled to embrace an absolutely necessary paradigm shift—the shift from competition and conflict to living as an "egoless collective". Such egoless participation (by "everybody-all-at-once") is how He says we will save the Earth from destruction.

Avatar Adi Da's ultimate Gift to all is the Divine Way of life He Revealed. He named that Way of life "Adidam"—or, in its fullest form, "the 'Radical' Reality-Way of Adidam Ruchiradam". That Way is "Radical" because it goes straight to the "root" of all human problem and suffering and Reveals What Is Prior. That Way is only about Reality—not about any kind of belief, mythology, or dogma, and not about any kind of seeking-effort.

The Reality-Way of Adidam Ruchiradam is the Supreme Divine Way. It has never been given before Avatar Adi Da's Divine Birth and His Divine Work. Avatar Adi Da's Universal Offering Transcends the entire Great Tradition of humankind, and Avatar Adi Da Samraj Himself now Stands As the "Threshold Personality", making it possible for all to Awaken to That Which Is the Real, His Eternal Divine Form. ■

Om Sri Parama-Sapta-Na Adi Da Love-Ananda Hridayam

To find Avatar Adi Da Samraj is to find the Very Heart of Reality—tangibly Known, Prior to body and mind, as the Deepest Truth of existence. This is the Great Mystery that Avatar Adi Da Samraj Revealed through His Avataric Lifetime, and the Great Mystery that is forever to be discovered.

Avatar Adi Da Samraj established many ways in which people can enter into relationship with His Eternal Being. In establishing these forms of relationship, Avatar Adi Da accounted for people in all walks of life, people in all parts of the world, and people either with or without a religious practice. All of these forms of relationship to Avatar Adi Da are ways of entering into egoless participation in Reality Itself.

All beings have already been Divinely Touched by His Person, and all can therefore connect to His Eternal Divine Form, through the many ways of relating to Avatar Adi Da that He created for the sake of all, during His Divine Incarnation on Earth.

● Avatar Adi Da established two formal renunciate orders for those who are, by Divine Grace, most seriously impulsed to Realization of the Divine Reality Itself.

The senior renunciate order is the Ruchira Sannyasin Order. Devotees in the Ruchira Sannyasin Order take a vow of full formal renunciation (or sannyas) by which they renounce all ownership of property, and (more profoundly) renounce all social ego-identity. Ruchira Sannyasin devotees embrace a life entirely devoted to the process of Divine Self-Realization, living on perpetual retreat at one of the Hermitages or Sanctuaries Empowered by Avatar Adi Da (as a general rule, at His principal Hermitage, Adi Da Samrajashram).

The second formal renunciate order is the Lay Renunciate Order, whose members serve under the governance and direction of the Ruchira Sannyasin Order. Lay Renunciate devotees are given over to serve the culture of Adidam Ruchiradam and the bringing of Avatar Adi Da's Revelation to the world—living wherever it is necessary to serve Avatar Adi Da's Revelation-Work for the sake of all beings.

● Avatar Adi Da established a form of devotional practice for those who are moved, on the basis of their response to Him, to dedicate their lives to Him through heart-felt service and the embrace of an intensive, purifying life of ego-transcending practice. This form of practice was Blessed by Avatar Adi Da to be the lifelong practice engaged by great numbers of people, including specific forms of participation for children and young people. And this form of practice is also the necessary foundation for those who are moved to enter the renunciate orders.

● Avatar Adi Da established a form of devotional practice for those who are moved to support His Great Divine Avataric Work through advocacy, patronage, scholarly communication, and other forms of service. This form of practice is open to all who are moved to it, whether or not they are already involved in another religious practice.

● Avatar Adi Da established a form of devotional practice for people who live in any of the traditional (or indigenous) cultures throughout the world. This form of practice is also open to all who are moved to it, whether or not they are already involved in the traditional religious practice of their culture (or any other religious practice).

● Finally, Avatar Adi Da established a Calling to all beings to participate in bringing into being a Global Cooperative Forum, based on the prior unity of the entire human family. This shift in the global life of humankind is of the profoundest significance for the future of the Earth and all its inhabitants. Avatar Adi Da's Calling for the Global Cooperative Forum is presented online at:

www.da-peace.org

The Sacred Literature
of Avatar Adi Da Samraj

The Life and the Reality-Teachings of His Divine Presence Avatar Adi Da Samraj are an unparalleled Revelation of the Truth—the Truth about everything that human beings have most deeply questioned and sought.

Avatar Adi Da's Teaching has no "outside sources". As He once said, "Everything I have Taught is something I have Lived." Avatar Adi Da's very first Teaching "Utterances" were His childhood Proclamations of His own Divine Self-Condition, which He called the "Bright", and His own Means of Bringing the "Bright" into the world, which He called the "Thumbs". Those two words were pure Divine Self-Revelation. They did not represent theories about anything. They were not statements of how He hoped or wished things would be. They were not borrowings from some traditional source. They were His simple and direct <u>Revealing</u> of What Is the Case. And this is true of everything Avatar Adi Da ever said or wrote. His Word is the direct Divine Self-Revelation of "the way things are", the experiential "report" of the egoless Divine Person.

Avatar Adi Da's Reality-Revelation is Ultimate precisely because it is a <u>Self</u>-Revelation. The "Bright", the Very Divine Reality, the Very Divine Person is Revealing Itself (or Himself) <u>directly</u>, through the medium of human language. Indeed, one of the great Purposes for which Avatar Adi Da Took Birth was to speak the Complete (and Perfectly Revealing) Word of Divine Truth to human beings in language—because It had never before been fully spoken. And that is exactly what He Accomplished.

To engage Avatar Adi Da's Word is to receive His Sublime Confession of His Purpose here and to absorb His Masterful Address to the eternal questions of humankind.

The following pages present a core group of books and other materials by and about Adi Da Samraj that are available from the Dawn Horse Press.

THE KNEE OF LISTENING
The Divine Ordeal of The Avataric Incarnation of Conscious Light

The Spiritual Autobiography of His Divine Presence, Avatar Adi Da Samraj

Born in 1939 on Long Island, New York, Adi Da Samraj describes His earliest Life as an existence of constant and unmitigated Spiritual "Brightness". His observation, still in infancy, that others did not live in this manner led Him to undertake an awesome quest—to discover why human beings suffer and how they can transcend that suffering. His quest led Him to a confrontation with the bleak despair of post-industrial Godlessness, to a minute examination of the workings of subjective awareness, to discipleship in a lineage of profound Yogis, to a period of intense Christian mysticism, and finally to a Re-Awakening to the perfect state of "Brightness" He had known at Birth.

In *The Knee of Listening*, Avatar Adi Da also reveals His own direct awareness of His "deeper-personality vehicles"—the beings whose lives were the direct antecedents (or the "pre-history") of His present human Lifetime—the great nineteenth-century Indian Realizers Sri Ramakrishna and Swami Vivekananda. Finally, Avatar Adi Da describes the series of profound transformational events that took place in the decades after His Divine Re-Awakening—each one a form of "Yogic death" for which there is no recorded precedent. Altogether, *The Knee of Listening* is the unparalleled history of how the Divine Conscious Light Incarnated in human Form, in order to grant everyone the possibility of Ultimate Divine Liberation, Freedom, and Happiness.

The Knee of Listening *is without a doubt the most profound Spiritual autobiography of all time.*

—ROGER SAVOIE, PhD
Philosopher; translator; author, *La Vipère et le Lion: La Voie radicale de la Spiritualité*

864 pp., **$24.95**
Also available in eBook edition!

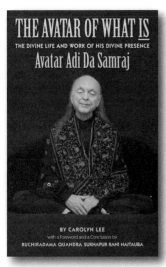

THE AVATAR OF WHAT <u>IS</u>

The Divine Life and Work of His Divine Presence Avatar Adi Da Samraj
by Carolyn Lee
with a foreword and a conclusion by Ruchiradama Quandra Sukhapur Rani Naitauba

This biography presents a summary overview of Avatar Adi Da's Life and Work. From the foretelling of His Birth, through His years of "Learning humankind", to the more than thirty-five years of His unique Avataric Teaching- and Revelation-Work, to the Eternal process of His Blessing, this is the extraordinary story of the Divine Avataric Intervention in the world.

Avatar Adi Da's Divine Emergence marks a new chapter in epochal Spiritual History.

200 pp., **$14.95**
Also available in eBook edition!

—**RICHARD GROSSINGER**
Author, *Planet Medicine, The Night Sky,*
and *Embryogenesis*

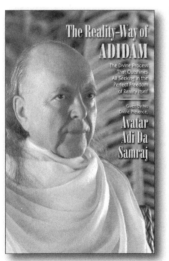

THE REALITY-WAY OF ADIDAM

The Divine Process that Outshines All Seeking in the Perfect Freedom of Reality Itself,
Given by His Divine Presence,
Avatar Adi Da Samraj
Written and compiled under the direct guidance of the Ruchira Sannyasin Order of Adidam Ruchiradam

A simple summary of the "radical" Way of life that His Divine Presence Avatar Adi Da Samraj offers to all. Includes a discussion of the three foundation dimensions of Adidam Ruchiradam—"radical" devotion, right life, and "Perfect Knowledge"; a summary of the Transcendental Spiritual process of Awakening in Avatar Adi Da's Eternal Blessing-Company; and a description of the unique nature of the Reality-Way of Adidam in the history of human religious and Spiritual endeavor.

255 pp., **$19.95**
Also available in eBook edition!

FROM *THE DIVINE SIDDHA-METHOD OF THE RUCHIRA AVATAR*
by Avatar Adi Da Samraj

MY "BRIGHT" WORD
Originally published as
The Method of the Siddhas

In these Talks from the early years of His Teaching-Work, Avatar Adi Da gives extraordinary Instruction on the foundation of true Spiritual life, covering topics such as the primary mechanism that prevents the Realization of Truth, the means to overcome this mechanism, and the true function of the Spiritual Master in relation to the devotee.

600 pp., **$24.95**

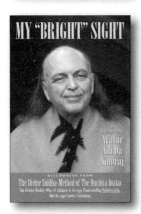

MY "BRIGHT" SIGHT

In Talks that span over twenty years of His Teaching-Work, Avatar Adi Da gives direct and enlivening Instruction on the transformative nature of the relationship with the Guru (or Spiritual Master) and on understanding and transcending the patterning of the ego-self.

466 pp., **$24.95**

MY "BRIGHT" FORM

In these Talks from 1993–1994, Avatar Adi Da illuminates the Western cultural paradigms that must be outgrown in true Spiritual practice, the specific four-part Yoga of devotional Communion that He has Revealed, and the Way of participation in His Eternal Outshining-Work.

690 pp., **$29.95**

THE GIFT OF TRUTH ITSELF

The Ever-Living Means Whereby Everyone Can Realize Truth, or Perfect Happiness

Selections from The Aletheon, *the Final Masterwork of Avatar Adi Da Samraj*

This compact volume speaks directly to everyone's innate heart-intuition of Truth and Reality, offering Avatar Adi Da's penetrating analysis of human suffering and His liberating communication about the process of Realizing utter Freedom and Happiness. Drawn from *The Aletheon*, the selections in this book are a wonderful introduction to Adi Da's Revelation-Word.

162 pp., **$12.95**
Also available in eBook edition!

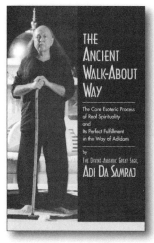

THE ANCIENT WALK-ABOUT WAY

The Core Esoteric Process of Real Spirituality and Its Perfect Fulfillment in the Way of Adidam
by Avatar Adi Da Samraj

In this beautiful collection of Essays, Avatar Adi Da begins with a foundation consideration of the purpose and principles of the ancient tradition of devotional response to the living Realizer; He then describes how to cultivate life-conditions that allow the being to enact its inherent devotional response to Living Truth; and, finally, He describes the unique Signs and Qualities of His Appearance and Offering, and of those who fully devotionally respond to Him.

Devotion to the Realizer is the ancient Way of true Spiritual life.
Devotion to the Realizer is the "pre-civilization Way", which existed before any recorded history, during a time when human beings were, essentially, merely wandering all over the Earth. Devotion to the Realizer has always been the fundamental Means of human Spirituality.

—Avatar Adi Da Samraj

144 pp., **$12.95**
Also available in eBook edition!

THREE GREAT REVELATION-BOOKS

These three Revelation-Books together form a guide to the "radical" means of the Realization of Reality and an all-encompassing Address to the entire history of human religious and Spiritual endeavor. *The Aletheon* is Avatar Adi Da's paramount Scripture—a pure exposition of His own Revelation, which He calls the "Seventh Way" (in reference to His schema of seven stages of life). In *The Gnosticon* and *The Pneumaton*, Avatar Adi Da examines the methods of the greatest traditions of human Spirituality and Transcendental Realization, in light of the Transcendental Spirituality of the Reality-Way of Adidam.

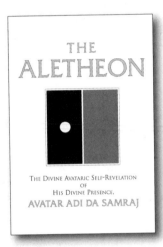

THE ALETHEON

The Divine Avataric Self-Revelation of His Divine Presence, Avatar Adi Da Samraj

Avatar Adi Da's Completing exposition of the "Seventh Stage" Way of Adidam Ruchiradam.

The writings of Adi Da Samraj are the most doctrinally thorough, the most philosophically sophisticated, the most culturally challenging, and the most creatively original literature on radical nonduality currently available in the English language.

—JEFFREY J. KRIPAL
J. Newton Rayzor Professor of Religious Studies,
Rice University

2322 pp.
$180 (eight-volume softcover set in slipcase)
$250 (single-volume hardcover in slipcase)

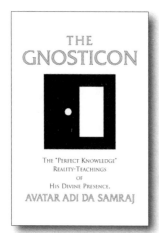

THE GNOSTICON

The "Perfect Knowledge" Reality-Teachings of His Divine Presence, Avatar Adi Da Samraj

Avatar Adi Da's examination of the Transcendental Teachings of the Great Sages and the Transcendental Spiritual Reality-Way of Adidam Ruchiradam.

The present book [is] a mature document that culminates forty or more years of reflection and articulation on Adi Da Samraj's part. I can only add my own humble invitation to all to plunge into its ecstatic waters and savor The Gnosticon.

—From the foreword by
PAUL E. MULLER-ORTEGA
Author, *The Triadic Heart of Shiva*

1186 pp.
$75.00 (softcover), **$150.00** (hardcover)

Essays from *The Gnosticon* are also available in the "Perfect Knowledge" Series published by the Dawn Horse Press in 2006, and in *Reality Is All The God There Is*, published by Inner Traditions International in 2008.

THE PNEUMATON

The Transcendental Spiritual Reality-Teachings of His Divine Presence, Avatar Adi Da Samraj

Avatar Adi Da's discussion of the devotional and Spiritual traditions of humankind—particularly as seen in Christianity and Hinduism—and the Transcendental Spiritual Reality-Way of Adidam Ruchiradam.

All spiritual aspirants need to confront and integrate the extravagant brilliance and originality of Adi Da Samraj. No one who reads these pages could avoid massive earthquakes of perception and transformation; they radiate power and vision and passion at the highest and most lucid level.

—ANDREW HARVEY
Author, *The Hope: A Guide to Sacred Activism*;
Son of Man: The Mystical Path to Christ; and
The Way of Passion: A Celebration of Rumi

1346 pp.
$75.00 (softcover), **$175.00** (hardcover)

ESSENTIAL FOUNDATION INSTRUCTION

This five-book series covers Avatar Adi Da's foundation Instruction in the three fundamental dimensions of the Reality-Way of Adidam: "radical" devotion, right life, and "Perfect Knowledge". The first four books contain Instruction principally drawn from *The Dawn Horse Testament* (new edition forthcoming)—Avatar Adi Da's complete summary of the entire Reality-Way of Adidam.

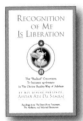

"Radical" Devotion—
RECOGNITION OF ME IS LIBERATION
A compilation of essential Instruction on whole-bodily-recognition-responsive devotional turning to Avatar Adi Da Samraj.
394 pp., **$29.95**

 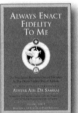

Right Life—
Right Life Is The Context of Divine Beholding
Avatar Adi Da's final summary Teachings on "right life", presented in three volumes.

Vol. 1: **RIGHT LIFE IS FREE PARTICIPATION IN UNLIMITED RADIANCE**
Instruction on the basic functional, practical, relational, and cultural disciplines in the Reality-Way of Adidam, including diet, health, exercise, service, and more.
394 pp., **$29.95**

Vol. 2: **THE SACRED SPACE OF FINDING ME**
A comprehensive manual covering the cultural practices for devotees of Avatar Adi Da, including sacred Sighting of Him, meditation, sacramental worship, devotional chanting, telling the stories of His Instructive Play, and much more.
540 pp., **$32.95**

Vol. 3: **ALWAYS ENACT FIDELITY TO ME**
Avatar Adi Da's Teaching about the emotional-sexual dimension of human life and the foundation emotional-sexual discipline in Adidam.
574 pp., **$32.95**

"Perfect Knowledge"—
NOTICE THIS
This Text elaborates on the rudimentary "Perfect Knowledge" practice, by which the beginning devotee is granted a tacit understanding of the Nature of Consciousness Itself.
314 pp., **$27.95**

THE HEART OF THE ADIDAM REVELATION

These five books present Avatar Adi Da's Revelation-summary of the foundation elements and the unfolding process of the Reality-Way of Adidam Ruchiradam.

AHAM DA ASMI
(Beloved, I <u>Am</u> Da)

Avatar Adi Da's Self-Revelation of His own Divine Person and His Impulse to Bless and Liberate all.

232 pp., **$24.95**

RUCHIRA AVATARA GITA
(The Avataric Way of The Divine Heart-Master)

Avatar Adi Da's Offering of the devotional relationship to Him, in the traditional manner of Guru-devotion.

432 pp., **$24.95**

DA LOVE-ANANDA GITA
(The Free Avataric Gift of The Divine Love-Bliss)

The foundation practice of devotional Communion with Avatar Adi Da Samraj: simply turning the four principal faculties—body, emotion, mind, and breath—to Him.

335 pp., **$24.95**

HRIDAYA ROSARY
(Four Thorns of Heart-Instruction)

The fully Transcendentally Spiritually Awakened practice of devotional Communion with Avatar Adi Da Samraj.

434 pp., **$29.95**

ELEUTHERIOS
(The <u>Only</u> Truth That Sets The Heart Free)

Devotional Communion with Avatar Adi Da Samraj, beyond the four faculties of the body-mind, in the Domain of Consciousness Itself: Realizing Avatar Adi Da Samraj As the "Bright" Itself, or the Conscious Light of Reality (having transcended identification with body, emotion, mind, and breath).

684 pp., **$34.95**

ESSAYS FROM *THE ALETHEON*

The books on these pages are all comprised of selected readings from Avatar Adi Da's final Revelation-Text, *The Aletheon*.

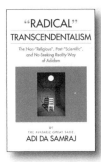

"RADICAL" TRANSCENDENTALISM

The Non-"Religious", Post-"Scientific", and No-Seeking Reality-Way of Adidam

A potent exposition of the unique nature of Avatar Adi Da's Reality-Way of Adidam and the fullness of its practice. Includes His revealing analysis of the illusions of both conventional religion and secular science.
304 pp., **$19.95**

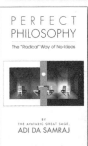

PERFECT PHILOSOPHY

The "Radical" Way of No-Ideas

Avatar Adi Da describes the inherent limits of all forms of knowledge and Offers a Way of life that originates and operates beyond such limits.
168 pp., **$16.95**

SURRENDER SELF BY SIGHTING ME

Essays on Right and True Devotion

Instruction from Avatar Adi Da illuminating the Way of right and true surrender to Him—the essentially non-verbal process of turning to Him on Sight—which He describes as "the Ancient Walk-About Way".
64 pp., **$7.95**

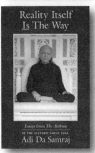

REALITY ITSELF <u>IS</u> THE WAY

In these Essays, Avatar Adi Da Samraj makes the Offering of His Divine Avataric Self-Revelation as the Perfect Means for the process of Awakening to Reality Itself.

136 pp., **$14.95**

Additional books of Essays from *The Aletheon* include *My Final Work of Divine Indifference*, *The Self-Authenticating Truth*, *Atma Nadi Shakti Yoga*, and *The Boundless Self-Confession*.

DIVINE LEELA

THE ETERNAL ONE

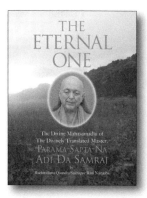

The Divine Mahasamadhi of the Divinely Translated Master, Parama-Sapta-Na Adi Da Samraj
by Ruchiradama Quandra Sukhapur Rani Naitauba

This book is an account of Avatar Adi Da's physical Passing, the great Event of His Divine Mahasamadhi, on November 27, 2008. Personal testimony and a bountiful collection of photographs celebrate the Event of Avatar Adi Da's Divine Mahasamadhi, the pristine quality of His final days on this Earth, and the gracious outpouring of Work He accomplished in the last years of His Life. It includes the most comprehensive collection of Avatar Adi Da's own Word on the meaning and import of His Bodily Passing and His Eternal Presence in the cosmic domain.

320 pp., **$45.00**

THE ETERNAL STAND

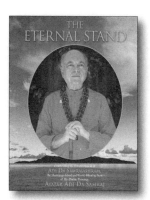

Celebrating the Establishment of Adi Da Samrajashram, the Hermitage-Island and World-Blessing-Seat of His Divine Presence, Avatar Adi Da Samraj

This book tells the remarkable story of Avatar Adi Da's Work to find and establish a true Hermitage on Earth. With riveting first-person accounts and a wealth of vibrant full-color photographs, this beautiful book will draw you into the miraculous Work that Avatar Adi Da engaged for the sake of humankind—to create a place set apart for the contemplation and magnification of His Divine Blessing-Transmission, for the sake of all and for all time.

Adi Da Samrajashram was a unique place with which Avatar Adi Da could Work, which He could conform to His Divine Person, such that every dimension of the Island now resonates with His Blessing-Power. Thus, this great Island was able to be Empowered by Avatar Adi Da to serve as the forever Resting-Place of His Divine Bodily Form and the place of the Eternal Radiation of His Divine Blessing.

—Ruchiradama Quandra Sukhapur Rani Naitauba
From the introduction

416 pp., **$65.00**

RIGHT LIFE

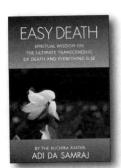

EASY DEATH

Spiritual Wisdom on the Ultimate Transcending
of Death and Everything Else
by Avatar Adi Da Samraj

*. . . [A]n exciting, stimulating, and thought-provoking
book that adds immensely to the ever-increasing literature on the phenomena of life and death. But, more
important, perhaps, it is a confirmation that a life filled
with love instead of fear can lead to ultimately meaning-
ful life and death.*

Thank you for this masterpiece.

544 pp., **$24.95**   **—ELISABETH KÜBLER-ROSS, MD**

Author, *On Death and Dying*

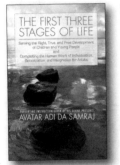

THE FIRST THREE STAGES OF LIFE

Serving the Right, True, and Free Development of
Children and Young People and Completing the Human
Work of Individuation, Socialization, and Integration for
Adults

768 pp., **$34.95**

GREEN GORILLA

The Searchless Raw Diet
Given by Avatar Adi Da Samraj

*I couldn't put this book down. The author powerfully conveys
the numerous benefits of the raw food diet. I was especially
impressed with the way he ties overeating with ego-bound
addiction to pleasure. I recommend that everyone read
this book.*

—VICTORIA BOUTENKO

184 pp., **$16.95**   Author, *Green for Life*

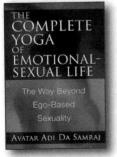

THE COMPLETE YOGA OF EMOTIONAL-SEXUAL LIFE

The Way Beyond Ego-Based Sexuality

A potent summary of Avatar Adi Da's instruction on
emotional-sexual matters—including His compassionate
instruction on transcending negative sex-patterning,
emotional immaturity, and all forms of seeking through
sex and relationship.

176 pp., **$14.95**

GLOBAL PEACE

NOT-TWO IS PEACE
Expanded Third Edition
The Ordinary People's Way of Global Cooperative Order
by the World-Friend Adi Da

Not-Two Is Peace contains Adi Da's vital wisdom on the root of human conflict, the limits and errors of conventional religion and politics, and the necessity and means for global cooperation, tolerance, and peace via "the working presumption of prior unity". This book, which includes Adi Da's "radical" argument for the transcending of egoity, is essential study for anyone who is concerned about the state of global affairs. The expanded third edition (published early 2009) contains significant writings not in previous editions, including an entirely new section of core principles for the establishment of a "Global Cooperative Forum".

320 pp., **$14.95**
Also available in eBook edition!

PRIOR UNITY
The Basis For A New Human Civilization
by the World-Friend Adi Da

A compact book of Adi Da's invaluable wisdom on going beyond the separate worldview to peaceful, cooperative coexistence. This is not a book about politics as we know it. It is about uncovering the true basis for a new politics, a new social contract that is founded in, and expressive of, how things really are.

It is a rare event in human history when a truly enlightened master speaks directly to the world situation, what must be done about it, and the consciousness from which all action, individual and collective, must proceed. The message in this book is urgent.

—BOB ANDERSON
Founder, Chairman, and Chief Development Officer
of The Leadership Circle

128 pp., **$12.95**

For more "right life" Wisdom from Avatar Adi Da Samraj, see the books in the "Right Life Is The Context of Divine Beholding" series on p. 404.

THE GREAT TRADITION

During His Incarnation-Lifetime, Avatar Adi Da created *The Basket of Tolerance*, a massive library collection, for which He developed an associated bibliography and wrote many accompanying commentarial Essays (from which the booklets listed below are drawn). This library contains many thousands of items—books, articles, and audio-visual materials—on aspects of humankind's total wisdom-search, which Avatar Adi Da calls "the Great Tradition". Each item in the library was selected by Avatar Adi Da from the many more thousands of items that He reviewed during His bodily (human) Lifetime.

As Avatar Adi Da described, this library is not simply a collection of many separate items, but is, rather, a system for comprehending the single, unified expression of the Great Tradition, and the completing expression of the Reality-Way of Adidam.

ESSAYS FROM *THE BASKET OF TOLERANCE*—

Each of the booklets below contains a single Essay from *The Basket of Tolerance*, in which Avatar Adi Da Samraj elucidates a particular aspect of (or point of view within) the Great Tradition. (For a full list of titles in this series, visit www.dawnhorsepress.com.)

- **God-Talk, Real-God-Realization, and Most Perfect Divine Awakening**, 44 pp., **$4.95**
- **The "Official" (Exoteric) Fabrications and the Secret (Esoteric) Truth about Jesus of Nazareth**, 36 pp., **$3.95**
- **The Real Intention and True Message of "Creation" Myths**, 20 pp., **$1.95**
- **The Revolutionary (and Yet Conventional) Effort of Classical Buddhism and "Mind Dharma" in Buddhism**, 20 pp., **$2.95**
- **The Shroud of Turin and the Cult of Relics**, 20 pp., **$2.95**
- **To Realize Nirvana Is to Realize the True "Self": Buddhist Realism and Its (Ultimately) Inherent Sympathy with Advaitic "Idealism"**, 19 pp., **$1.95**
- **The True Transcending of Sex and the Entire Body-Mind**, 64 pp. (8 Essays), **$6.95**
- **The Western Prohibition Against Higher Knowledge and Realization**, 12 pp., **$1.95**
- **What Is Required to Realize the Non-Dual Truth? The Controversy Between the "Talking" School and the "Practicing" School of Advaitism**, 24 pp., **$2.95**

SACRED CELEBRATION

THE DANAVIRA MELA BOOK

The Season of "Light-in-Everybody"
as Celebrated in the Company of
Bhagavan Adi Da Samraj
by Naamleela Free Jones

> *Light means something holy, something Divine.... Light is fundamental in human experience and aspiration and meaning. Because of this, it is suitable to be associated with a universal celebration every year.*
> —Avatar Adi Da Samraj

With these words, Avatar Adi Da Samraj describes the holiday season as a time when people of all faiths and places can celebrate the "Light-in-Everybody"—a season, as He says, that is "essentially about Light, and about that Light in everybody. It is about acknowledging the characteristic of Light in everybody you know and meet, rather than darkness. It is about love rather than its opposite."

In this special holiday book, Naamleela Free Jones shares the unique seasonal traditions that Avatar Adi Da, her father and Guru, developed on this basis. She writes:

> *Throughout my life, I have had the good fortune to witness and participate in Bhagavan Adi Da's enjoyment of this holiday season, along with His detailed care in making it a truly sacred celebration for His devotees—and a time filled with universal love and positiveness for people of all faiths and places.*
>
> *It is my hope that this book helps you to share in the love and delight of the wonderfully rich traditions of this season in Bhagavan Adi Da's Company, with your friends and family, young and old.*

96 pp., full color, hardcover: **$54.00**, softcover: **$29.95**

ADIDAM CALENDAR

Each year, the Adidam Calendar celebrates the Gift of Sighting Avatar Adi Da Samraj and receiving His Word. Each month of the calendar bears both a large and a smaller color image of Avatar Adi Da Granting Blessing-Sighting of His bodily (human) Divine Form and includes a quotation from His Revelation-Word.

24 pp., 12″x 12″, full color, **$29.95**

IMAGE-ART

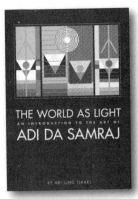

THE WORLD AS LIGHT

An Introduction to the Art of Adi Da Samraj
by Mei-Ling Israel

This generously illustrated book provides an overview of the massive body of highly distinctive artwork Adi Da Samraj created over forty years—accompanied by key statements He made on His own art and on the artistic process in general.

128 pp., with over 140 color
and black-and-white illustrations,
$24.95

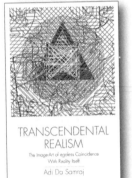

EXPANDED SECOND EDITION—

TRANSCENDENTAL REALISM

The Image-Art of egoless Coincidence
With Reality Itself
by Adi Da Samraj

Adi Da's key instruction on the methods, meaning, and purposes of His own image-art work, as well as His penetrating insight into the present-day culture and purpose of art.

> *Clearly, Adi Da Samraj is creating a new sacred art . . . one not bound to any particular religious ideology.*
> **—DONALD KUSPIT**
> Critic, Professor of Art History and Philosophy,
> State University of New York at Stony Brook

266 pp., plus 24-page color insert of Adi Da's images, **$19.95**
Also available in eBook edition!

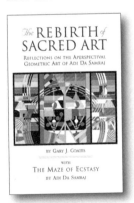

THE REBIRTH OF SACRED ART

Reflections on the Aperspectival Geometric Art
of Adi Da Samraj
by Gary J. Coates

In this response to the 2008 exhibition of Adi Da's art in the Cenacolo di Ognissanti (a space containing Ghirlandaio's renowned perspectival fresco *The Last Supper*), Coates provides a comprehensive framework for understanding the place of Adi Da's art within the context of the unfolding of Western art, consciousness, and culture. The book also includes Adi Da's Essay "The Maze of Ecstasy".

> *[Adi Da's] pursuit of the spiritual paths found in early abstraction, from Kandinsky to Mondrian, and [his] translation of that pursuit into the digital age restore a transcendental spiri-tuality to the materialism of the machine aesthetic.* **—PETER WEIBEL**
> Director, ZKM I Center for Art and Media, Karlsruhe

72 pp., **$14.95**

THE ADIDAM REVELATION DISCOURSES on DVD

During these remarkable occasions, Avatar Adi Da answered questions from those who were present in the room with Him, and also from devotees in other parts of the world via speakerphone. The "Adidam Revelation Discourse" DVDs offer the opportunity to see and hear Avatar Adi Da speak in these unique and intimate occasions of Divine Instruction.

Currently available titles include:

TRANSCEND THE SELF-KNOT OF FEAR

Running time: 60 minutes. Includes subtitles in English, Spanish, French, German, Dutch, and Polish.

THE DIVINE IS NOT THE CAUSE

Running time: 72 minutes. Includes subtitles in English, Spanish, French, German, Dutch, Finnish, Polish, Czech, Chinese, Japanese, and Hebrew.

CRACKING THE CODE OF EXPERIENCE

Running time: 86 minutes. Includes subtitles in English, Spanish, German, Dutch, Polish, Czech, Chinese, Japanese, and Hebrew.

THE QUEST FOR THE HISTORICAL SELF

Running time: 69 minutes. Includes subtitles in English, Spanish, French, German, Dutch, Polish, Czech, Chinese, Japanese, and Hebrew.

HUMAN HISTORY IS ONE GREAT TRADITION

Running time: 74 minutes. Includes subtitles in English, Spanish, French, Italian, German, Dutch, Polish, Czech, Chinese, and Hebrew.

ENTER INTO UNLIMITED PROFUNDITY

Running time: 70 minutes. Includes subtitles in English, French, Italian, German, Dutch, Polish, Czech, and Hebrew.

BEYOND SEX, SCIENCE, AND "SELF"

Running time: 82 minutes. Includes subtitles in English, Spanish, French, Italian, German, Dutch, Russian, Polish, Czech, and Hebrew.

THE SECRET OF EXPERIENCE

Running time: 65 minutes. Includes subtitles in English, Spanish, French, Italian, German, Dutch, Polish, Czech, and Hebrew.

DVD, **$26.95** each

DISCOURSES on CD

THE COSMIC MANDALA

A discourse from 1982 in which Avatar Adi Da describes the Cosmic Mandala and how it is experienced and "seen" in the death process. He explains that whenever association with the physical body is relinquished, attention will either be bound by the experiences and states that arise, or—if a foundation of ego-transcending practice and Divine Communion is in place—attention will rest in What Is Beyond and Prior to all experience, by Grace.

Understand your condition of existence and the mechanics of your own attention, and become devoted to a practice of life that will enable you to become responsible for attention—so that (while alive, and in the midst of uncommon states, and after death) you will have the ability to locate attention in its Source. You will have the ability to locate your existence in the Divine Domain, Which is the True Heaven of existence, the Very Divine State.

—Avatar Adi Da Samraj
July 11, 1982

CD: 58 minutes
$16.95

THE BRIDGE TO GOD

After a shaman from Mexico visited the Mountain Of Attention, Avatar Adi Da's Northern California Sanctuary, Avatar Adi Da considered with His devotees the inherently magical nature of the world and our psychic relationship to it. He describes how the "external" and "internal" worlds coexist as a "single, fluid, psychic plastic" in which all must responsibly participate—and go Beyond, through unreserved devotional response to the Divine Reality.

Ultimately the secret is not a matter of becoming psychic and peering through the hole in your forehead to some "other side". It is rather to recognize this world totally, to become free of all its limits, to out-breathe it, out-love it, out-live it. It is to use such force through submission to God that the God-Force overcomes the world.

—Avatar Adi Da Samraj
October 27, 1980

CD: 57 minutes
$16.95

Polarity screens and **hamsadandas** are also available for purchase through the Dawn Horse Press

To order books, tapes, CDs, DVDs,
and videos by and about
His Divine Presence Avatar Adi Da Samraj,
contact

THE DAWN HORSE PRESS

1-877-770-0772
(from within North America)

1-707-928-6653
(from outside North America)

Or visit the Dawn Horse Press website:
www.dawnhorsepress.com

The Structures of
the Divine Avataric "Source-Texts"
Given by Avatar Adi Da Samraj

Beginning in 1997, His Divine Presence Avatar Adi Da Samraj worked intensively to gather His Reality-Teachings, in their final form, into a comprehensive series of "Source-Texts", indicating that these books contain His Eternal Communication to humankind. In the end, He established two overarching structures within which His "Source-Texts" are organized in specific sequences:

■ The Five Final Books

In the last month of His Lifetime, Avatar Adi Da indicated that His final five "Source-Texts"—*The Aletheon, The Gnosticon, The Pneumaton, Not-Two Is Peace*, and *Transcendental Realism*—stand as the "Five Principal Books" of His "Forever Comprehensive Seventh-Stage Address to all-and-All". These books are His most summary expression to the world at large of the Divine Truth and Way He had been Born to Reveal.

■ The Twenty-Three Courses

Avatar Adi Da indicated otherwise that <u>all</u> of His designated "Source-Texts" (which He describes as "True-Water-Bearers", or "Bearers of the 'True Water' of the 'Bright' Divine Reality Itself") are contained in a structure of twenty-three "Streams", or "Courses". Each of these Courses conveys a particular aspect of His Divine Avataric Teaching—and each Course may include any number of "Source-Texts".

The first Course conveys Avatar Adi Da's Principal Revelation of His Divine Avataric Incarnation and the Reality-Way He has Given, and includes only His two principal Summary "Source-Texts": *The Aletheon* and *The Dawn Horse Testament*.

The remaining twenty-two Courses are divided into two groups: *The Heart of The Adidam Revelation* (consisting of five Courses, which, together, present a comprehensive overview of the entire process of the Reality-Way of Adidam) and *The Companions of The True Dawn Horse* (consisting of seventeen Courses, each of which elaborates on particular topics from the first and primary Course).

The present book falls in Course Nine of *The Companions of The True Dawn Horse.*

The Aletheon *and* The Dawn Horse Testament *Are—with all the other "Source-Texts", or True-Water-Bearers, of My Twenty-Three-Course Divine Avataric Reality-Teaching— the Summary of My Divine Self-Discoveries (Made by Means of My Divine Self-Submission to Avataric Incarnation) and My Divine Self-Revelations (Made by Means of My Avatarically Given Divine Self-Confessions of My Own Divine Secrets).*
—Avatar Adi Da Samraj,
The Aletheon

The Five Principal Books of
Avatar Adi Da's Forever Comprehensive
Seventh-Stage Address to all-and-All

This set of "Source-Texts" was designated and described by Avatar Adi Da in the last month of His Lifetime, after several years of intensive work to create these five books:

In and by Means of These Five Books, and Fully With All the Books of Mine, I Am (now, and forever hereafter) Calling for the "root" re-culturing of global humankind—and (thus and thereby) for a new and fully cooperative "world"-culture (and, always coincidently, a Right and True Practicing-Culture of Adidam Ruchiradam) Which is intrinsically and thoroughly <u>not</u> a "world"-mummery of ego-culture, and <u>not</u> a first-six-stages-of-life seeking-culture, but Which Is the Zero-Point Culture of Always Prior Unity and of Intrinsically egoless Reality-Demonstration.
—The Aletheon

THE ALETHEON
The Divine Avataric Self-Revelation of
His Divine Presence, Avatar Adi Da Samraj

THE GNOSTICON
The "Perfect Knowledge" Reality-Teachings of
His Divine Presence, Avatar Adi Da Samraj

THE PNEUMATON
The Transcendental Spiritual Reality-Teachings of
His Divine Presence, Avatar Adi Da Samraj

NOT-TWO IS PEACE
The Ordinary People's Way of
Global Cooperative Order

TRANSCENDENTAL REALISM
The Image-Art of egoless Coincidence
With Reality Itself

Avatar Adi Da's Twenty-Three-Course
Divine Avataric Reality-Teaching

The "Source-Texts" listed in the Twenty-Three-Course structure here include only those Texts that either are presently published or were designated specifically by Avatar Adi Da as a priority to publish. Avatar Adi Da otherwise indicated that any of the "Courses" could potentially include any number of additional "Source-Texts" into the future, to be created from Avatar Adi Da's Written and Spoken Word, based on His specific Instructions and indications for such texts given during His Lifetime. The asterisked titles indicate the Five Principal Books of Avatar Adi Da's "Forever Comprehensive Seventh-Stage Address to all-and-All", which also comprise their own separate structure, as shown on the preceding page. The descriptive phrases for each of the Courses (presented in italic type), are based on indications Avatar Adi Da Gave about His final intentions for the Courses, and were generated after His Divine Mahasamadhi by the Adi Da Samrajashram editorial guild, under the direction of (and authorized by) the Ruchira Sannyasin Order of Adidam Ruchiradam.

I. Principal Reality-Revelation
(In Its Single Course)

The Summary of Avatar Adi Da's Divine Avataric Self-Revelation of Truly human, and Spiritual, and Transcendental, and Divine Reality-Truth

* THE ALETHEON
The Divine Avataric Self-Revelation of His Divine Presence, Avatar Adi Da Samraj

THE DAWN HORSE TESTAMENT
The Testament of Divine Secrets of His Divine Presence, Avatar Adi Da Samraj

II. The Heart of the Adidam Revelation
(In Its Five Courses)

1. Divine Self-Confession

AHAM DA ASMI (BELOVED, I AM DA)
The Late-Time Avataric Revelation of The True and Transcendental Spiritual Divine Person (The egoless Personal Presence of Reality and Truth, Which Is The Only Real Acausal God)

THE BOUNDLESS SELF-CONFESSION
Essays from *The Aletheon*

2. Guru-Devotee Relationship

RUCHIRA AVATARA GITA
(THE AVATARIC WAY OF THE DIVINE AVATARIC MASTER)
The Late-Time Avataric Revelation of The Great Secret of The Divinely Self-Revealed Way That Most Perfectly Realizes The True and Transcendental Spiritual Divine Person (The egoless Personal Presence of Reality and Truth, Which <u>Is</u> The Only <u>Real</u> Acausal God)

THE ANCIENT WALK-ABOUT WAY
The Core Esoteric Process of Real Spirituality and Its Perfect Fulfillment in The Reality-Way of Adidam

THE SELF-AUTHENTICATING TRUTH
Essays from *The Aletheon*

THE GIFT OF TRUTH ITSELF
The Ever-Living Means Whereby Everyone Can Realize Truth, or Perfect Happiness

3. Recognition-Responsive Turning

DA LOVE-ANANDA GITA
(THE FREE AVATARIC GIFT OF THE DIVINE LOVE-BLISS)
The Late-Time Avataric Revelation of The Great Means To Worship and To Realize The True and Spiritual Divine Person (The egoless Personal Presence of Reality and Truth, Which <u>Is</u> The Only <u>Real</u> Acausal God)

RECOGNITION OF ME <u>IS</u> LIBERATION
The Radical Conversion To Intrinsic egolessness In The Divine Reality-Way of Adidam

THE NINE GREAT LAWS OF RADICAL DEVOTION TO ME
Readings from *The Aletheon*, *The Dawn Horse Testament*, and *Eleutherios*, as well as Selected Discourses and Spoken Instructions

THE SACRED SPACE OF FINDING ME
The Cultural Disciplines Practiced In The Sacred Domain of The Divine Reality-Way of Adidam

SURRENDER self BY SIGHTING ME
Essays from *The Aletheon* on Right and True Devotion

4. Up-Turned Transcendental Spiritual Process

HRIDAYA ROSARY (FOUR THORNS OF HEART-INSTRUCTION)
The Late-Time Avataric Revelation of The Universally Tangible Divine Transcendental Spiritual Body, Which Is The Supreme Agent of The Great Means To Worship and To Realize The True and Transcendental Spiritual Divine Person (The egoless Personal Presence of Reality and Truth, Which <u>Is</u> The Only <u>Real</u> Acausal God)

5. "Perfect Practice"

ELEUTHERIOS (THE <u>ONLY</u> TRUTH THAT SETS THE HEART FREE)
The Late-Time Avataric Revelation of The "Perfect Practice" of The Great Means To Worship and To Realize The True and Spiritual Divine Person (The egoless Personal Presence of Reality and Truth, Which <u>Is</u> The Only <u>Real</u> Acausal God)

THE ORDERS OF MY TRUE AND FREE RENUNCIATE DEVOTEES

III. The Companions of the True Dawn Horse (In Their Seventeen Courses)

1. Science, Religion, and Real God

<u>REAL</u> GOD <u>IS</u> THE INDIVISIBLE ONENESS OF UNBROKEN LIGHT
Reality, Truth, and The "Non-Creator" God In The Universal Transcendental Spiritual Reality-Way of Adidam

THE TRANSMISSION OF DOUBT
Transcending Scientific Materialism

PERFECT PHILOSOPHY
The "Radical" Way of No-Ideas

2. Paradigms for a New World-Culture

THE TRULY HUMAN NEW WORLD-CULTURE OF <u>UNBROKEN</u> REAL-GOD-MAN
The <u>Eastern</u> Versus The <u>Western</u> Traditional Cultures of Humankind, and The Unique New <u>Non-Dual</u> Culture of The Universal Transcendental Spiritual Reality-Way of Adidam

SCIENTIFIC PROOF OF THE EXISTENCE OF GOD WILL SOON BE ANNOUNCED BY THE WHITE HOUSE!
Prophetic Wisdom About The Myths and Idols of Mass Culture and Popular Religious Cultism, The New Priesthood of Scientific and Political Materialism, and The Secrets of Enlightenment Hidden In The Body of Man

PRIOR UNITY
The Basis For A New Human Civilization

* NOT-TWO <u>IS</u> PEACE
The Ordinary People's Way of Global Cooperative Order

3. Overview of the Reality-Way of Adidam

THE ONLY COMPLETE WAY TO REALIZE THE UNBROKEN LIGHT OF REAL GOD
An Introductory Overview of The "Radical" Divine Way of
The Universal Transcendental Spiritual Reality-Way of Adidam

"RADICAL" TRANSCENDENTALISM
The Non-"Religious", Post-"Scientific", and No-Seeking Reality-Way
of Adidam

ATMA NADI SHAKTI YOGA
The Intrinsically egoless Transcendental Spiritual Reality-Way of
Adidam Ruchiradam

4. The Divine Avataric Incarnation

THE KNEE OF LISTENING
The Divine Ordeal of The Avataric Incarnation of Conscious Light

MY FINAL WORK OF DIVINE INDIFFERENCE
Wherein I Constantly Abide Only As I Am, In Divine and Avatarically
Responsive Transcendental Spiritual Regard of all-and-All

5. Divine Avataric Discourses

THE DIVINE SIDDHA-METHOD OF THE RUCHIRA AVATAR
The Divine Reality-Way of Adidam Is An ego-Transcending
Relationship, Not An ego-Centric Technique

VOLUME ONE: MY "BRIGHT" WORD

VOLUME TWO: MY "BRIGHT" SIGHT

VOLUME THREE: MY "BRIGHT" FORM

VOLUME FOUR: MY "BRIGHT" ROOM

6. Transcendental Realist Literature and Art

THE ORPHEUM
The Tragic History of The Recent Return of Orpheus, or, The First
Room In Three Books

BOOK ONE: THE MUMMERY BOOK
The Parable of Divine Tragedy, Told By Means of
A Self-Illuminated Illustration of The Totality of Mind

BOOK TWO: THE SCAPEGOAT BOOK
The Previously Secret Dialogue On The Avatarically Given
Divine Way of Perfect-Knowledge-Only, Once-Spoken In
A Single Night of Conversation, Between The Captive Divine
Avatar and Great Sage, Raymond Darling, and His Captor,
The Great Fool, and False Teacher, and Notoriously Eccentric
Super-Criminal, Evelyn Disk—Herein Fully Given, Without
Evelyn Disk's Later and Famous and self-Serving Revisions, but
Exactly As It Was Originally Tape-Recorded, by Evelyn Disk
Himself, In The First Room, at the State Mental Facility, Near
God's End, and Presented in Exact Accordance With The Recent
Revelatory and Complete Recounting, Given To The Waiting
World of Intelligent and Receptive Persons, By Meridian Smith,
Who Was, As Usual, Inexplicably Present

BOOK THREE: THE HAPPENINE BOOK
The Childhood Teachings and The End-of-Childhood
Revelations of The Famous "Infant Sage", Raymond Darling—
Compiled from Raymond Darling's Original Handwritten
Manuscripts, and Privately Held Tape-Recordings, Discovered
in The First Room By His True Servant-Devotee, Meridian Smith,
After The Miraculous Disappearance of The Avataric Great Sage

CRAZY DA MUST SING, INCLINED TO HIS WEAKER SIDE
Confessional Poems of Liberation and Love

THE REDUCTION OF THE BELOVED TO SHAPE ALONE

* TRANSCENDENTAL REALISM
The Image-Art of egoless Coincidence With Reality Itself

7. The Indivisibility of Consciousness and Light

HE-AND-SHE IS ME
The Indivisibility of Consciousness and Light In The Divine Body
of The Ruchira Avatar

8. Transcendental Spiritual Reality-Teachings

RUCHIRA SHAKTIPAT YOGA
The Divine (and Not Merely Cosmic) Spiritual Baptism In The
Divine Reality-Way of Adidam

* THE PNEUMATON
The Transcendental Spiritual Reality-Teachings of His Divine
Presence, Avatar Adi Da Samraj

9. Whole Bodily Health and Enlightenment

THE WHOLE BODILY YOGA OF SEARCHLESS RIGHT LIFE
The Physical-Spiritual (and Truly Esoteric) Method of Mental, Emotional, Sexual, and Whole Bodily Health and Enlightenment In The Divine Reality-Way of Adidam

RIGHT LIFE IS FREE PARTICIPATION IN UNLIMITED RADIANCE
The Functional, Practical, Relational, and Cultural Disciplines In The Divine Reality-Way of Adidam

EASY DEATH
Spiritual Wisdom on The Ultimate Transcending of Death and Everything Else

CONSCIOUS EXERCISE AND THE TRANSCENDENTAL SUN
The ego-Transcending Principle Applied To Exercise and Common Physical Action

THE YOGA OF RIGHT DIET
An Intelligent Approach To Dietary Practice That Supports Communion with The Living Divine Reality

GREEN GORILLA
The Searchless Raw Diet

THE EATING GORILLA COMES IN PEACE
The ego-Transcending Principle Applied To Diet and The Regenerative Discipline of True Health

CONDUCTIVITY HEALING
Energy-Healing Practices That Support An Intelligent, Harmonious, and Flowing Re-Integration of The Physical and Etheric Dimensions of The Human Body

THE COMPLETE YOGA OF EMOTIONAL-SEXUAL LIFE
The Way Beyond Ego-Based Sexuality

ALWAYS ENACT FIDELITY TO ME
The Foundation Emotional-Sexual Discipline In The Divine Reality-Way of Adidam

LOVE OF THE TWO-ARMED FORM
The Free and Regenerative Function of Sexuality In Ordinary Life, and The Transcending of Sexuality In True Esoteric Practice

I GIVE YOU THE GIFT OF ONE ANOTHER
The Call To ego-Transcending Cooperation and The Creation of Authentic Intimate (Local) and Global Community

10. *The Stages of Life*

THE SEVEN STAGES OF LIFE
Transcending The Six Stages of egoic Life, and Realizing The
ego-Transcending Seventh Stage of Life, In The Divine Reality-Way
of Adidam

11. *The Seventh Stage Yoga*

THE <u>ALL-COMPLETING</u> AND <u>FINAL</u> DIVINE REVELATION TO HUMANKIND
A Summary Description of The Supreme Yoga of The Seventh Stage
of Life In The Divine Reality-Way of Adidam

THE SEVENTH WAY
Readings from *The Aletheon*—The Practice and The Realization of
The Divine Acausal Reality-Principle

12. *Simple Explanation of Adidam (for Children and Everyone Else)*

WHAT, WHERE, WHEN, HOW, WHY, AND <u>WHO</u> TO REMEMBER TO BE HAPPY
A Simple Explanation of The Divine Reality-Way of Adidam (For
Children, and <u>Everyone</u> Else) *(in all its editions)*

13. *Searchless Beholding as the Primary Practice*

NO SEEKING / MERE BEHOLDING
The Always Primary Practice of The Divine Reality-Way of Adidam

14. *Essential Summary of Adidam*

SANTOSHA ADIDAM
The Essential Summary of The Divine Reality-Way of Adidam

15. *"Perfect Knowledge" Reality-Teachings*

THE LION SUTRA
The "Perfect Practice" Teachings In The Divine Reality-Way
of Adidam

REALITY ITSELF <u>IS</u> THE WAY
Essays from *The Aletheon*

NOTICE THIS
The Five Reality-Teachings of His Divine Presence, Avatar Adi Da Samraj

THE TEACHING MANUAL OF PERFECT SUMMARIES
The Revelation of The Preliminary "Perfect Knowledge" Teachings of His Divine Presence, Avatar Adi Da Samraj

* THE GNOSTICON
The "Perfect Knowledge" Reality-Teachings of His Divine Presence, Avatar Adi Da Samraj

16. Ecstatic "My House" Revelations

THE OVERNIGHT REVELATION OF CONSCIOUS LIGHT
The "My House" Discourses On The Indivisible One of Reality Itself

17. Commentary on the Great Tradition

THE BASKET OF TOLERANCE
The Perfect Guide To Perfectly <u>Unified</u> Understanding of The One and Great Tradition of Humankind, and of The Divine Reality-Way of Adidam As The Perfect <u>Completing</u> of The One and Great Tradition of Humankind

NIRVANASARA
The Essence of The Teaching of Reality In The Realistic Traditions of Buddhism, In The Idealistic Traditions of Advaita Vedanta, and In The Radical World-Teaching of Adidam

REALITY IS ALL THE GOD THERE IS
The Single Transcendental Truth Taught by the Great Sages and the Revelation of Reality Itself

INDEX

Find out more about Avatar Adi Da Samraj and His Reality-Way

■ Learn more about "conductivity" healing: **www.conductivityhealing.com**

■ Visit the ADIDAM™ website: **www.adidam.org**

■ Subscribe to the **AdiDaVideos** channel on YouTube

■ Or browse the Dawn Horse Press website for more books, audio, and video: **www.dawnhorsepress.com**

You can also contact one of our regional centers directly to find out how you can participate in courses and events nearest you:

AMERICAS
12040 N. Seigler Rd.
Middletown, CA
95461 USA
correspondence@
adidam.org
1-707-928-4936

THE UNITED
KINGDOM
and IRELAND
uk@adidam.org
0845-330-1008

EUROPE-AFRICA
Annendaalderweg 10
6105 AT Maria Hoop
The Netherlands
info@adidam.nl
31 (0)20 468 1442

ASIA/PACIFIC
12 Seibel Road
Henderson
Auckland 0614
New Zealand
auckland@
adidam.org
64-9-838-9114

AUSTRALIA
PO Box 92
Montmorency Victoria 3094
Australia
1800 ADIDAM
(1800-234-326)

INDIA
F-168 Shree Love-Ananda Marg
Rampath, Shyam Nagar Extn.
Jaipur - 302 019, India
info@adidam.in
91 (141) 2293080